WARMACHINE®

COLOSSALS

CREDITS

WARMACHINE created by
Matthew D. Wilson

Project Director
Bryan Cutler

Game Design
Matthew D. Wilson

Lead Designer
Jason Soles

Development Manager
David Carl

Associate Developer
William Schoonover

Creative Director
Ed Bourelle

Lead Writer
Douglas Seacat

Additional Writing
Simon Berman
Matt DiPietro
Aeryn Rudel
William Shick

Continuity
Douglas Seacat
Jason Soles

Editorial Manager
Darla Kennerud

Additional Editing
John Michael Arnaud

Graphic Design Director
Josh Manderville

Graphic Design & Layout
Shona Fahland
Matt Ferbrache
Laine Garrett
Josh Manderville

Art Director
Chris Walton

Cover Illustration
Andrea Uderzo

Illustrations
Alberto Dal Lago
Mariusz Gandzel
Néstor Ossandón
Andrea Uderzo
Matthew D. Wilson

Concept Illustrations
Roberto Cirillo
Nate Feyma
Chris Walton
Matthew D. Wilson

Studio Director
Ron Kruzie

Staff Sculptors
Sean Bullough
Brian Dugas
Ben Misenar

Miniature Sculpting
Thomas David
Julie Guthrie
Jose Roig
Jeff Wilhelm

Staff Miniature Painters
Matt DiPietro
Meg Maples

Hobby Manager & Terrain
Stuart Spengler

Hobby Apprentice
Leo Carson-DePasquale

Photography
Matt Ferbrache
Stuart Spengler

Video Producer
Tony Konichek

President
Sherry Yeary

Chief Creative Officer
Matthew D. Wilson

Project Manager
Shona Fahland

Director of Business & Branding Development
William Shick

Marketing Manager
Lyle Lowery

Retail Support & Development
Bill French

Convention Coordinator
Jason Martin

Community Manager & Staff Writer
Simon Berman

Organized Play Coordinator
Jen Ikuta

Volunteer Coordinator
William Hungerford

No Quarter EIC
Aeryn Rudel

Licensing & Contract Manager
Brent Waldher

Sys Admin/Webmaster
Chris Ross

Executive Assistant
Chare Kerzman

Customer Service
Adam Johnson

Customer Support
Jack Coleman

Production Director
Mark Christensen

Technical Director
Kelly Yeager

Packaging/Shipping Manager
Joe Lee

Production
Bryan Adler
Mark Arreola
Oren Ashkenazi
Nelson Baltzo
Max Barsana
Brandon Burton
Thomas Cawby
Johan Cea
Henry Chac
Phillip Chinzi
Alex Chobot
Bryan Dasalla
Cody Ellis
Joel Falkenhagen
Michael Hang
Alex Leyva
Jared Mattern
Mike McIntosh
Spencer Newman
Phuong Nguyen
Antwan Porter
Marcus Rodriguez
Benjamin Sanders
Jon Schectman
Nick Scherdnik
Ryon Smith
Trevor Snow
Jacob Stanley
Chris Tiemeyer
James Thomas
Ben Tracy
Dara Vann
Hector Villarreal
Matt Warren

Infernals
John Morin
Peter Gaublomme
Joachim Molkow
Brian Putnam
Gilles Reynaud
Donald Sullivan

Playtest Coordination
David Carl
William Schoonover

Internal Playtesters
Simon Berman
Ed Bourelle
David Carl
Jack Coleman
Leo Carson-DePasquale
Cody Ellis
William Hungerford
Jen Ikuta
Ben Sanders
William Schoonover
Nate Scott
Douglas Seacat
William Shick
Jason Soles
Brent Waldher
Matthias Warren

External Playtesters
Ray Bailey
Brad Casey
Todd Crow
Eric Ernewein
Logan Fisher
Stephen Forston
Peter Gaublomme
Tommy Geuns
Devon Goda
Andrew Hartland
William Hayes
Andrew Inzenga
Geoffrey Long
Wout Maerschalck
Rob Miles
Jeremy Miller
Dirk Pintjens
Craig Poche
Owen Rehrauer
Jarred Robitaille
Josh Saulter
Derek Scott Jr
Tim Simpson
Michael Stubbs
Mark Thomas
Anthony Woods

Proofreading
Bryan Cutler
Darla Kennerud
Lyle Lowery
William Shick
Brent Waldher

BRACE YOURSELF FOR FULL-SCALE WARFARE!

At Privateer Press, we firmly believe bigger is better—bigger models, bigger games, and bigger stakes. For more than half a decade we have been working on how and when to crank the dial up to 11, and finally the time is right. *WARMACHINE: Colossals* is here. It's time to go big.

Easily the most notable additions to the game are the massive colossals themselves. These warjacks are awesome, not only in scale but also in tabletop might. Each is a mobile weapons platform bristling with destructive power that commands respect and attention. With thick armor and double-sized damage grids, the colossals are able to endure punishment that could reduce entire battlegroups to wreck markers. They can also perform two exciting new power attacks befitting their impact on the game: power strike and sweep. To say they have a major presence on the table would be an understatement.

Colossals kick up the intensity in games of any size, but they truly begin to feel epic when fielded in large-scale battles of 150 points or more. WARMACHINE players have been clamoring for large-scale game rules, and Unbound makes playing games of this size easier and more dynamic than ever before. Now you can experience firsthand what it is like to command the earth-shaking armies of the Iron Kingdoms.

To lead these giant monstrosities of robot destruction and the massive forces supporting them onto the fields of battle, *Colossals* features six warcasters. Four of our most iconic characters have gone epic a second time to reflect how the twists and turns of the evolving story have shaped them. We are also excited to unveil a third Rhulic warcaster, enabling Rhulic armies to field three-warcaster armies in Unbound games.

Battles of this massive scale require stout and decisive leadership, and these warcasters fit the bill. They are going to need all their resolve and every technological advantage they can innovate as Cryx raises the stakes. The various lich lords are on the move as the Nightmare Empire prepares to unleash the once-hidden might of its army. So dire is their situation that even long-time enemies have entered into an uneasy alliance, putting aside their animosity to prevent western Immoren from being transformed into a blighted wasteland.

Colossals is a project that has fueled a great deal of excitement at Privateer. The colossals have been in various forms of development since well before Mk II, and we are thrilled to see them finally become a reality. With these giant death-dealing mountains of steel and steam and the Unbound rules for epic-sized battles, you have the tools to translate the escalating scale of the Iron Kingdoms setting to your tabletop.

Now take to the field and crush your enemy beneath your colossal might!

TABLE OF CONTENTS

Visit: www.privateerpress.com

Privateer Press, Inc. 13434 NE 16th St. Suite 120 • Bellevue, WA 98005
Tel (425) 643-5900 • Fax (425) 643-5902

For online customer service, email frontdesk@privateerpress.com

IN THE DARKEST PLACE
PART ONE

POINT BOURNE, LATE FALL 608 AR

Skarre leapt down from the low wall to land behind the bulky Man-O-War soldier, who whirled to face her only to be knocked off his feet as her horns smashed into his helmet. He flew to the ground with a crash of heavy armor hitting cobblestones. The Khadoran kept a strong grip on his ice maul but was too slow to defend himself as the satyxis queen drove Takkaryx through his breastplate and into his heart.

Satyxis blood witches charged from the shadowed alleyway to blindside the other Man-O-War corpsmen with their sharpened blades, turning the blood of their own bodies against the enemy as the air filled with a red mist. Skarre's Harrower emerged from behind the Winter Guard riflemen, scything through several with a single sweep of its claw. Those remaining fled with shocked looks, staggering toward the cover of a half-shattered wall. Skarre lazily lifted her hand cannon, fired a booming shot into the back of one, and watched him stagger another two steps and collapse in a heap. The Harrower fired a pulsing shot of necromantic darkness to explode into several more, while her satyxis raiders and blood witches finished off the rest of the ill-fated expedition.

She sighed in a dissatisfied way, taking none of the delight from this clash that the rest of the satyxis enjoyed. She strode toward the figure watching from the nearby darkness and leaning upon a lengthy and distinct polearm, once the weapon of a lich lord. The sight of that weapon in Deneghra's hands always prompted fresh indignation from Skarre—it was a reminder of the treachery of the woman and her master, Asphyxious. "'Ardly a proper battle," she snarled. "Ye ought purge the Khadorans from their warren and be done with 'em."

Deneghra stepped forward and shook her head, an insincere smile visible below the masked helmet. "No need to expend unnecessary resources. You'll want to save your strength for when Venethrax arrives with his prize."

"I need no reminder of my duty from the likes of ye," Skarre snapped. "Were it not for Lord Terminus' orders, I'd not be here. Don't be thinking I'll dance at yer whim. Where be Lich Lord Venethrax anyhow? I would like to get back to sea."

"Lord Asphyxious has informed me Venethrax is delayed," Deneghra said with a frown. "The tunnels he used to expedite his journey collapsed, taking with them a sizable portion of his escort and damaging the athanc transport. He has continued overland. It is unfortunate; I am weary of this city and would prefer to be gone as well."

"The screams do be tiresome," Skarre agreed. Point Bourne was largely theirs, despite the Khadorans and Cygnarans hunkered down in their respective neighborhoods. Asphyxious had begun the systematic purging of its inhabitants, an operation conducted with an odd mix of brutal efficiency and apparent caprice; Skarre could see no pattern to how he was selecting areas to target. There were more people here than could easily be turned into thralls, even with the necrosurgeons and necrotechs working tirelessly. Skarre suspected they had long since filled every soul cage they had. "All the more reason for taking the fight to the Khadorans and rooting 'em out for good."

"They are penned in where we can keep an eye on them, so leave them be for now. My only interest is in stopping those they keep sending forth to interfere with our operations." Deneghra looked down at a Winter Guardsman who groaned as he bled out. "Strange they can't seem to help themselves. It's not their own citizens being slaughtered."

"What about the Cygnarans up behind their walls?" Skarre jerked her chin vaguely in the direction of the other side of town. Both Cygnar and Khador had periodically sent small patrols out into the city to test the Cryxian defenses and try to come to the aid of the remaining citizens. "Gun mages over there shot up an ogrun boarding party. The others want a little payback."

"Unless you're eager to eat a sniper's bullet, stay away from them," Deneghra said with a sharper tone. "It's your own fault for looking for plunder where we told you not to go."

Skarre's eyes narrowed. "Seems time I talked to Asphyxious. Would like to give 'im a piece of my mind about this whole raid."

Deneghra's voice was hard. "I speak for Lich Lord Asphyxious. Do not provoke either the Khadorans or the Cygnarans. Not until I tell you otherwise. You may be here on Terminus' orders, but so long as you are in this city, you fall under Asphyxious' dominion and will do as told."

Skarre took some satisfaction in having gotten under the wraith witch's skin. "So ye keep telling me. If ye don't want my advice, we'll call it a day. I'll be back by the river should ye have need of me. Send a messenger when Venethrax arrives." She turned and walked away, pretending not to hear Deneghra's parting rejoinder. Her satyxis followed swiftly behind her.

RHYDDEN IN LLAEL

Grand Exemplar Kreoss looked out across the roiling horde of mechanithralls beyond a bristling wall of swords, spears, and halberds. Around him a mingled army of Steelheads and his own troops stood against the tide of undead. The current alliance was one of necessity forced upon him and the mercenary captain Amador Damiano. Kreoss had come to Rhydden to ensure the new temples and the converted Menites among the populace were protected from the oncoming Cryxian menace. Damiano and his Steelheads had been hired to safeguard the city from all threats—among which they apparently counted Kreoss' army.

After the mercenaries had proven unwilling to allow him access to the city, Kreoss had reluctantly entered battle with Captain Damiano and the defenders of Rhydden, but the arrival of Lich Lord Terminus and a monstrous host of undead had cut the fighting short. Faced with the greater threat, Kreoss and Damiano had ended their own conflict to stand together against the lich lord. Together they had blunted the impact of the first Cryxian advance, but at a heavy toll.

Kreoss had expected the dead to simply overwhelm them with a crushing onslaught of numbers. He had committed to the battle knowing very well it might be his last. Yet Terminus had broken off the initial attack and regrouped, a tactic entirely at odds with what they had come to expect from Cryx—and Terminus' reputation. Kreoss had taken advantage of the short reprieve to send a messenger toward the nearest encampment. Two nightmarish days of intermittent battle had followed, with the undead attacking in staggered waves for hours at a time. Although his forces had kept the enemy outside Rhydden itself, the men were exhausted and fewer in number with every clash. It was clear to Kreoss that unless he could find a way to change the dynamic of this battle, their defeat was inevitable.

The Steelheads and Exemplars braced for another charge from the massed mechanithralls. Overhead, Kreoss heard Rhydden's battlement cannons thunderously discharge, sending their projectiles shrieking into the Cryxians. Each blast destroyed dozens of undead in a plume of dirt, smoke, and broken bodies, but there were always more advancing.

Kreoss ordered Fire of Salvation forward. The men in front of the 'jack moved aside to allow it room to swing its great flaming mace. Kreoss, too, moved forward, taking a position among several Exemplar knights. Under his breath he offered a silent prayer to Menoth, using the mantra to focus his will and make it tangible. Holy fire bloomed to life around him, licking along the edges of the Exemplar relic blades.

The undead rushed forward, heedless of the swords and halberds arrayed against them. They struck the Exemplar and Steelhead line, driving it back a step, but failed to gain appreciable ground. Then the tide of battle changed, and the defenders pushed back, hacking down mechanithralls

with the precision of those well versed in the task. Kreoss focused his attacks on the few bonejacks mixed in with the lesser Cryxian troops, channeling his will into Justifier to bolster each skewering thrust. A dozen yards away, Fire of Salvation swung its mace in wide, sweeping arcs at Kreoss' mental urging, swiftly reducing a dozen thralls to burnt flesh and charred mechanika.

The charge ended abruptly, and once more the Cryxian army pulled back, leaving hundreds of motionless mechanithralls across the ground. It looked to Kreoss like Terminus was probing their lines for a weak point where a concerted strike would have the best chance of breaking through. Looking to the north, he saw that the far end of the Cryxian line had been breached by several hundred mounted Exemplar vengers, who had smashed through with lances and then entered the fray with drawn swords to clear their way.

Their presence could mean only one thing: his message requesting urgent reinforcement had reached the sizable cavalry force stationed to secure a recently converted Menite community to the northwest of Rhydden.

> EACH BLAST DESTROYED DOZENS OF UNDEAD IN A PLUME OF DIRT, SMOKE, AND BROKEN BODIES.

The ranking venger seneschal rode up, quickly dismounted, and dropped to a knee at Kreoss' feet. "Grand Exemplar," the man said. "We rode straight here when we received your orders."

"Rise," Kreoss commanded. "How many are you?"

"Three hundred," the seneschal replied as he stood.

Kreoss glanced to the east, where Captain Damiano and the bulk of the Steelhead halberdiers and riflemen formed the iron center of Rhydden's defensive line. He then looked back at the gathered vengers and noticed they had brought a thick-bodied Khadoran destrier, huge and imposing in its heavy armor. Strapped to its sides were his shield and cavalry spear, Conviction.

"I see you brought my mount, as I required. You have done well," Kreoss said. The seneschal inclined his head and gestured for the great horse to be brought forth. Kreoss touched Agon briefly along the neck, and the steed whickered in recognition. The grand exemplar mounted and raised his voice to the others. "Pull back to Rhydden!"

Rhydden's defenders had opened the gates to allow Kreoss' and Damiano's forces behind the relative safety of the walls again. Cannon crews and riflemen along the battlements took shots of opportunity on any enemy that came too close, although the dead too had largely pulled back. The Cryxians still seemed reluctant to challenge the walls of the city. As grateful as he was for their restraint, Kreoss knew it couldn't last, and the town lacked the firepower to drive the dead away if they attacked in full force. It was almost as though Terminus were toying with them, allowing them to feel the despair of being trapped—or else withholding the deathblow deliberately for some sinister purpose. He had no desire to leave his fate in the hands of the Cryxian lich lord. Their only hope to avoid a slow and withering defeat was to mount an offensive. He laid out his thoughts succinctly.

"It's a bold plan. I'll give you that," Captain Damiano said, shaking his head. "But blind faith is not a good replacement for common sense."

Kreoss gritted his teeth behind his mask. Despite the mercenary captain's competence on the battlefield, he found the man's irreverence profoundly irritating. They were hardly equals. Nevertheless, Kreoss had need of these men, and therefore he indulged them with a brief explanation, "If we simply stand here, we will be overrun."

"And if you go gallivanting off with your cavalry, we'll be overrun even sooner," Damiano shot back. "We need that heavy horse here to bolster our line."

"Bolstering a line would be an improper use of cavalry against such numbers, as I would expect a veteran captain to understand," Kreoss said with calm intensity. "My plan will make far better use of them. We will use our speed to get behind them."

"The grand exemplar is right, sir," a Steelhead lieutenant standing next to Damiano said. This was Damiano's adjutant Lorio Jaspar, a man who seemed possessed of more wisdom and patience than his commander. "Remember the Idrians north of Tower Judgment?"

Damiano nodded. "I do, but that was a bit different," he said. "We had Major Laddermore and her Storm Lances to back us up. Plus, that was a few hundred Idrians, not a horde of walking corpses led by a millennia-old warcaster."

"But the idea is the same," Lorio replied. "Box them in, don't allow them time to regroup or react, then crush them despite their numerical advantage."

Damiano seemed unconvinced—likely simple pigheadedness, Kreoss expected, resistance to a plan not of his own design. It did not matter. "Captain, this is not a debate. I am telling you what I intend to do. Prepare your men. The dead will not wait."

Damiano grimaced. "We'll do our part. But we'll have to stretch our lines thin, and if you fail, they'll break us and be inside Rhydden by nightfall."

"I will not fail," Kreoss said.

Kreoss rode at the head of a long column of vengers, with the line of armored horses and riders flowing behind him like a great steel serpent. He'd left Rhydden soon after meeting with Captain Damiano, leading his knights north into the foothills that ringed the small valley where the Llaelese city rested. They'd worked their way south, skirting the city and finally exiting the hills directly behind the Cryxian host. As Resistance scouts had surmised, the Cryxians had no Soulhunters or other swift forces to screen their perimeter or intercept incoming cavalry.

When they were a mile or so away from the enemy, Kreoss reigned to a halt and raised his spear, signaling the vengers to form ranks around him. They quickly moved into position, creating a wide, shallow wedge of armored horses and men with the grand exemplar at its head. Kreoss could see that the mercenary captain had kept to his part of the plan. A thin line of Menite and Steelhead troops surrounded the Cryxian host on three sides, pushing the enemy closer together, which would allow his own comparatively smaller force to drive them forward.

Kreoss brought Conviction down and urged his horse into a slow trot. Behind him the vengers followed suit. They were close enough now that he could pick out individual shapes in the mass ahead. He saw primarily mechanithralls, but there were a number of helljacks and bonejacks within the Cryxian ranks. Terminus was likely holding those in reserve to lay siege to Rhydden once the outer defenders fell.

Seeing them approach, the Cryxian army quickly made preparations to meet the cavalry. The majority of the helljacks were pushed to the rear of the army, forming a ragged line of towering black shapes. There was no sign of Terminus. Instead, a number of strange, multi-armed constructs of bone and steel floating behind the helljacks seemed to be directing their actions.

Kreoss lowered Conviction into position for a charge, resting the butt of the heavy spear against his saddle to brace it. He leaned forward, pushed his feet tight against the stirrups, and drew his shield tight to his body. Trained for battle, Agon responded to these subtle movements and broke into a gallop. Behind Kreoss his vengers spurred their horses to match his pace.

He charged directly at the center of the helljack line. Seconds before impact, he unleashed his will and faith in a wave of holy power. He felt the dark presence of enemy sorcery crumble beneath the sacred onslaught, and the cascade of power coursing through him gave his mind superior concentration and force. A litany of prayers tumbled from his lips, imbuing the lances of the vengers beside him with unerring accuracy and limning their steel tips with fire.

They hit the Cryxian line like the fist of Menoth. Conviction's point clipped the carapace of the first Slayer in Kreoss' path, spinning the necromechanikal construct around and into the charging vengers behind him. Strikes from two more lances reduced it to burning scrap.

Empowered by his blessings and skilled at estimating the foe, they struck the other helljacks at the fore of the line, delivering enough punishment to shatter them one after the next. Once past these and into the main body of the Cryxian army, Kreoss shortened his grip on Conviction, allowing him to thrust with the mighty spear. The vengers abandoned their lances and drew the long swords hanging from their saddles. They continued their charge, unslowed by the lesser Cryxian troops massed ahead of them. Kreoss felled every mechanithrall he could reach with Conviction and reduced bonejacks to dust with blasts of magical force.

Unable to stand against the charging vengers, the undead horde showed typical mindlessness at the new threat, clumping together and pushing chaotically against their fellows. Kreoss and his vengers slowed and fanned out, pressing the Cryxian army into itself with steel and horseflesh. As Kreoss had anticipated, there were too few intelligent masters to direct so many. Terminus' attention seemed focused at the vanguard.

Kreoss was driving back toward the gates of Rhydden, where Damiano and the bulk of his Steelheads waited. The rest of the army defending the city had spread out considerably. Together with Kreoss' charging cavalry, the Steelheads and Menites were pushing the Cryxian horde into a tightly compacted mass.

His plan was working, and Kreoss allowed himself a moment's satisfaction. Then a great winged shadow passed overhead and its fleeting darkness sent a horrid chill through his body. Terminus had joined the battle.

Damiano stood behind the triple row of halberdiers and riflemen positioned in front of Rhydden's gates. Rocinante towered next to him, periodically firing its cannon over the Steelhead lines and into the Cryxians beyond. The battle had reached a fevered pitch, and it was clear Kreoss had begun his attack. The ranks of mechanithralls were becoming tighter and tighter, denying them sufficient space to dodge Steelhead halberds and thus making them easier to destroy.

It wasn't over yet. Damiano cursed under his breath as the hellish, smoke-shrouded form of Lich Lord Terminus came looming through the air from the south. The iron lich was not alone. Four small dark shapes flew beside him—Scavengers, bonejacks kept aloft more by magic than by their tattered, leathery wings. Terminus landed almost on top of the first rank of Steelhead halberdiers, loosing a jet of blistering green flame from his skeletal jaws. The Steelheads caught in the blast died instantly, leaving behind charred, withered shapes that hardly resembled the corpses of men. With each swipe of Terminus' lengthy sword or razor-taloned claw more men died, and their souls were ripped from their bodies to feed the unholy hunger of the Cryxian lord. With each soul Terminus grew stronger, his sword strokes faster and more accurate, and his dire spells struck down Steelheads with hellfire and bolts of necrotic energy.

The Scavengers flew directly at Damiano and Rocinante. Damiano urged the big warjack to discharge its cannon, putting his will into the shot. The cannonball struck one of the bonejacks in midair, and it fell from the sky in a shower of debris.

"Take them," Damiano said aloud, urging Rocinante to engage the remaining bonejacks. He then drew his hand cannon Judgment and moved toward Terminus, trying to ignore the rising dread he felt as he neared the iron lich. Behind him, Rocinante brought its battle blade to bear on the remaining Scavengers, and he felt the warjack cut one in half with a brutal overhand strike.

The Steelheads that had survived Terminus' initial attack were bravely facing down the iron lich, but their halberds glanced off his armor, and he continued to reap death and feast on souls.

Damiano aimed carefully and fired Judgment again. The heavy lead ball struck Terminus' armored skull with a clang, causing the iron lich to stumble back a step. The momentary reprieve granted his Steelheads a few precious seconds to reform their ranks.

"Steelheads! To me!" Damiano screamed when he reached the line. In response, the halberdiers nearest the iron lich pulled back and gathered around their commander, pressing tightly together to form a mobile hedge of halberd spikes with Damiano at the center.

"Push!" Damiano shouted, harnessing his sorcerous ability to lend strength and determination to the Steelheads around him. The halberdiers advanced, thrusting at Terminus as a single unit. Individually, a Steelhead halberd posed little threat to the iron lich, but a dozen thrusting together and bolstered by Damiano's magic was a different matter entirely. Multiple halberd spikes struck Terminus' armor, driving the iron lich back a few steps and into a wall of mechanithralls coming from the other direction. The

Cryxian troops flowed around their master, engulfing him. Behind the onrush of mechanithralls Damiano could see a line of vengers advancing inexorably, pushing the undead toward the walls of Rhydden.

The Cryxian troops were now so tightly compacted they could hardly move, and Damiano could see Steelheads and Exemplars cutting them down at will. Terminus had become swamped by his own troops, unable to reach his enemy. With a soul-curdling screech of rage, the iron lich ripped his massive sword through the mechanithralls around him, cutting them down in a wide swathe.

Terminus leveled his sword at Damiano, and the blazing green fire burning in the empty sockets of his iron skull pulsed with unbearable brightness. The iron lich leapt into the air, his wings stirring up a whirlwind of dirt and battlefield debris and casting a blanketing shadow across the battlefield. Terminus retreated over his swiftly dwindling army before disappearing to the south.

POINT BOURNE, WEST GATE

Supreme Kommandant Irusk directed his Destroyers to obliterate the last of the sizable brick building nearest to the fortified western gatehouse region they had occupied and reinforced. They now had a wide, clear lane around their position, making it impossible for any corporeal Cryxian force to approach them unobserved.

Snipers and riflemen were perched anywhere they could fit along the walls, with mortar and field guns situated at strategic positions. Spotters in the highest remaining towers with telescopes yelled down directions for those sending high-arcing mortar fire into the alleys and streets beyond their open firing lanes. Every access route to the region was faced by a formidable array of warjacks and Man-O-War, and Greylords stood ready to reinforce the newly erected mystical barriers keeping the incorporeal dead at bay. Since clearing a perimeter, things had been eerily quiet in the immediate vicinity. Once the sounds of explosive blasts and falling stone had faded, though, the distant sounds of human misery and a city being torn apart by horrors returned.

Irusk spotted several of his men rushing back to their position and moved his Devastators aside to let them pass. They were Winter Guardsmen, several injured and others simply broken, the last of a group that had volunteered to advance on the nearest Cryxians collecting civilians for slaughter. Irusk had been persuaded to allow this by one of his kovniks who felt the men needed to try to do something against the barbarism taking place in the streets of this enemy city. Four separate small efforts had been mounted, but only two had managed to return with civilians. Now several hundred refugees were taking precious space among the buildings garrisoning his men, where they glared suspiciously at the Khadorans and muttered curses about their liberators under their breath. Irusk accepted this.

Their fortified position held, and Cryx seemed reluctant to move against them, for now. But how long would this last? They gained nothing by staying here except survival, and Cryx conducted their depravities unchecked. Irusk had long prided himself on his ability to see the path to victory, but now he felt blind and deaf. Their capacity to gain useful intelligence on the disposition of the enemy had diminished to almost nothing. He felt conflicted in a way that was new to him: he knew they must act, but all choices felt ruinous. He heard footsteps behind him and knew from their distinct weight and cadence it was Kommander Strasvite, his subordinate who led the 4th Assault Legion.

"Kommandant," the approaching man began, "we must reassess our position." His tone suggested tremendous frustration.

"I agree absolutely, old friend," Irusk said without turning toward him. "I had just come to the same conclusion." He felt another pang of deep pain from his shoulder, where the wound from the sniper's shot still bled, despite bandaging. He did not allow any sign of this to show on his face. The hole in his warcaster armor had been sealed, and he knew that considering their situation it would be easy for his men to forget he had been struck, which suited him. Many bore worse wounds.

The kommander continued, "I think we have no choice but to retreat from the city and make egress across the countryside." He indicated the barricaded gateway leading to the western road from the city.

"To what end, Kommander?" Irusk asked, his tone neutral.

The man seemed nonplussed. "To evade the Cryx, return to the north shore, and rejoin our forces in the Thornwood."

Irusk looked sidelong at him. "We are behind enemy lines, Strasvite, on the wrong side of the Dragon's Tongue. There are no easy crossings. East is Stonebridge, Cygnar's strongest remaining northern fortress. Beyond that, Corvis. We could go west, to be chased by both Cygnaran and Ordic border patrols while Cryx harries us from the rear. Otherwise you suggest the 4th Assault Legion and a large portion of my army live off the land in unfamiliar and unfriendly territory. If we take over Tarna, perhaps you and I can learn how to wrap hooaga cigars. A profitable trade, I hear."

Kommander Strasvite pulled himself up, his face reddening. "Better to take our chances outside the city than wait here for Cryx."

"A better way to die, without question. It may come to that. But I have another idea." He turned to face the kommander. "A chance to strike a meaningful blow against the enemy—and perhaps live to serve the Motherland."

ONCE THE SOUNDS OF EXPLOSIVE BLASTS AND FALLING STONE HAD FADED, THOUGH, THE DISTANT SOUNDS OF HUMAN MISERY AND A CITY BEING TORN APART BY HORRORS RETURNED.

Whatever offense the kommander had taken at his superior's earlier words was transformed into tentative hope. "You have a plan?"

Irusk smiled grimly and said, "Less a plan than a desperate contingency. The only one available to us. The thought has been growing from the first time our men volunteered to risk death on the chance of saving the civilians in this accursed town." Irusk spoke slowly, as if the words were difficult to form. "We have common cause, rooted in the simple kinship of life. Lest Cryx feast on us both, we must enter into an alliance with Cygnar."

Kara Sloan's body ached. She had gone without rest for days, pacing the upper battlements of Point Bourne's military quarter. Long hours of standing absolutely still at the best vantage points while staring fixedly through the scope of her sniper rifle had begun to take their toll. There had been little activity in the nearby streets, but occasionally she spotted and targeted Cryxians trying to close on the quarter unseen. She had also provided cover to several retaliatory ranger expeditions into the nearest streets, until the general had ordered such operations halted. She chafed at the helpless feeling of waiting here while the citizens of Point Bourne were mercilessly slaughtered. Reinforcements were supposedly on the way from Stonebridge, and the general did not wish to jeopardize their chances. Despite having rescued several thousand people from the nearest areas the morale of the soldiers was flagging, a situation worsened by their rapidly diminishing food stores.

She heard what sounded like gunfire or cannons from one of the nearby streets. So far as she was aware, there should be no Cygnaran patrols in that region. She wondered if some reckless junior officer had decided to mount a rescue effort despite the general's orders. She scanned the approach of Falls Road and saw nothing, then turned and crossed the battlement to the main gateway, moving past a number of soldiers on post with rifles ready. All were tense, having heard the gunshots. She saw movement at the far end of Academy Way, the wider approach to the main gate, and once again brought her scope to her right eye.

Rather than the drab motley of fleeing Cygnaran civilians she had expected, she was bewildered at the sight of red, black, and gold armor. Adjusting the rotating lens, she pulled the focus back to take in Khadorans rushing swiftly toward the barricaded gates of the quarter. Her pulse increased as she spotted the distinct form of Supreme Kommandant Gurvaldt Irusk, shouting orders. He raised his pistol and fired behind him, sending a heavy bullet to impact a flying Scavenger that had been swooping toward them. Additional Cryxians were closing from behind. "Looks like your time is up," she muttered under her breath, feeling no sympathy for the enemy that had brought this ruin on the city. Irusk's path was easy to follow now, and this time there were no Man-O-War shocktroopers surrounding him with their impenetrable shields. She aimed slightly ahead of his path, feeling a moment of perfect tranquility, then held her breath and let her finger begin to tighten on the trigger.

The colonel in charge of the outer wall shouted, "Captain Sloan, hold!" She almost squeezed anyway; the moment was so close, and the shot would have been so clean. Training and discipline froze her muscles. "They bear a flag of truce—do not fire!"

With a growl in her throat she looked through the scope again and moved her focus to one of the massive brute thralls rushing down the street toward the wounded Khadorans falling behind the squad. Her rifle gave a loud report, and a rune-scribed round took the creature's head clean off. She quickly reloaded, and her next shot shattered the skull of a closing bonejack. The sharpshooters on the wall followed suit, picking apart the Cryxian pursuit, and she urged her nearest Defenders to add their fire. "Very well, Colonel," Sloan said in a resigned tone. "Open the portcullis and let's find out what they want."

CORVIS

When the official message sealed with the king's signet arrived, Sebastian Nemo was confined to a hospital bed. His injuries had been tended by a veteran medic of the First Army and then greatly diminished by the prayers of a seasoned battle-chaplain of the Church of Morrow, but they wanted him to rest. Still, the intruding emissary was no ordinary military courier but a Stormguard major and officer of the Royal Guard as well as a sworn and decorated officer of the Cygnaran Royal Assembly.

Major Sterling was a man Nemo knew in passing from previous visits to the court, a reliable man known to King Leto personally. Nonetheless, each of them knew commissions at this level were usually delivered by the

king personally or by the warmaster general in his stead. The warmaster's health had taken a bad turn, however, and the situation in Corvis was too unstable to summon Nemo to court, which meant promotion by proxy.

It seemed very strange to Nemo that he was being given titles and praises while lying in a hospital bed after a failed Cryxian assassination attempt. Furthermore, the city was still besieged by Khador. He looked down at the pieces of parchment, decorated with florid script and embossed sigils. "Artificer General, eh?" His chuckle prompted coughing and additional pain from his wrapped chest. "Is that a promotion or a demotion?"

The major was a good man, but he was rather tightly wound and clearly mindful of representing the highest echelons of the Cygnaran Army. "It is a singular honor, General. A new post and commission specifically created to recognize your contributions to Cygnar's war arsenal. You now have total authority over the Cygnaran Armory as well as all privately owned military contractors. Projects you deem vital are to be given priority. The first of the Stormwalls will be arriving in a matter of days, and I am sure they will provide a decisive advantage against the Khadorans."

"Perhaps," Nemo allowed. "Although as you know, CRS reports confirm the Khadorans learned of our colossal project and promptly built their own. They have already staged parades in Korsk to display their oversized machines." He sighed heavily and said, "Impossible to keep secrets anymore, on either side. We each have our spies."

The major paused and said with forced enthusiasm, "Even a few weeks with such machines in our hands while theirs slog through the forest should give us the edge."

"Yes. I'm very glad the Khadorans are finding the Thornwood as troublesome as we ever did. It's a bad place for colossals, although perhaps these newer ones will fare better." Nemo decided he had enjoyed the company of the royal emissary long enough. "I appreciate your confidence, Major. Send my regards to the warmaster general and King Leto, and thank them for the honor. Tell them I'd like more reinforcements and supplies. Ammunition especially: Defender, Cyclone, Charger, and Sentinel. We have every gun shop in Corvis making bullets, and it's not enough."

The major bowed deeply and took his leave, making way for a man wearing the distinct attire of an arcane scholar of the Order of Illumination. He was in his early fifties, but to Nemo's eyes he looked young despite his wispy, mostly gray hair and his thick goggles. His white and gold formal robes hung loosely from his thin frame, and he wore the symbols of Morrow and his order prominently displayed. Nemo impatiently waved him forward and sat up in bed, ignoring the pain from the exertion.

"Been waiting out in the hall all this time, Dolan?" Nemo asked irritably. "Should have come in at once; the major could have waited. Speak plainly—how is she?"

Vigilant Peer Carrick Dolan took no umbrage at Nemo's abrupt manner. Many of the Illuminated were grim-faced and battle-hardened witch hunters who spent their lives trying to eradicate necromancers and infernalists, but Carrick was different. He was a scholar, occultist, and alchemist who spent his time amid dusty ancient tomes and in laboratories. He was also the Church of Morrow's foremost expert on supernatural afflictions and poisons, having experience with the effects of blight, exposure to necrotite, and other Cryxian calamities. He had been rushed to Corvis after Nemo had sent word by telegraph of Major Victoria Haley's condition.

There were dark wells under his eyes, as he had slept little in the two nights since his arrival. He frowned, opened his mouth, closed it again, and finally said, "Most perplexing. An altogether unusual situation." He was in the habit of speaking slowly, something Nemo found grating.

"Will she live? Out with it, man!" Nemo exclaimed.

Dolan did not flinch. "Her condition has stabilized, and she does not appear to be in imminent mortal danger. But the situation remains severe. I have found no means to purge the toxin."

"Have you learned anything useful at all?" Nemo asked, exasperated.

"Quite a bit," Dolan replied seriously. "This poison is not entirely new to me, albeit clearly modified. Very rare. Requires prohibitively expensive ingredients. Likely originated in Blackwater. A finicky bit of alchemy, requiring time and skill. Not widely used, as it affects only those who practice the arcane. Behaves more like an illness than a traditional poison, and requires magical energy to sustain itself."

Nemo's eyes narrowed. "Warcaster poison? Hard to believe Cryx wouldn't find a use for that."

Dolan shook his head. "Not worth the trouble. A dose the size the major received may have taken years to distill and isn't even fatal. Mostly an alchemical oddity. Those afflicted should simply be overcome with nausea as their magic fails them for several hours. I expect Cryx is investigating it while they try to develop something to permanently eradicate arcane potential in their enemies."

"Wonderful," Nemo muttered sourly. "But why is Haley still suffering its effects, then?"

The alchemist pressed on, clearly warming to the topic. "I presume the assassin hoped the poison would stifle your magic long enough that he could murder you by more traditional means. A suicide mission, but one that might have succeeded if not for Major Haley's intervention. Ordinarily, when a victim's magic is extinguished, the process by which the poison sustains itself fails and it dissipates. Major Haley's power is too strong to extinguish entirely, so the poison reached an equilibrium where it continually feeds on the source of her magic to sustain itself. Quite fascinating, really."

"What does that mean for her?" Nemo prodded.

> HER RIFLE GAVE A LOUD REPORT, AND A RUNE-SCRIBED ROUND TOOK THE CREATURE'S HEAD CLEAN OFF.

"While the poison is in her system it is continually spilling a small quantity of toxins into her blood. She is in constant pain, but she should develop a tolerance for it. To prevent the poison from becoming stronger she will need to suppress her arcane powers entirely. She cannot rely on magic, not until we find a cure. I suggest she be confined to administrative duty, indefinitely."

"Effectively she is a warcaster no longer." Nemo pronounced the sentence in any icy tone.

"I will do everything I can, but this is an unprecedented circumstance. A cure may not even be possible."

Feeling an intense desire to get back into his armor, Nemo ignored the pain that washed over him as he stood from the bed. He said, "I suggest you get back to your laboratory immediately. Pray while you work, if it'll help. Just restore her."

POINT BOURNE

The northern section of the city, abandoned by civilians long before the attack by Khador, had become the site of frantic Cryxian activity. It served as the coordination point for sorting the city's plunder and shipping it north into the Thornwood as efficiently as possible. This included a continuous line of wagons hauling corpses, although not all captives had been slain or turned over to the necrosurgeons for transformation to thralls. In accordance with the arrangements made with Lich Lord Asphyxious' allies, a percentage of those civilians were shackled, blindfolded, and hauled off to the cephalyx, who would eventually transform them into drudges. Deneghra walked past all this activity with a critical eye, scanning to ensure everything was proceeding as planned.

They did not have unlimited time. More resources had been invested in the city's seizure than she would prefer. Asphyxious had hoped to regain clout with the other lich lords by playing an instrumental role in assisting Venethrax with securing his prize. Lord Toruk would be watching for the successful delivery of this athanc, and it behooved the dragon's servants to ensure that came to pass. Were it not for this, there would have been little reason to occupy Point Bourne at all, aside from the always useful tactic of exploiting vulnerabilities left by the mainland armies as they fought their trivial wars. Already the gains here had been substantial; Asphyxious had declared the plan, orchestrated and initiated by Deneghra, a complete success. All that remained was for Venethrax to be sent on his way with Skarre escorting.

Deneghra descended steep steps into one of the most heavily fortified of the buildings remaining amid a cluster of lower outlying structures in the northern region: a former Cygnaran military command station and stockade. She moved into the lower chambers with the smooth, fluid grace of a stalking cat. As she neared her destination she could hear the laboring machines making their rhythmic susurrations. The holding cell was dimly lit, and its vents did not completely clear the noxious fumes that came from the machinery surrounding the individual at its center. He was suspended from chains that wrapped his chest and shoulders but exposed the stumps where his arms and legs had been torn from him nearly a century ago. Piping and tubes sunk into the lower section of his torso connected him to bellows and pumps. While technically his heart and lungs did not need these in order to function, the devices augmented his ancient organs, as he had long exceeded his natural lifespan.

Covered in a thin sheen of sweat, Alexander Karchev's bald head gleamed beneath the gaslights. The kommander had already been subjected to a taxing and intensive regimen of pain and agony. His flesh had proven remarkably resilient. He should have been at her mercy: helpless, weak, and alive only by the functions of the redundant support systems. She had eagerly anticipated breaking his will and shaping his mind like clay, pulling forth his inner shames and repressed desires, making him her puppet. She did not understand these reserves of will. There must be a limit.

His eyes met hers as she approached and she gave him a sly smile, walking with swaying hips toward him. He radiated nothing but raw aggression and hatred. Her smile faltered as she felt the temperature in the room increase dramatically and saw the air shimmer around his torso. "Now, now, none of that!" She yanked a lever attached to one of the nearest machines, prompting a flat metal slab set with a tightly packed row of nails coated with a burning liquid to slam into his naked back, piercing through the skin in dozens of places.

His entire frame went rigid as his muscles tightened and his jaw clenched involuntarily, but he did not scream. The shimmering haze around him faded and the temperature returned to normal, to Deneghra's relief. Every time this happened she half-expected the mechanism would fail and then the room would explode with power, tearing her asunder. The image was so vivid in her mind she had to blink and shake her head to clear it. She met his bloodshot eyes.

"You will regret not killing me," he muttered through clenched teeth. "Very soon."

"Hush, now," she crooned, running her cool hand along his sweat-streaked face. "Death's embrace will come, in time. But we must not be hasty. I have plans for you. Wondrous plans. You must feel so helpless, but you will become a weapon again. I dream of the day I can send you against your own countrymen. Imagine their horror, their despair. Their national treasure, the Hero of the First Thornwood War, become a vassal of Lich Lord Asphyxious."

"That will not be," he said flatly. "I serve the Motherland."

Green runes manifested around her hand as she gathered her will. She leaned close, placing her fingers against his forehead, and sent her thoughts wriggling into his mind. Despite his ancient injuries and subsequent modifications, he was still a man, with the desires and weaknesses of his gender. Though her flesh was dead, she knew he must desire her. His will was softening, the pain splitting cracks in his resolve. He must seek comfort, release, oblivion. Somewhere in him was the key to a keening desperation and despair she could use to unravel him. "Surrender to me," she whispered, her lips only inches from his ear. She reversed the lever to retract the spiked plate and sensed his intense relief. Her fingers traced his skin softly.

The same training that allowed a warcaster to connect his mind to cortexes made using such manipulations against one extremely difficult, but Karchev's diminished state had finally given her an opening. For a moment she felt rising excitement as she sensed the chaotic storm of his surface thoughts. She pressed in deeper, deeper. Then his mental barriers slammed back into place with the strength of a steel wall. She had committed so much of her will into the effort that his hatred and defiance sent her staggering, her mind reeling. She snarled and pulled a different lever even as she felt the shimmering signs of his power being mustered once more. This time a nozzle directed at the side of his neck sprayed a thin mist of corrosive bile across his skin, sizzling and popping as it ate the upper layers. The pain overwhelmed him again and his concentration was lost, even as his eyes remained defiant.

Deneghra glared back at him, considering that perhaps keeping him alive was not worth the effort. For a crippled man, he had been a most troublesome captive. She refused to admit defeat; Asphyxious had taken to the idea of transforming Karchev into a weapon to be used against his own nation, and such a transformation would require work. Asphyxious would assist once they had him back at the Thornwood necrofactorium, but her failure to break the man's will before turning him over to the lich lord vexed her.

She turned a geared dial attached to the wheezing bellows, reducing the rate of their compressions. Karchev's breathing became strained, his eyelids flickered, and his head fell as the lack of oxygen forced him unconscious. Satisfied he was in no position to demolish the chamber with the force of his hatred, Deneghra turned the dial in the other direction, just enough to ease his breathing, and stepped back.

"Mistress, I have urgent news." The hissing words did not startle her. She had been aware of the approach of the pistol wraith, who drifted serenely through the intervening walls to reach her side. He knelt and bowed his head. She recognized him as a creature once named Thomas Ketchum, one of several wraiths she had sent outside the city to watch for unexpected trouble.

"Speak," she commanded him.

"While patrolling the eastern road, I spied a mortal attempting to flee the city unseen and followed him. He bore the colors and wore the cloak of a ranger of Cygnar. I might have killed him, but his manner suggested a man on a mission, and he was protective of a satchel he bore—"

"Get to the point." Ketchum was an old wraith and slightly eccentric. Deneghra put up with him only because he was also keenly intelligent and observant.

"I went ahead of him, having heard the sound of hooves, and discovered a large column of Cygnarans advancing down the mountain roads from Stonebridge or Bainsmarket. By the banners I mark it as the Storm Division, with Lord Commander Stryker commanding. A large force, well equipped. I returned and killed the ranger I had followed, lest his communications be delivered. I then came to you." He bowed again.

"How long until they arrive?"

"Three days at most, although such a force will take time to ready for assault. Of course, the Cygnaran-occupied military quarter holds the gate to that road."

Deneghra showed no outward reaction, although her mind was leaping ahead. "And the satchel? Did you bring the messages he bore?"

"Of course, mistress." The wraith became substantial and offered a leather case bearing the Cygnus. After taking it, she dismissed him to vanish once more through the walls.

> ## "IT WOULD NOT BE BEYOND LORD TORUK TO OBLITERATE HIS PRESENT SERVANTS IN THEIR ENTIRETY AND START ANEW."

Deneghra quickly skimmed and her eyes narrowed through the intercepted missives. It was too much to hope this had been the only copy. The Cygnarans would have dispatched a dozen rangers or more. If it was no ruse, Khador would have done the same. Deneghra had eyes and ears scattered around the periphery of the city, but they were primarily to watch for the approach of armies. Single elusive couriers would be easy to miss. She looked back to the unconscious Khadoran and her mouth tightened. Savoring that project would have to wait. She sent her will lashing out like a whip to crack against the mind of her nearest necrotech, who was two chambers away working on a piece of delicate apparatus. He abandoned his work and came at once.

Deneghra barely acknowledged his arrival as she ordered, "Prepare Karchev for travel."

Deneghra found Asphyxious regally surveying the harvest of bodies and souls from one of the taller buildings just south of the central river locks. From here he could oversee the operation and issue commands to his skarlocks and other subordinates. He was suffused with a spectral green glow as the tormented essence of the slain howled and swirled around him. His soul cages pulsed with necromantic energy, filled beyond their ordinary capacity, and now he was sampling the essence of the newly slain as a connoisseur of the ineffable and immortal essence of life.

Next to him stood his battle skarlock, Vociferon, who held aloft a bladed staff with a crossbar from which dangled a mass of gleaming soul cages.

As souls of greater potency emerged from below, Asphyxious cast aside weaker ones, discarding them to fall shrieking and moaning amid the streets of Point Bourne. Ghosts birthed by violence, some might pass on to Urcaen, traumatized and reduced by their rough handling, while others would haunt this place to act out their final moments. While invisible to most mortal eyes, their presence would be felt in subtler ways. Most of these shades were insubstantial and impotent, in life possessed of inadequate ambition, but some few might learn to sustain themselves by preying on the living. The scars that would be left on Point Bourne would be deeper than the bullet holes pocking its walls and the rubble in its streets.

Deneghra was not immune to the rush and euphoria of this influx of fresh-spilled soul energy. Her own cages were also brimming with power, and she could feel vitality pouring through her dead flesh. The only time she had felt similar overwhelming potency had been atop the Temple Garrodh while it swept in the souls of the slain as armies clashed around it. Most of that power had flowed directly to Asphyxious, but she had been able to sample the currents as they spilled through the machine and its vault-like core. The secrets of that facility had been lost when it tumbled beneath the earth, buried beyond even Cryx's attempts at recovery. There was still much the Orgoth had known that they had yet to understand.

Asphyxious turned as she approached and said, "Dost thou come to savor the harvest? The selection is rather flavorless, I am afraid. But their bodies will serve."

"Lord Asphyxious, I bring urgent news," she responded, feeling urgency. "First, I have word of a Cygnaran army marching here from the east, to arrive very soon." She described what she knew of the force her pistol wraith had encountered. "Clearly Iron Lich Virulex was defeated."

"Virulex has a talent for survival. I feel certain we shall see him again." His tone suggested this was unfortunate. He had sent the iron lich to conduct raids deeper in the interior quite deliberately; Virulex's true loyalties rested with Lich Lord Terminus.

"Additionally," Deneghra continued, "Khador and Cygnar have entered into an alliance against us. Those remaining here in the city will work together now."

Asphyxious did not seem alarmed. "Thou did predict this alliance; I thought their enmity too deep."

"I did not think it would happen so quickly," Deneghra admitted. "I had hoped to be gone from the city first."

"It would seem we have no choice but to establish a stronger defensive perimeter and weather their attacks until the arrival of Venethrax. Not an ideal situation, to be sure, but one we considered. I may need thee to hasten north to gather reinforcements, including Mortenebra and her special project." Asphyxious peered out above the rooftops, looking first to the west, then the east. "It may be time to exterminate those forces barricaded within the walls, before the arrival of external armies bolster them. Which to slaughter first? Khador, I think. Their position is improvised and considerably less secure."

"A different plan occurred to me," Deneghra said, choosing her words carefully. "I believe we need to rethink our contingencies."

Asphyxious seemed in a receptive mood, perhaps sated by the ample influx of souls and corpses. "Oh?" he asked. "I will hear thy mind."

She smiled and continued, "Given Lich Lord Venethrax is delayed and we cannot know when he will arrive, I suggest we abandon the city entirely and retreat to the Thornwood. There is no point in wasting resources becoming embroiled in an escalating battle here, against both Khador and Cygnar at once." She was careful not to suggest they might be defeated in such a clash, knowing such a statement would prick his pride.

"My sweet Deneghra, it was at *thine* urging that we took this city at the outset, a course I was initially loath to follow. I know thee too well to think thou shirks from battle. The resources we have gathered exist solely for the purpose of being expended where and when we wish. Thou knowest this, so perhaps I have mistaken thy meaning."

She said, "We must think first and foremost of the athanc borne by Lich Lord Venethrax—am I correct in this?"

"Of that there is no doubt. Even were Lord Toruk's eye not fixed hungrily upon this freshly discovered prize, it would behoove us at this time to bestow upon the other lich lords our cooperation in this matter. There is much capital to be won, should our efforts prove instrumental in its recovery. Similarly, its loss would prompt repercussions. It would not be beyond Lord Toruk to obliterate his present servants in their entirety and start anew."

Deneghra had never heard this particular scenario spoken and shuddered at the thought. She had never seen the dragon with her own eyes but had learned to respect and fear him based upon the manner in which Asphyxious referred to him. Her master was not easily cowed by the might of others. "Consider then, the consequences if we linger. Yes, we would hold Point Bourne secure, providing the means for Venethrax to escape west, but by the time he arrives this entire region will be embroiled in open war. The

chances of his exodus being detected would become all the greater. Khador's and Cygnar's navies might coordinate to intercept. If we are careful executing our retreat, however, leaving some lingering forces to slow the enemy and allowing them to witness our reversal, they will be drawn after us like flies to carrion. Their armies will chase on our heels to finish us, underestimating our reserves. We have worked to convince them the bulk of our strength lies on the Broken Coast, and they believe it. If they smell blood and think they can finish us, they will not hesitate to do so. They will chase us north, toward the necrofactorium, with armies as large as they can muster."

Asphyxious seemed to consider her words and then said, "All the while, Venethrax can continue south, unimpeded."

"Precisely. Skarre and her riverboats can linger behind, staying unseen among the detritus on the river. There has been little river trade since the war reached these waters. When Venethrax nears, they will make use of Malathrax's agents in Five Fingers to expedite their exodus past the Bay of Stone as planned. The fleet will rendezvous and see them home while the might of Cygnar and Khador follows us."

It was a long moment before Asphyxious replied. "We would be taking considerable risk in so doing. Exposing the heart of my power to their eyes."

"True," she admitted, "but we will be ready to make battle on ground of our choosing. By your power, we can withstand them. If the recovery of the athanc is of prime importance, I believe this is the better course."

"Thou serves me well," Asphyxious said after a lengthy pause, prompting in her a rush of pleasure and contentment that momentarily overwhelmed her. He waved dismissively. "I leave it to thy discretion to relate the plan to Skarre Ravenmane; I feel no need to speak with the satyxis."

Lord Commander Coleman Stryker was proud of how swiftly the men of his division had made the march to Point Bourne, particularly as they were already battered and weary. Given what he knew of the city's fortifications and the measures taken to secure the northern shore, he had been skeptical of the news of its capture. Now, though, he saw the proof in thick plumes of smoke that poured from the city to darken the sky.

His mind went to those he knew in the city, including both Major Haley and Captain Sloan as well as his old instructors at the Strategic Academy. He thought of them as he marched alongside Ol' Rowdy, remembering the days before his journeyman tour, when he had first become acquainted with the stubborn warjack that would become his most loyal battlefield companion. It was during those years at the Strategic Academy that he had confronted his power, which he had once sought to suppress, and come to grips with what he could be. He never would have imagined Khadoran boots treading on those streets, let alone putting old and familiar buildings to the torch. His anger increased as he imagined it, and he knew similar thoughts added urgency to the footsteps of his soldiers.

"That smoke seems very thick," Constance Blaize observed as they neared. Her smaller force of Morrowan knights and the remnants of the ruined Paulson Barracks had joined him a week previous. Stryker appreciated the presence of another experienced warcaster, particularly since Captain Kraye had been sent to Corvis, he had left Major Brisbane at Stonebridge, and Caine had been requested for some special mission to the south. His own force was outfitted with ample warjacks, but he had too few warcasters to properly exploit them. Blaize continued, "Why would the Khadorans burn the town?"

Stryker's lip curled. "It would not be completely out of character for them to burn what they cannot pillage. We saw similar acts in Llael." He reconsidered this even as he spoke: This situation was not like Llael, he reminded himself. With Point Bourne's strategic location, it would be to Khador's advantage to keep the city intact. They should have been fortifying. Casting about for an explanation, he added, "Resistance was likely more fierce than they anticipated." He could not imagine Major Haley in particular giving up the city. He hoped she had learned the value in a strategic retreat after the fall of Northguard.

One of his advance rangers reached him from ahead, her expression difficult to read. "Lord Commander, take a look!" She offered her spyglass to him and pointed toward the wall.

Stryker felt some slight annoyance at this lack of proper protocol. Rangers were supposed to offer reports to their superiors, not goad their curiosity. But members of the CRS had been long accustomed to looser practices, as was likely necessary in their role. He took the lens and peered through it. The battlements seemed surprisingly intact. This nearest section of the city was the military quarter where the northern Strategic Academy was located, and his hopes increased as he saw familiar uniforms atop the wall. "Looks like things are not as bleak as we feared," he said. "We still have the military quarter, certainly the most secure area of the city."

"Look to the inner wall," the ranger advised, pointing.

He squinted into the distance at the limits of the spyglass' effective range. After a bit of searching he found a narrow section of the inner battlements facing into the city and caught a glimpse of crimson. He adjusted the focus, and this became red uniforms. He saw the silhouette of an oversized scoped rifle, what had to be a Widowmaker. His

eye flinched; he half-expected to see the enemy sniper fire on the Cygnarans atop the adjacent wall. When this did not happen, he walked several paces ahead to find a better angle and at last confirmed Khadorans and Cygnarans occupying the same battlement, with perhaps a dozen yards between. Neither looked at the other, staring instead down into the city streets. He lowered the glass, dumbfounded. "Morrow above, how can this be?"

The Cygnaran soldiers cheered the arrival of the Storm Division and ushered the leading officers into the overcrowded military quarter. The lord commander had been forced to leave most of his soldiers outside the gates, instructing them to watch their perimeter and be ready for anything. It looked as though what remained of the Point Bourne garrison, a sizable portion of Cygnar's First Army, was crammed into every possible building of the district. Many of those Stryker passed showed signs of recent injuries, including some who were seriously maimed.

Stryker acknowledged their enthusiasm but kept his attention focused ahead, where his escort had been instructed to take him immediately to their senior-most officer. When he'd heard Lord General Olan Duggan was still alive—and actively involved in making plans with the senior Khadoran officer!—it had been more than he could believe. The Duke of the Northforest's lands had been claimed by northerners during the retreat. He had fought at Fellig, Deepwood Tower, and Northguard, making the defense of Cygnar's borders against Khadoran and Khadoran-paid mercenary incursions his life's work. Yet as the lord commander walked forward to the western plaza where rows of sword knights, long gunners, and trenchers were gathered in formation, he saw the grizzled lord general standing at a map-strewn table alongside a Khadoran in warcaster armor festooned with awards and medals.

"Supreme Kommandant Gurvaldt Irusk." Stryker found it impossible to hide the animosity in his voice.

The Khadoran turned at the sound of his name and their eyes locked for a long moment before he offered a slight inclination of his head, the smallest of smiles touching his lips. "Lord Commander Stryker," he said in accented but clear Cygnaran, greeting him as if his arrival was neither unexpected nor notable.

"Lord General Duggan, may I have a word with you?" Stryker inclined his head to show respect to the duke and lord general, but the edge to his tone was unmistakable. The Morridane general did not seem surprised that the warcaster wished to speak to him in private. They walked to the side behind the shelter of a battered Defender being seen to by mechaniks, who made themselves scarce at a glare from Duggan.

Stryker had not had occasion to spend much time with the lord general since the First Army withdrawal to the Dragon's Tongue River, or even since his elevation to Lord Commander. That he had been taken out of the normal chain of command was not widely appreciated by the generals, but Duggan had never shown him any resentment. There was mutual respect between them; Duggan had fought on the front line as a proven leader and was not simply a military bureaucrat. On a personal level, Stryker liked the man. Yet he could not understand finding him in civil discourse with the Khadoran supreme kommandant.

Before he said anything else, Stryker felt compelled to ask, "Where is Major Haley, General?"

Duggan started, clearly having expected different first words. He said, "She left for Corvis just days before the battle. Didn't inform her superiors, either. She was sorely missed." His angry expression suggested volumes unspoken.

While the news was puzzling, Stryker felt a powerful surge of relief that she was likely safe. He kept it from his face. "I'm sure you can rebuke her later. But about this . . ." The wave of his hand was vague, but the general understood his meaning.

"Before you say anything," Lord General Duggan began, "keep in mind you weren't here, and you didn't see the horrors we have dealt with. These are desperate times, Lord Commander." Duggan quickly described what had happened in Point Bourne: the Khadoran assault, the seizure of the locks, and the Cryxian army moving in behind them. He spoke of the slaughter in the streets and of their difficulty mounting expeditions to save more civilians.

"Cryx in the numbers you suggest, so deep within the mainland . . ." Stryker said.

"We knew they lingered in the Thornwood, saw them many times on our retreat from Northguard. They kept nipping at our heels. But those were small, harassing forces. Every time we sought to confront them they retreated into their holes. Reports had suggested that clash at the Orgoth temple had wiped out most of them. Clearly not." His face showed deep-set weariness, and he looked aged beyond his years. "You know me. Do you think I like working with the reds? Even in Llael we had Cryx chewing on our leavings every time we turned around. How long can this continue? We can't keep killing each other just to feed Cryx our dead. We need to purge the Thornwood."

Stryker's expression hardened and he said, "All these horrors are ultimately the fault of Irusk and his empress. Your city could have withstood Cryx had he not paved the way."

"You think I don't know that? I loathe the man, but we need him. And his men."

The lord commander scowled, unconvinced. "You do not speak for the king. What terms did you offer? We cannot trust them. They will turn on us the moment they sense an advantage."

Duggan smiled slightly and said, "They assume we will do the same. I do not expect this arrangement to last. But we are all alive, and that gives us common cause against Cryx. Irusk and his ilk would force us to bow to their empress if they could, but what they want is our lands. What Asphyxious wants is death and our immortal souls. Our two nations cannot endure the spread of the Nightmare Empire. As to terms, that will be between King Leto and the empress. We've sent messages to them. What we did here and what follows is on *my* head; I take full responsibility."

> "WHAT ASPHYXIOUS WANTS IS DEATH AND OUR IMMORTAL SOULS. OUR TWO NATIONS CANNOT ENDURE THE SPREAD OF THE NIGHTMARE EMPIRE."

Stryker could think of nothing more to say and was keenly aware not only that Irusk waited nearby but also that every minute they delayed gave Cryx time to murder and reanimate innocent citizens. "Very well, let us see what comes of your infernal bargain."

They returned to where Irusk was standing. He spoke as if there had been no interval, addressing the lord general. "We should begin the operation to unite our forces."

Lord Commander Stryker interrupted, "How large of a contingent do you have? I hear your army suffered when Cryx took advantage of your distraction to attack from the rear."

Irusk's eyes were piercing, but Stryker did not flinch or look away. The Khadoran said, "Our numbers do not matter to the initial operation."

"It seems to me you have gained a detailed survey of *our* strength by your visit here," Stryker said with a tight smile. "If we are to effectively coordinate, why withhold?"

"Our force will be sufficient to do what must be done," Irusk answered.

Lord General Duggan made a noise and then shook his head when Stryker looked at him. "We're wasting time. Let him talk."

The supreme kommandant looked to the map and said icily, "I have marked blockades and the largest concentrations of Cryxians known to us. Any of these could have shifted.

I will join Lord Commander Stryker and two battalions of his freshly arrived forces as a vanguard along this route," he indicated a street with a gloved finger, "to reach the western gate, at which point my reserves can join us and we can clear these two courtyards. That will give us room to deploy our forces and coordinate strikes against Cryx-held positions, prioritizing the lock bridges."

Stryker frowned but could find no fault. He had studied Irusk's writings in the halls of the academy just a few blocks from where he stood. There was no disputing the man knew how to wage war. "Very well. I'll gather my men. But Irusk," he said sternly, locking eyes once more with the Khadoran, "remember, I am in charge here."

"Of course, Lord Commander," the supreme kommandant said, his back ramrod straight. "We are at your service in these endeavors. Let us cleanse Point Bourne of the dead." He offered an open hand across the map, and Stryker paused only briefly before taking it in his own, feeling unclean as he entered into this conspiracy.

The spirit of Irusk's men was revitalized after his return and as they began to fight back against the Cryxians in the street. They should still have been exhausted, having been afforded so little rest since the first assault on the city. The short reprieve while holed up near the western gate must have helped, but it did not fully explain how they surged against the forces of the dead without hesitation, screaming resounding war cries. They fought alongside his warjacks as an invincible tide, showing no sign of the desperation that had gripped them just the day before.

> **THE CYGNARANS COULD HEAR THE SCREAMS OF THEIR COUNTRYMEN BEING SLAUGHTERED AND SAW THE TOO-FRESH SIGNS OF MASSACRE.**

Kommander Strakhov led his forces and warjacks while Irusk directed his, and their subordinate officers followed their kommandant's plans with expert precision. They did the Motherland proud, even fighting alongside the repugnant blue uniforms of the Cygnarans that had relieved them. As much as possible he and Cygnar's lord commander sought to maintain the integrity of their own companies, but as the battle became more chaotic the two sides increasingly were forced to share the same lanes. Irusk expected tempers to flare, but the soldiers showed admirable restraint and discipline.

Still, the hatred between the two sides was clear. There was no kinship or camaraderie. The Cygnarans could hear the screams of their countrymen being slaughtered and saw the too-fresh signs of massacre. Not just civilians, but innocents that should have been spared such horrors: the elderly, children, even pregnant mothers. Cryx spared no one. Point Bourne had been ravaged. Irusk could not blame the Cygnarans for their simmering anger. He knew his role in this.

Pushing against Cryx, sweeping street to street, they directed that hatred at their mutual foe. Storm Knights and Iron Fangs marched resolutely to the fore as lightning leapt deep into the ranks of mechanithralls and blasting pikes toppled helljacks. There was a sense of competitive pride between the two armies. The Cygnarans resented the Khadorans and hoped to free the city by their own strength of arms, rushing into harm's way rather than holding back and letting the toll fall on their rivals. Similarly, the Khadorans had their dignity to recover after the defeat that had been dealt to them by Cryx. There was vengeance owed, and this day it was the walking dead who paid.

Irusk observed the battling Cygnarans with a critical eye, taking in their tactics and techniques and orders as he always had, knowing he would face them soon enough as adversaries again. He had not entered into this alliance insincerely, as he believed this blight must be rooted out and dealt with, but he knew there could be no lasting accord between their nations.

The Storm Division was Cygnar's finest, hand-picked by their lord commander, veterans one and all and as tightly knit as brothers. They were like unto his own 4th Assault Legion, though the comparison left a sour taste in his mouth. Stryker showed no hesitation to wade into battle at the front, his armor glowing with galvanic power. The Morrowan warcaster, a woman unfamiliar to Irusk, also showed her courage alongside the gleaming knights in silver as she directed her warjacks. Irusk observed that many of the Cygnaran machines were as damaged as his own. Clearly there had been hard fighting before they had arrived at Point Bourne.

Storm Striders advanced behind the front lines, firing sheets of lightning overhead, with Irusk's battered warjacks standing as a wall of iron between them and the enemy. His remaining Devastators, Spriggans, and Demolishers filled the role of moveable barricade, and his mind was split between them even as he barked orders to his subordinates and occasionally invoked his magic to empower his soldiers. Some of his warjacks were entirely out of ammunition, and there was no time to reload them. They pressed on, smashing through dead flesh and trampling thralls underfoot, all the while enduring bile sprays and the pounding of steam-powered fists battering their armored surfaces.

Irusk orchestrated his part of the battle with familiar ease, able to interpret the noises amid the din to determine how the clash transpired despite intervening buildings and distance. He could easily differentiate the sound of Cygnaran and Khadoran firearms in the distance and the noise of more antique Cryxian pistols and rifles, fired by revenants that had boiled forth from the river to join the fight. The booming of mortars and cannons joined the tumult, and he directed the aggressive advance of his remaining artillery batteries. For this fight it was something of an ironic boon he had more artillery crew than pieces to man, allowing him to cycle them as needed. Other soldiers spent their time running to bring water or soaked cloth to cool overheated barrels, sending plumes of scalding steam into the air.

With increasing speed the Cryxian menace was pushed from the southern city. Indeed, the allied force advanced through the streets with a rapidity that surprised Irusk and made him suspicious. By the third day of battle he believed Cryx was not actually committed to the defense. He shared a few brief words with the lord commander, who had come to the same conclusion. They kept their thought to themselves, not wishing to undermine the morale of their men, but Irusk was convinced Cryx did not intend to contest them. Although the number of thralls they fought was staggering, the quality and composition of the force spoke to a token defense. It implied Asphyxious had already accomplished whatever he had intended.

Irusk was shouting orders to get his artillery advanced into higher positions as they neared the largest lock bridge crossing the Dragon's Tongue when something caught his attention across the river. He felt a familiar twinge in the back of his mind and shared a look with Kommander Strakhov, who was organizing his battle-weary assault kommandos. Strakhov yelled for a spyglass from the nearest mortar crew spotter. He used this to peer across the tumult, then he pushed his way back toward the supreme kommandant. "It's Kommander Karchev! I see him—he's alive!" Irusk took the spyglass from the junior warcaster and put it to his eye as Strakhov continued, "I can get to him. This is our chance!"

Irusk saw a number of skittering necrotechs attaching some sort of peculiar piped machinery onto the back of a modified Leviathan. They were clamping it in place and working quickly, but amid the nest of pipes he saw a familiar face: that of Alexander Karchev. Karchev suddenly looked up, his eyes intense and brooding. Across such a distance it seemed impossible he could have seen Irusk, yet there was a sensation of mental contact. Karchev seemed to recognize his supreme kommandant and shook his head once in negation to some unasked question.

"No," Irusk found himself saying. "It is a ruse to draw us forth."

"Kommandant!" Strakhov's face was red and his expression defiant. "I can get to him—I swear it. We cannot leave him in their hands!" Already the Leviathan to which Karchev had been strapped was trundling north. A wall of mechanithralls surged down the street toward the bridge to engage their forces and was met by the shriek of incoming mortar fire. Rifles crackled as revenants emerged from a street to their west.

"Listen to me!" Irusk said in low but intense tones. "He does not wish us to rescue him, not now. He knows his duty. We are being shown him deliberately. Asphyxious seeks to goad us, likely into an ambush. Even were that not so, even if we could bring him back, we would not." Seeing Strakhov did not comprehend his meaning, Irusk turned and scanned the faces of his subordinates to find the bearded face he sought. "Koldun Jielvich!"

He waved to summon the veteran Greylord, whose stern and lined face betrayed his age even more than the white streaks in his beard and hair. He was a powerfully built Khard who held his runed axe in a sure grip. His companion, an old and battered Juggernaut, came with him. "Yes, Kommandant?"

"Are you prepared to use your powers to locate Kommander Karchev, as I asked?"

"Absolutely. We recovered blood from his warjack frame. The rite to locate him requires both time and concentration, but I can begin when you command." He looked at the booming artillery as if suggesting his surroundings were less than ideal.

"Not yet. Return to the fight." He indicated the bridge ahead, where Iron Fangs and mechanithralls clashed. Irusk turned back to Strakhov and said, "The Cryxians are delaying us while their masters retreat. They will set traps for us in the northern city and melt into the Thornwood. They will vanish into their tunnels, confident we cannot follow. Amid that endless forest they could be anywhere, and it would take an age to root them out. But so long as Karchev is with them, we will find their heart and can reach it overland. Let him do his duty."

Strakhov considered this, and although he did not look pleased at last he nodded. There was no question Karchev being alive was no mercy, not in Cryx's grasp. Strakhov turned away and summoned his warjacks as he rejoined the battle. The purging of Point Bourne would bring little satisfaction, and Irusk knew it was only a precursor to the more harrowing fight ahead.

COLOSSAL RULES

COLOSSALS

For the first time in centuries colossals tower over the battlefields, dwarfing men and warjacks alike. Centuries of mechanikal progress have birthed modern colossals that make their predecessors seem primitive in comparison. The colossals of the present day utilize sophisticated cortexes and some of the most advanced and experimental weaponry ever seen in the Iron Kingdoms, making these machines the most powerful weapons in a warcaster's battlegroup.

A **colossal** is a **huge-based** (120 mm) warjack.

HUGE BASE

A huge-based model occupies the space from the bottom of its base to a height of 5″.

FACING & LINE OF SIGHT

A colossal's front arc is marked on its base. Its front arc is further divided into two 90° **fields of fire**. These fields of fire determine which models a colossal can target with its weapons depending on their location. Weapons located on a colossal's left side (L) can target only models in its left field of fire. Weapons located on a colossal's right side (R) can target only models in the colossal's right field of fire. Weapons with locations "S" or "—" can target models in either field of fire. If any part of a model's base is on the line separating the left and right fields of fire it is considered to be in both fields of fire.

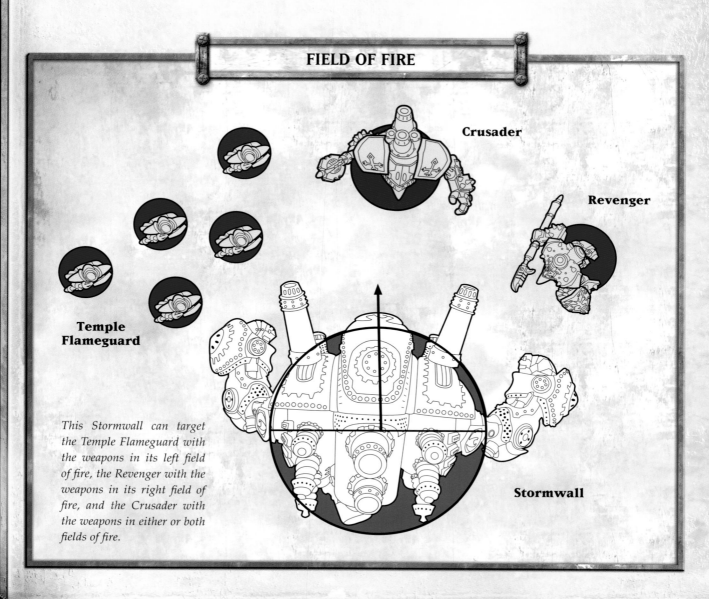

FIELD OF FIRE

Crusader

Revenger

Temple Flameguard

Stormwall

This Stormwall can target the Temple Flameguard with the weapons in its left field of fire, the Revenger with the weapons in its right field of fire, and the Crusader with the weapons in either or both fields of fire.

TARGETING A COLOSSAL

A colossal never gains a DEF bonus from concealment, cover, or elevation.

CLOUD EFFECTS AND FOREST TERRAIN

Cloud effects and forest terrain do not block line of sight to a colossal.

TARGETING A COLOSSAL IN MELEE

A model targeting a colossal with a ranged or magic attack does not suffer the target in melee attack roll penalty. If a ranged or magic attack misses a colossal in melee, that miss is not rerolled against another model. It misses completely.

A colossal can be targeted by combined ranged attacks while it is in melee.

PREDEPLOYMENT

Colossals must be placed before normal deployment. If both players have models to predeploy, they predeploy their models in standard deployment order.

MASSIVE

A colossal cannot be slammed, pushed, thrown, knocked down, or made stationary.

COLOSSAL MOVEMENT

A colossal can only advance during its normal movement and cannot be placed.

PATHFINDER

Although the icon does not appear on their stat lines, all colossals have the Pathfinder advantage.

CONTROLLING A COLOSSAL

Colossals must be assigned to a battlegroup and cannot begin the game under the control of a 'jack marshal. If a 'jack marshal reactivates a colossal, the colossal becomes autonomous instead of coming under the 'jack marshal's control.

Your opponent can never take control of your colossal by any means.

GREAT MACHINE

A colossal never suffers Disruption.

A colossal can never gain Advance Deployment, Incorporeal, or Stealth.

COLOSSAL COMBAT RULES

RANGED ATTACKS WHILE IN MELEE

A colossal can make ranged attacks while in melee. A colossal never suffers the firing in melee penalty when targeting a model it is in melee with.

A colossal cannot gain the aiming bonus while engaged.

COLOSSAL MELEE RANGE

Colossal melee weapons and colossal melee attacks have a 2″ melee range unless otherwise noted. This includes all power attacks made by a colossal.

COLOSSAL POWER ATTACKS

A colossal can make all the power attacks available to a warjack. In addition, it can make two power attacks available only to colossals: power strike and sweep.

POWER STRIKE

A colossal making a **power strike** power attack uses the force of its tremendous melee power to send a smaller-based model flying. A colossal must have at least one non-

crippled Open Fist to make a Power Strike power attack. Its target must be in the Open Fist's field of fire and have a smaller base than the colossal.

The colossal makes a melee attack against the target. If the attack hits, the target is slammed d6 + 2″ directly away from the colossal. The POW of the slam damage roll and the POW of collateral damage rolls resulting from the slam are equal to the STR of the colossal.

SWEEP

A colossal can use its arms to scythe through models within its reach. A colossal must have at least one non-crippled melee weapon to make a sweep power attack. This model makes one melee attack with the weapon against each model in the weapon's field of fire that is within the model's 2″ melee range. Models hit suffer a damage roll with a POW equal to the colossal's STR.

SLAM POWER ATTACK REVISITED

Smaller-based models hit by a slam power attack made by a colossal are moved an additional 2″.

DAMAGING A COLOSSAL

Colossals have two damage grids—right and left—but otherwise suffer damage like a smaller warjack.

When a colossal is damaged, the damage grid to be marked is determined by the origin of the damage suffered. If the origin of damage is in the colossal's right field of fire, the attack will damage the colossal's right damage grid. If the origin of damage is within the colossal's left field of fire, the attack will damage the colossal's left damage grid.

If the colossal suffers damage from an attack and the attacker is in the colossal's back arc or any part of the attacker's base is directly in front of the colossal, the attacker chooses which damage grid takes the damage. If the origin of damage is in the colossal's back arc or directly in front of the colossal and the source of the damage was not an attack, randomize which damage grid takes the damage.

When a colossal suffers damage without a point of origin, such as from a continuous effect, roll a d6 to determine which damage grid takes the damage. On a roll of 1-3 the damage is marked on the colossal's left damage grid. On a roll of 4-6 the damage is marked on the colossal's right damage grid.

Once the damage grid taking the damage has been determined, randomize which column takes the damage.

If all the damage boxes in column 6 of a colossal's damage grid are filled, continue recording damage in column 1 or the next column that contains an unmarked damage box within that same grid. If all the damage boxes in a colossal's grid are filled, continue recording damage on the other grid. Roll a d6 to determine where to apply this damage.

Note that on a colossal, the L and R system locations refer not only to the arm on that side but rather to the entire suite of weapons on that side. For example, if the R system is crippled, all weapons located in location R suffer the effects under Crippled Weapon.

ATTACKER LOCATION DIAGRAM

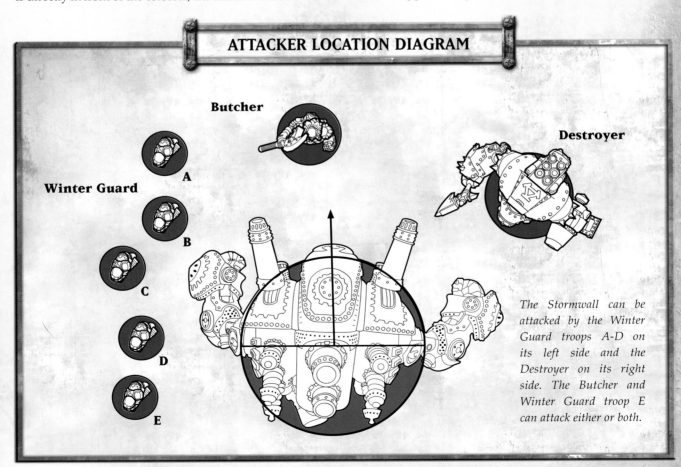

The Stormwall can be attacked by the Winter Guard troops A-D on its left side and the Destroyer on its right side. The Butcher and Winter Guard troop E can attack either or both.

UNBOUND RULES

LARGE-SCALE BATTLES IN THE IRON KINGDOMS

Before you stands an enormous force not even the greatest enemy could dismiss. Rank upon rank of anxious soldiers ready their weapons behind a solid wall of heavily armored warjacks whose heartfires burn with eagerness for the coming fight. In the early dawn, the rising sun begins to illuminate the vast expanse of land that will soon become riddled with craters, wreckage, and the broken bodies of the unfortunate. Weeks of coordination, months of planning, and years of training have gone toward mustering this immense military force, and just across the field prepares an equally impressive collection of determined soldiers and massive machines awaiting the order to attack. Your people and superiors have placed their trust in your ability to lead this army to victory, and the coming battle will decide how history will remember you. Your legacy and the fate of your people are now intertwined.

This is the fire in which heroes are forged. This is WARMACHINE Unbound.

OVERVIEW

The following rules are an optional system for playing large-scale WARMACHINE and HORDES games. These rules feature a new alternating sequence of play that keeps both players involved constantly throughout the game. Though the standard rules can accommodate large-scale play, these rules present a new way to play WARMACHINE and HORDES that keeps the action fast and furious by removing downtime between players' turns. Instead of each player taking a turn and moving all his models each round and then waiting while his opponent takes a turn and moves all *his* models, Unbound rounds are divided into several turns in which players alternate activating *portions* of their armies. In this way, Unbound simulates the ebb and flow of actual battle, giving players ample opportunity to act and react to the fortunes of war.

Instead of completely replacing the rules of WARMACHINE and HORDES, these rules modify only the structure of play while leaving the core mechanics untouched.

As a result of this alternating sequence of play, some model rules have been modified to integrate better into Unbound games. A list of these changes can be found in the Unbound Rules Appendix, pp. 156–159.

Unbound has been designed with multiplayer and team play in mind in addition to two-player games. These rules are covered below.

UNBOUND ARMY CONSTRUCTION

In Unbound games, each player fields 150-point or larger armies with three or more warcasters or warlocks on each side. An additional warcaster or warlock is added to each army for every additional 50 points of models fielded by each player.

Players can also benefit from Formations when building their armies. Formations are bonuses based on different combinations of models in the army. For a list of Unbound Formations, see pp. 32–38.

TABLE SIZE

Due to the scope of Unbound games, it is recommend that players use a 4′ × 6′ table instead of the standard 4′ × 4′ table. Truly massive games may require even larger tables to accommodate play.

DEPLOYMENT ZONES

Unless otherwise noted, players deploy their armies into standard 10″ deployment zones, giving each player a 10″ × 72″ deployment area.

SEIZING THE INITIATIVE

Unless the scenario dictates otherwise, at the start of the game each player makes a starting roll to determine which player will be the first player. The first player sets up first and takes the first turn as in a normal WARMACHINE or HORDES game.

When playing Unbound, the order of play is not static. Instead, beginning with the second round, at the start of each round players roll to determine which player takes the first turn that round. Each player rolls a d6, just as for the starting roll. The player with the higher roll (or the highest roll, in a multiplayer game) has **seized the initiative** and takes the first turn that round.

Note that any modifiers to the starting roll, such as those from the Intelligence ability, do *not* affect the roll to seize the initiative.

DOMINATION BONUS

The more ground a player controls, the greater his chances of seizing the initiative. When playing Unbound, the table is divided into eight 24″ × 18″ territories. Starting with the beginning of the second round, a player gains +1 on his roll to seize the initiative for each territory he controls at that time. A player controls a territory if he has one or more models completely within it and his opponent does not.

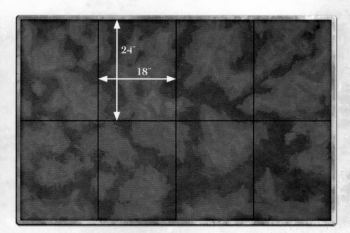

ALTERNATING PLAY

Unbound rounds are divided into a variable number of turns based on the number of warcasters and/or warlocks each player has at the start of the game.

The number of turns each player takes during a round is equal to the number of warcasters and/or warlocks each player has at the start of the game +1. Once the number of turns a player takes during each round has been determined, it does not change as play progresses and warcasters and warlocks are destroyed or removed from play.

PLAY ACCORDINGLY!

The round structure of Unbound games substantially changes the familiar timing of the game and forces players to approach their model and unit activations carefully. Notably, many spells and feats that can be stacked in normal WARMACHINE and HORDES games are limited to affecting only the models activating in the current turn.

As in a standard WARMACHINE and HORDES game, a player must activate each model/unit in his army once each round. Contrary to standard games, however, only a subset of models will activate in a given turn. During each of his turns each round, a player can activate one battlegroup and an assortment of other models and units.

During each round, players alternate taking turns, starting with the player who has the initiative. Once both players have completed all their turns, the round ends. A new round then begins starting with a new roll to seize the initiative.

For game effects, a **round** is measured from the current turn to the end of the last turn of the round. A game effect with a duration of one round expires at the end of the current round.

THE ANATOMY OF A ROUND

Each round has three **phases**: Maintenance, Control, and Activation.

MAINTENANCE PHASE

During the Maintenance Phase players take turns performing the following steps, beginning with the player who has the initiative that round. Once the player with the initiative completes all these steps, the next player will resolve them.

1. Remove all focus points from your models. For each of your models with the Fury Manipulation ability, remove all fury points in excess of its FURY stat. Leave fury points on warbeasts at this time.

2. Check for expiration of continuous effects on any models you control. After removing all expired continuous effects, resolve the effects of those that remain in play. All damage dealt by continuous effects is resolved simultaneously.

3. Resolve all other effects that occur during the Maintenance Phase.

CONTROL PHASE

During the Control Phase, players take turns performing the following steps beginning with the player who has the initiative that round. Once the player with the initiative completes all of these steps, the next player will then resolve them.

1. Each of your models with the Focus Manipulation ability, like warcasters, replenishes its focus and receives a number of focus points equal to its current FOCUS. Each of your models with the Fury Manipulation ability can leach any number of fury points up to its current FURY from warbeasts in its battlegroup in its control area.

2. Each model with the Focus Manipulation or Fury Manipulation abilities can spend focus or fury points to maintain its upkeep spells in play. If a model does not spend focus or fury points to maintain a spell requiring upkeep, the spell expires and its effects end immediately.

3. Make a threshold check for each of your warbeasts with 1 or more fury points left on it. Any warbeasts that fail the check immediately frenzy.

4. Resolve all other effects that occur during the Control Phase.

Note that shaking knockdown and stationary effects in an Unbound game occurs at the start of a turn in which a model activates.

Focus is allocated at the start of each turn, rather than at the start of the round.

ACTIVATION PHASE

During the Activation Phase, players take turns activating their models as defined in the Taking Turns section below. All models you control must be activated once per round.

MARKING ACTIVATED UNITS

We strongly recommend marking your models and units as you activate them. This can be accomplished by placing a token next to each model and unit as it activates. Remove those tokens at the end of the round.

During your final turn of each round, it may be helpful to mark activating units with tokens of a different color to denote they activated during your last turn of the round. Leave these off-color tokens in place when the other activation tokens are removed at the end of the round so players will remember which models/unit cannot activate during the first turn of the next round. After that turn ends, remove the off-color tokens since these models are now eligible to activate this round.

TAKING TURNS

Except for his last turn each round, a player must declare his intention to activate one warcaster- or warlock-controlled battlegroup at the start of each of his turns. Though the models in the battlegroup are still activated separately, all models in the declared battlegroup must be activated that turn.

During a turn in which a player activates a battlegroup, he can also activate any combination of the following:

- Up to 4 units
- Up to 4 solos
- Up to 2 independent warjacks
- Up to 2 battle engines

A player can exercise any of these options or none, as he chooses.

Models and units can be activated in any order during a turn. The models in a battlegroup do not have to be activated before other models and units a player is activating that turn.

All of a player's warcaster- or warlock-controlled battlegroups will have activated before his last turn each round. During his last turn each round a player activates his remaining models and units. If a player has already activated all of his models and units before this turn, he will not be able to activate any models or units during his last turn of the round. Models and units activated during a player's last turn of the previous round cannot be activated during his first turn of a given round. This means that a model can never activate two turns in a row. Note that this rule only applies to models that were activated during each player's last turn of the round (the turn after all warcaster or warlock battlegroups have already been activated).

When a model or unit activates, any warjacks or warbeasts the model or unit controls must also activate that turn. This includes warjacks and warbeasts controlled by 'jack marshals and lesser warlocks.

EXAMPLE: *Brent and Jack are playing a 150-point Unbound game and each player is fielding 3 warcasters. Because the players are fielding 3 warcasters each, each will take 4 turns each round. During each player's first 3 turns each round he must activate one battlegroup. In addition to activating the models in the battlegroup, each player can also activate any combination of the following: up to 4 units, 4 solos, 2 independent warjacks, and 2 battle engines. During each player's fourth turn of the round he must activate any model or units that he has not yet activated that round. Any models/units activated during that fourth turn cannot be activated during the first turn of the upcoming round.*

LOST WARCASTERS AND WARLOCKS

If one or more of a player's warcasters or warlocks have been destroyed or removed from play, that player is not required to activate a warcaster- or warlock-controlled battlegroup during each of his turns and can choose which turns to activate his remaining warcaster or warlock-controlled battlegroups. However, he must still activate all of his remaining battlegroups each round, can only activate one warcaster- or warlock-controlled battlegroup each turn, and cannot activate a warcaster or warlock-controlled battlegroup during his last turn each round.

EXAMPLE: *Jason and DC are playing a 150-point game with each player taking 4 turns each round. Ordinarily, each player must activate a battlegroup during his first 3 turns each round. However, if one of Jason's warcasters is destroyed, he can activate his remaining two battlegroups on the first, second, or third turns and must activate both by his third turn each round. If Jason loses another warcaster, he can choose to activate his remaining battlegroup during the first, second, or third turns but cannot activate it on his fourth.*

FOCUS ALLOCATION

At the start of each of a player's turns, each model with the Focus Manipulation ability activating that turn can allocate focus points to warjacks in its battlegroup that are in its control area.

In order to allocate focus, a player must declare at the start of the turn that the models allocating focus will be activating that turn. This includes non-warcaster models with the Focus Manipulation ability he wants to allocate focus that turn.

SHAKE EFFECTS

Instead of spending focus to shake effects during the Control Phase, a model that can spend focus to shake knock down or stationary does so at the start of its activation.

Instead of being forced to shake effects during the Control Phase, a model that can be forced to shake knock down or stationary does so at the start of its activation.

MULTIPLAYER GAMES

FREE-FOR-ALL GAMES

Unbound can accommodate three or four players in free-for-all games. At the start of the game, all players roll as normal to determine the order of play. At the start of subsequent rounds, players roll to seize the initiative. Reroll ties, with the highest reroll winning the roll, followed by the next highest, and so on.

In a three-player game, each player deploys his models into a 10″ × 34″ deployment zone. One player deploys in the middle of the west table edge, the next player in the northeast corner of the table, and the third player in the southeast corner of the table.

For a four-player game, increase the table size to 4′ × 8′. Each player deploys his models into a 14″ × 38″ deployment zone, each in a different corner of the table.

TEAM GAMES

Team games are played with two or more players on each team, with each player controlling one or more battlegroups. Each team plays a single faction, but its army can include non-faction models that will work for that team faction. Players should decide which battlegroups each player will control before the start of the game. Generally, fielded models that are not part of a battlegroup are not assigned to a specific team member. Instead, players on the team take turns controlling the models that are not part of one of their battlegroups. Remember that each team army can include only one of any character model.

At the start of the game, the teams roll to determine which will set up first and take the first turn. Starting on the second turn, teams will roll to seize the initiative. When calculating a team's domination bonus, count all models on the team.

Throughout each round, teams alternate taking turns. Except for their last turn each round, the players on a team must declare their intention to activate one warcaster- or warlock-controlled battlegroup at the start of each of their turns. The player in control of that battlegroup will then activate all the models in the battlegroup that turn. Additionally, other team members can activate and move additional team models and units that are not part of a battlegroup. On a turn he activates his battlegroup, a player cannot also activate other team models and units. Those are left to his teammates to activate.

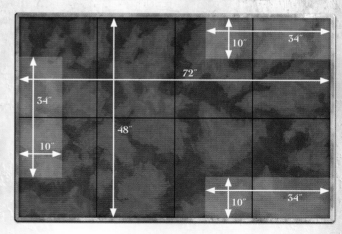

THREE-PLAYER GAME

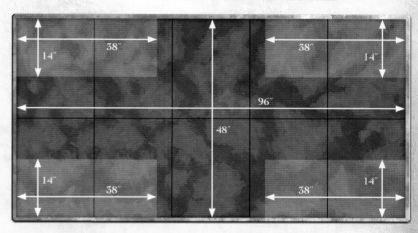

FOUR-PLAYER GAME

During a turn in which a player activates a battlegroup, the other members of the team can activate any combination of the following:

- Up to 4 units
- Up to 4 solos
- Up to 2 independent warjacks
- Up to 2 battle engines

EXAMPLE: *Ed and Chris are playing a 150-point game against Bryan and Will. Ed controls two warcasters and Chris controls one. During their first turn of the game, they decide that Ed will activate one of his battlegroups. In addition to Ed activating the models in his battlegroup, Chris can activate up to four units, up to four solos, up to two independent warjacks, and up to two battle engines.*

FORMATIONS

Formations provide benefits to players in Unbound games based on the composition of their armies. There is no maximum number of Formation benefits a player can gain for his army. Although Formations are broken down by faction, the benefits are granted based on the models in the army, not its primary faction.

EXAMPLE: *If Magnus the Traitor controls three Freebooter warjacks while part of a Khador army, the Freebooters in the army still benefit from the Dockside Brawlers Formation.*

Note that some Formations require a grouping of three or more warjacks or warbeasts in a battlegroup. These requirements must be met at the start of the game, and the Formation benefits are not contingent on the models remaining in play.

CYGNAR

CHARGER WARJACKS - TARGET PRACTICE

Requirement: The army includes three or more Charger warjacks.

Benefit: Charger warjacks gain Swift Hunter. (When a model with Swift Hunter destroys an enemy model with a normal ranged attack, immediately after the attack is resolved it can advance up to 2".)

CENTURION WARJACKS - FORTIFIED POSITION

Requirement: The army includes three or more Centurion warjacks.

Benefit: Reduce the cost of Centurion warjacks by 1. Additionally, Centurion warjacks gain Lash. (A model with Lash and friendly warrior models B2B with it cannot be knocked down.)

DEFENDER WARJACKS - HUNTER-KILLERS

Requirement: One or more of your battlegroups includes three or more Defender warjacks.

Benefit: Defender warjacks in a battlegroup with three or more Defenders gain Concerted Fire. (This activation, models with Concerted Fire in the same battlegroup gain a +1 cumulative bonus to ranged damage rolls for each other model in the battlegroup with Concerted Fire that has hit an enemy model with a ranged attack this activation.)

STORMWALL COLOSSALS - CONVERGENCE

Requirement: The army includes two or more Stormwall colossals.

Benefit: Reduce the cost of Stormwall colossals by 1. Additionally, when resolving a Stormwall colossal's Electro Leap ability ignore models with Immunity: Electricity when determining what model the Electro Leap arcs to.

LONG GUNNER INFANTRY UNITS - INFANTRY LINE

Requirement: The army includes three or more Long Gunner Infantry units.

Benefit: Long Gunner Infantry units gain Reform. (After all models in a unit with Reform have completed their actions, each can advance up to 3")

TRENCHER INFANTRY UNITS - FIRE SUPPORT

Requirement: The army includes two or more Trencher Infantry units.

Benefit: Add a Trencher Chain Gun Crew or a Trencher Cannon Crew unit to the army free of cost. For every additional Trencher Infantry unit in the army after the first two, add an additional Trencher Chain Gun Crew or a Trencher Cannon Crew unit to the army free of cost. These units ignore FA restrictions.

STORM STRIDER BATTLE ENGINES - THUNDERSTORM

Requirement: The army includes two or more Storm Strider battle engines.

Benefit: When a Storm Strider battle engine makes a d3 roll for Lightning Generator, roll 2d3 and discard the lower die roll.

PROTECTORATE OF MENOTH

REPENTER WARJACKS - FIRESTARTERS

Requirement: The army includes three or more Repenter warjacks.

Benefit: Repenter warjacks gain Firestarter (★Action). (When a model makes a Firestarter special action, place a 3″ AOE anywhere completely within 6″ of the warjack. The center point of the AOE must be in the warjack's LOS, ignoring intervening models. A model entering or ending its activation in the AOE suffers a POW 12 fire damage roll ⬤ and Continuous Effect: Fire ⬤. The AOE remains in play for one round or until this model is destroyed or removed from play.)

CASTIGATOR WARJACKS - FIRE WALKERS

Requirement: The army includes three or more Castigator warjacks.

Benefit: Castigator warjacks gain Righteous Flames. (An enemy model that ends its activation within 2″ of a model with Righteous Flames suffers the Fire continuous effect ⬤.)

CRUSADER WARJACKS - CONVOCATION OF FIRE

Requirement: One or more of your battlegroups includes three or more Crusader warjacks.

Benefit: Crusader warjacks in a battlegroup that includes three or more Crusaders gain Soul Drive. (A model with Soul Drive is allocated 1 additional focus point during your Control Phase. A warjack cannot exceed normal focus allocation limits as a result of Soul Drive.)

JUDICATOR COLOSSALS - FORTRESSES OF RIGHTEOUSNESS

Requirement: The army includes two or more Judicator colossals.

Benefit: Reduce the cost of Judicator colossals by 1. Additionally, Judicators gain Divine Influence. (Once per activation when the AOE ranged attack of a model with Divine Influence deviates, you can reroll the direction and/or distance of deviation.)

EXEMPLAR BASTIONS AND EXEMPLAR CINERATOR UNITS - HEAVY ARMOR

Requirement: The army includes two or more Exemplar Bastion units and two or more Exemplar Cinerator units.

Benefit: Exemplar Bastion and Exemplar Cinerator models gain Advance Move. (Before the start of the game but after both players have deployed, a model with Advance Move can make a full advance.)

KNIGHTS EXEMPLAR UNITS - HAND OF GOD

Requirement: The army includes three or more Knights Exemplar units.

Benefit: Knights Exemplar units gain Relentless Charge. (Models with Relentless Charge gain Pathfinder ⬤ during activations they charge.)

VESSEL OF JUDGMENT BATTLE ENGINES - MIRACLES OF WAR

Requirement: The army includes two or more Vessel of Judgment battle engines.

Benefit: Each time you activate a Vessel of Judgment battle engine, at the start of that activation remove d3 damage from the battle engine.

KHADOR

DESTROYER WARJACKS - BOMBS AWAY

Requirement: The army includes three or more Destroyer warjacks.

Benefit: Destroyer warjacks gain Quick Work. (When a model with Quick Work destroys one or more enemy models with a melee attack during its combat action, immediately after the attack is resolved it can make one normal ranged attack. Attacks gained from Quick Work do not count against a weapon's ROF.)

DEVASTATOR WARJACKS - CONVOY

Requirement: The army includes three or more Devastator warjacks.

Benefit: Reduce the cost of Devastator warjacks by 1. Additionally, Devastator warjacks gain Heavy Boiler. (A model with Heavy Boiler can run without spending focus.)

MARAUDER WARJACKS - STEAMROLLER

Requirement: The army includes three or more Marauder warjacks.

Benefit: Marauder warjacks gain Follow Up. (When a model with Follow Up slams an enemy model, immediately after the slam is resolved the slamming model can advance directly toward the slammed model up to the distance it was moved.)

CONQUEST COLOSSALS - MOVING MOUNTAINS

Requirement: The army includes two or more Conquest colossals.

Benefit: Reduce the cost of Conquest colossals by 1. Additionally, Conquest colossals gain Bulldoze. (When a model with Bulldoze that is not making a trample power attack advances into B2B contact with an enemy model during its activation, it can push that model up to 2" directly away from it. A model can be pushed by Bulldoze only once per activation.)

IRON FANG PIKEMEN UNITS - WALL OF IRON

Requirement: The army includes three or more Iron Fang Pikemen units.

Benefit: Iron Fang Pikemen units gain Stalwart. (While B2B with another model in its unit, a model with Stalwart cannot be knocked down.)

MAN-O-WAR BOMBARDIERS AND MAN-O-WAR DEMOLITION CORPS UNITS - MECHANIZED INFANTRY

Requirement: The army includes two or more Man-O-War Bombardiers units and two or more Man-O-War Demolition Corps units.

Benefit: Man-O-War models gain Advance Move. (Before the start of the game but after both players have deployed, a model with Advance Move can make a full advance.)

GUN CARRIAGE BATTLE ENGINES - ROLLING BARRAGE

Requirement: The army includes two or more Gun Carriage battle engines.

Benefit: Gun Carriage battle engines gain +1 RAT.

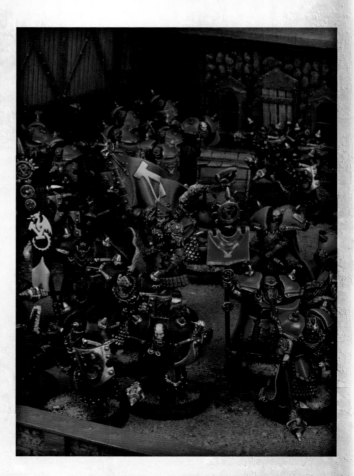

CRYX

DEATHRIPPER BONEJACKS - BONEPICKERS

Requirement: The army includes five or more Deathripper bonejacks.

Benefit: Deathripper bonejacks gain Dodge. (A model with Dodge can advance up to 2″ immediately after an enemy attack that missed it is resolved unless it was missed while advancing. It cannot be targeted by free strikes during this movement.)

SLAYER HELLJACKS - DEATHMONGERS

Requirement: One or more of your battlegroups includes three or more Slayer helljacks.

Benefit: Slayer helljacks in the battlegroup with three or more Slayers gain Deathdealer. (Models with Deathdealer gain +2 on melee attack rolls against trooper models.)

LEVIATHAN HELLJACKS - SUPPRESSION FIRE

Requirement: The army includes three or more Leviathan helljacks.

Benefit: Leviathan helljacks' Spiker weapons gain Covering Fire (★Action). (A model with a weapon with Covering Fire (★Action) can place a 3″ AOE anywhere completely within the weapon's RNG as a ★Action. The center point of the AOE must be in the model's LOS, ignoring intervening models. A model entering or ending its activation in the AOE suffers a damage roll with POW equal to the POW of the weapon with Covering Fire (★Action). The AOE remains in play for one round or until the model is destroyed or removed from play.)

KRAKEN COLOSSAL - MORTUARY SCIENCE

Requirement: The army includes two or more Kraken colossals.

Benefit: Reduce the cost of Kraken colossals by 1. Additionally, Kraken colossals begin the game with one corpse token.

MECHANITHRALL UNITS - SHAMBLING DEAD

Requirement: The army includes five or more Mechanithrall units.

Benefit: Mechanithrall units gain Shambling. (When a model with Shambling is disabled by blast damage, it heals 1 damage point, is no longer disabled, and is knocked down.)

REVENANT CREW OF THE *ATRAMENTOUS* - GUN DECK

Requirement: The army includes two or more Revenant Crew of the *Atramentous* units.

Benefit: Add a Revenant Cannon Crew unit to the army free of cost. For every additional Revenant Crew of the *Atramentous* unit in the army after the first two, add an additional Revenant Cannon Crew unit to the army free of cost. These units ignore FA restrictions.

WRAITH ENGINE BATTLE ENGINES - NIGHTMARE LEGION

Requirement: The army includes two or more Wraith Engine battle engines.

Benefit: Wraith Engine battle engines each begin the game with three soul tokens.

RETRIBUTION OF SCYRAH

BANSHEE MYRMIDONS - HYMNS OF DESTRUCTION

Requirement: The army includes three or more Banshee myrmidons.

Benefit: Increase the range of the Banshee's Wailing ability to 7″.

HYDRA MYRMIDONS - ARCANODYNAMICS

Requirement: The army includes three or more Hydra myrmidons.

Benefit: At the start of each of its activations, a Hydra myrmidon is allocated 1 focus point. (A warjack cannot exceed normal focus allocation limits as a result of Arcanodynamics.)

PHOENIX MYRMIDONS - AVENGING ANGELS

Requirement: The army includes three or more Phoenix myrmidons.

Benefit: Phoenix myrmidons gain Righteous Flames. (An enemy model that ends its activation within 2″ of a model with Righteous Flames suffers the Fire continuous effect .)

HYPERION COLOSSALS - RAGE OF AEONS

Requirement: The army includes two or more Hyperion colossals.

Benefit: Reduce the cost of Hyperion colossals by 1. Additionally, Hyperion colossals gain Phoenix Field. (Remove d6 damage points from the force field of a model with Phoenix Field after resolving continuous effects during your Maintenance Phase. While its Field Generator system is crippled, the model loses Phoenix Field.)

DAWNGUARD SENTINEL UNITS - BLADES OF DAWN

Requirement: The army includes three or more Dawnguard Sentinel units.

Benefit: Dawnguard Sentinel units gain Stalwart. (While B2B with another model in its unit, a model with Stalwart cannot be knocked down.)

HOUSEGUARD HALBERDIER UNITS - MINOR HOUSES

Requirement: The army includes three or more Houseguard Halberdier units.

Benefit: Houseguard Halberdier units' Halberds gain Powerful Charge. (A model gains +2 to charge attack rolls with a weapon with Powerful Charge.)

ARCANTRIK FORCE GENERATOR BATTLE ENGINES - ARCANTRIK CONVERGENCE

Requirement: The army includes two or more Arcantrik Force Generator battle engines.

Benefit: If an Arcantrik Force Generator forfeits its movement during its activation for the aiming bonus, friendly myrmidon models within 2″ of it are affected by Range Booster.

MERCENARIES

NOMAD WARJACKS - HOT RODS

Requirement: The army includes three or more Nomad warjacks.

Benefit: Nomad warjacks gain Heavy Boiler. (A model with Heavy Boiler can run without spending focus.)

ROVER WARJACKS - COUNTING COUP

Requirement: The army includes three or more Rover warjacks.

Benefit: Rover warjacks gain Retaliatory Strike. (When a model with Retaliatory Strike is hit by a melee attack made by an enemy model during your opponent's turn, after the attack is resolved the model hit can immediately make one normal melee attack against the enemy model. A model can make one Retaliatory Strike per turn.)

GALLEON COLOSSAL - SQUARE-RIGGED

Requirement: The army includes two or more Galleon colossals.

Benefit: Reduce the cost of Galleon colossals by 1. Additionally, Galleon colossals gain Assault. (As part of a charge, after moving but before making its charge attack, a model with Assault can make one ranged attack targeting the model charged unless they were in melee with each other at the start of the activation of the model with Assault. When resolving an Assault ranged attack, the attacking model does not suffer the target in melee penalty. If the target is not in melee range after moving, the model with Assault can make the Assault ranged attack before its activation ends.)

STEELHEAD RIFLEMEN UNITS - BEST THAT MONEY CAN BUY

Requirement: The army includes three or more Steelhead Riflemen units.

Benefit: The RNG of the Military Rifles of Steelhead Riflemen units in increased to 12.

SEA DOG CREW UNITS - POWDER MONKEYS

Requirement: The army includes two or more Sea Dog Crew units.

Benefit: Add a Sea Dog Deck Gun unit to the army free of cost. For every additional Sea Dog Crew unit in the army after the first two, add an additional Sea Dog Deck Gun unit to the army free of cost. These units ignore FA restrictions.

GHORDSON AVALANCHER WARJACKS - EXPERIMENTAL ARTILLERY

Requirement: The army includes three or more Ghordson Avalancher warjacks.

Benefit: Ghordson Avalancher warjacks' Avalanche Cannons gain Quake. (On a direct hit with a weapon with Quake against an enemy model, all models hit are knocked down.)

HORGENHOLD FORGE GUARD UNITS - THE BIG GUNS

Requirement: The army includes two or more Horgenhold Forge Guard units.

Benefit: Add a Horgenhold Artillery Corps unit to the army free of cost. For every additional Horgenhold Forge Guard unit in the army after the first two, add an additional Horgenhold Artillery Corps unit to the army free of cost. These units ignore FA restrictions.

OGRUN ASSAULT CORPS UNITS - MOBILE ARTILLERY

Requirement: The army includes three or more Ogrun Assault Corps units.

Benefit: Ogrun Assault Corps units gain Assault (Order). (Affected models must charge or run. As part of a charge, after moving but before making its charge attack, an affected model can make one ranged attack targeting the model charged unless they were in melee with each other at the start of the affected model's activation. Models that received this order cannot make combined ranged attacks this activation. When resolving an Assault ranged attack, the attacking model does not suffer the target in melee penalty. If the target is not in melee range after moving, the affected model must still make the ranged attack before its activation ends.)

UNBOUND SCENARIOS

The following scenarios have been designed for Unbound games. They reflect titanic clashes between armies in the midst of war and cover a broad selection of missions and battlefield conditions. Unbound scenarios are narrative and mission-oriented and are not purely competitive. These scenarios do not simply create an alternate win condition but instead frequently alter how the game itself is played.

Unless otherwise noted, these scenarios are intended to be played on a 4′ × 6′ table.

When selecting a scenario, players either agree on which scenario to play or roll on the appropriate table below. It is best for players to determine which scenario they will play prior to building their armies since the scenario rules can introduce significant twists, such as building destruction or board-wide flooding.

TERRAIN PLACEMENT

Before choosing their deployment zones, players take turns placing terrain features. Players alternate placing terrain features until one player wishes to stop. The other player is then allowed to place one additional terrain feature. Each player must place a minimum of three terrain features unless otherwise dictated by a scenario's special rules.

Terrain features should be moderately sized, no more than 12″ across. A terrain feature cannot be placed within 3″ of another terrain feature. The exceptions to this are that terrain features can be placed on hills and that trench terrain features can be placed where they touch other trench terrain features.

MULTIPLAYER PLAY

Many of the following scenarios are suitable for play with three or four players. Additional rules for each of those scenarios are described in its Multiplayer Game section.

RANDOM SCENARIO DETERMINATION

If both players agree, instead of choosing a scenario for the battle, you can roll 2d6 and consult this table to determine the scenario you will play.

ROLL	RESULT
2	Basic Battle
3	Treasure Hunt
4	Battle in the Wilderness
5	Occupation
6	The Great Divide
7	No Man's Land
8	Barnstormers
9	Last Stand
10	King of the Hill
11	Scorched Earth
12	Floodland

For multiplayer battles, you can roll a d6 and consult this table to determine the scenario you will play.

ROLL	RESULT
1	Barnstormers
2	Battle in the Wilderness
3	Floodland
4	King of the Hill
5	Occupation
6	Treasure Hunt

BASIC BATTLE

Mortal man is never so close to the divine as when he commands a great army in battle.

—Kommandant Gurvaldt Irusk

DESCRIPTION

The loss of the army's commanders will deal a crippling blow to any force and may shatter the morale of an entire army. In this battle, two armies clash with the goal of destroying the opposing commanders.

SPECIAL RULES

There are no special rules for this scenario.

VICTORY CONDITIONS

A player wins the game when he has the only remaining warcaster(s) or warlock(s) in play.

MULTIPLAYER GAME

This scenario is suitable for multiplayer play.

BARN STORMERS

That fortification not only offers sanctuary but is the key to this battle.

—Grissel Bloodsong

DESCRIPTION

The significance of any refuge from the guns of the enemy cannot be overstated. In the maelstrom of war, any townhouse, ruin, or standing structure can become a de facto fortress.

SPECIAL RULES

Before placing any other terrain features, place a 6″ × 10″ structure in the center of the table, as shown on the diagram below. That structure is an obstruction that cannot be damaged. It should have entryways large enough to accommodate large-based models on two opposite sides.

Throughout the scenario, players will attempt to hold the structure. At the end of each round, a player holds the structure and scores 1 victory point if he has one or more models completely in the structure and his opponent has none. Ignore models that are fleeing or out of formation, inert warjacks, and wild warbeasts when determining whether a player holds the structure.

VICTORY CONDITIONS

A player wins the game when he has 3 victory points or if he has the only remaining warcaster(s) or warlock(s) in play.

MULTIPLAYER GAME

This scenario is suitable for multiplayer play.

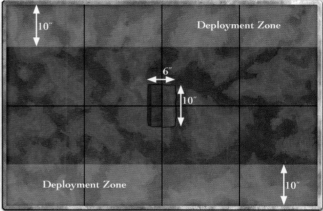

BATTLE IN THE WILDERNESS

Vhat none remember is that the roots of these great trees have long drunk of the blood of the dead and dying.
—The Old Witch of Khador

DESCRIPTION

Two vast armies fall upon each other in the midst of an ancient forest. Only the more tenacious will be able to oust the enemy and take the day.

SPECIAL RULES

Before placing any other terrain features, place an 8"-diameter forest in the center of the table. Players then take turns each placing four additional 8"-diameter forests anywhere within 8" of the center forest. These forests cannot be placed within 3" of each other or the center forest.

Throughout the scenario, players will attempt to hold these sections of forest. A player holds a forest if he has one or more models completely within the area of a forest and his opponent has none. Ignore models that are fleeing or out of formation, inert warjacks, and wild warbeasts when determining whether a player holds a forest.

After the forests are placed, players takes turns placing up to two additional terrain features each. Remember that a terrain feature cannot be placed within 3" of another terrain feature, including a forest.

VICTORY CONDITIONS

Starting at the end of the second round, a player wins the game if at the end of the round he holds five or more of the forests. A player also wins if he has the only remaining warcaster(s) or warlock(s) in play.

MULTIPLAYER GAME

In a three-player game, do not place a forest in the center of the table. Instead, players take turns each placing three 8"-diameter forests anywhere within 18" of the center of the table. These forests cannot be placed within 3" of each other.

In a four-player game, place an 8"-diameter forest in the center of the table. Players then take turns each placing two additional 8"-diameter forests anywhere within 8" of the center forest. These forests cannot be placed within 3" of each other or the center forest.

FLOODLAND

A great tide is coming that will wash our enemies from these sacred lands.

—Hierarch Severius

DESCRIPTION

Endless rains are taking their toll, and it is only a matter of time until the floodwaters rise. The army that succeeds in holding the high ground will be the one to take the day.

SPECIAL RULES

Before placing any other terrain features, place five 10″-diameter hills on the table. The first hill is placed in the center of the table. The next hill is centered on a point 14″ from the north table edge and 14″ from the east table edge. The third hill is centered at a point 14″ from the north table edge and 14″ from the west table edge. The fourth hill is centered at a point 14″ from the south table edge and 14″ from the east table edge. The final hill is centered at a point 14″ from the south table edge and 14″ from the west table edge.

After placing the hills, players take turns placing terrain normally. Remember, terrain features can be placed on the hills.

At the start of every round beginning with the second, roll a d6. On a 5 or 6, the floods come. During the round the floods come, all non-elevated portions of the table are covered by shallow water. After the end of that round, all non-elevated portions of the table are considered to be rough terrain for the rest of the game.

Players score victory points by holding the 10″-diameter hills. A player holds a hill if he has one or more models on it and his opponent has none. At the end of each round, a player scores 1 victory point if he holds three or more of the hills. Ignore models that are fleeing or out of formation, inert warjacks, and wild warbeasts when determining whether a player holds a hill.

VICTORY CONDITIONS

A player wins the game when he has 3 victory points or if he has the only remaining warcaster(s) or warlock(s) in play.

MULTIPLAYER GAME

This scenario is suitable for multiplayer play. A player wins the game when he has 2 victory points or if he has the only remaining warcaster(s) or warlock(s) in play.

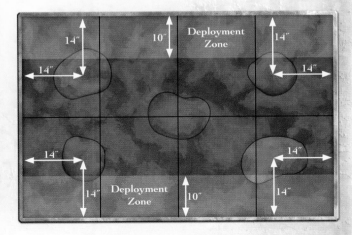

THE GREAT DIVIDE

Wheel your horses around the right flank and I'll strike their center. By Morrow, we will meet in the middle and send them all screaming to Urcaen.

—*General Adept Nemo*

DESCRIPTION

The surest path to victory is to flank your opponent, to divide his forces, and watch his army collapse under the weight of your assault.

SPECIAL RULES

This scenario is played on a table turned lengthwise with players deploying to the 4′ table edges.

Models with Ambush cannot be placed within 30″ of the rear of your opponent's deployment zone.

A player scores 1 victory point at the end of his last turn each round if he has one or more models in his opponent's deployment zone and his opponent has no models in his deployment zone.

VICTORY CONDITIONS

A player wins the game when he has 2 victory points or if he has the only remaining warcaster(s) or warlock(s) in play.

MULTIPLAYER GAME

This scenario is not suitable for multiplayer play.

KING OF THE HILL

With the high ground we assure their death.

—*Lylyth, Shadow of Everblight*

DESCRIPTION

Many battles are fought over strategic locations of uncertain value, but all military strategists know the importance of taking a significant hill before securing ancillary vantage points.

SPECIAL RULES

Before placing terrain features, place a hill at least 10″ in diameter in the center of the table. No other terrain features can be placed on this hill. After the hill is placed, players take turns placing terrain normally.

At the end of each round, a player scores 1 victory point if he has more models on the hill than his opponent does. Ignore models that are fleeing or out of formation, inert warjacks, and wild warbeasts when counting models on the hill.

VICTORY CONDITIONS

A player wins the game when he has 3 victory points or if he has the only remaining warcaster(s) or warlock(s) in play.

MULTIPLAYER GAME

In a three-player game, center the hill at a point in the middle of the table 28″ from the west table edge.

In a four-player game, the hill remains centered in the middle of the table.

Deployment Zone

10″

10″

Deployment Zone

LAST STAND

Archdomina, their forces are surrounded. We begin the final assault at your pleasure.

—Tyrant Xerxis

NO MAN'S LAND

Supreme Kommandant, the only thing standing between us and victory is a maze of trenches, death traps, and those pitiful ruins our enemies call fortifications. It is going to be a glorious day!

—Karchev the Terrible

DESCRIPTION

Last Stand is a desperate battle for survival. Surrounded and cut off from support, one army prepares for the onslaught of its enemies while the other moves to capitalize on its fortunes or be destroyed in the attempt.

SPECIAL RULES

Before placing terrain, players each roll a d6. The high roller chooses whether to be the attacker or the defender.

The attacker sets up first and takes the first turn, but his models lose the Advance Deployment advantage.

The defender's deployment zone is a 12″ × 36″ area in the southeast table edge. The attacker can deploy his forces anywhere within 10″ of the north and west table edges.

The defender can place two terrain features up to 10″ wide within his deployment zone. After these two terrain features are placed, players take turns placing terrain. The defender cannot place terrain within either player's deployment zone, and the attacker cannot place terrain within the defender's deployment zone.

VICTORY CONDITIONS

A player wins the game when he has the only remaining warcaster(s) or warlock(s) in play.

MULTIPLAYER GAME

This scenario is not suitable for multiplayer games.

DESCRIPTION

The battlefield is a blasted wasteland divided by twisted networks of winding trenches where death lurks behind every corner. The only measure of victory is in territory gained.

SPECIAL RULES

Each player begins with a 5″ × 8″ command trench in the middle of his deployment zone, 5″ from his rear table edge. Players take turns each placing fifteen 3″ × 5″ trench terrain features. Trench terrain features can be placed in contact with other trench terrain features. After these trenches have been placed, each player can place one additional terrain feature no more than 10″ in diameter on his side of the table at least 10″ from the nearest trench terrain feature.

VICTORY CONDITIONS

A player wins the game at the end of any of his turns if he has more models completely in his opponent's command trench than his opponent has in that trench. Ignore models that are fleeing or out of formation, inert warjacks, and wild warbeasts when counting models in a command trench. A player also wins the game when he has the only remaining warcaster(s) in play.

MULTIPLAYER GAME

This scenario is not suitable for multiplayer games.

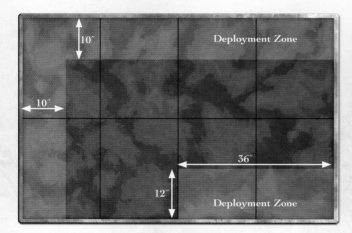

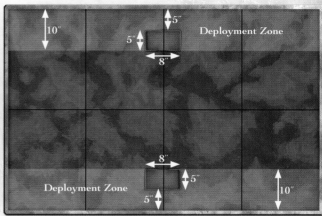

OCCUPATION

Only two blocks of blasted and burning buildings stand between us and the enemy. However, my orders say to take and hold this town and that is exactly what I intend to do.

—*Captain Kara Sloan*

DESCRIPTION

This battle takes place within the sprawling confines of a small town. Its outer defenses are breached, and two great armies now rush to secure the town before it is consumed by the flames of war.

SPECIAL RULES

In the center of the table is an 18″ × 18″ area representing the Town Square. In the middle of the Town Square is 5″-diameter raised fountain. The fountain area is shallow water that provides cover. Place eight 4″ × 6″ structures around the Town Square as shown on the map. These structures are ARM 16 and collapse after taking 80 points of damage.

Players then take turns placing terrain normally. Each player must place at least three terrain features, which is limited to structures, ruins, walls, and up to one forest. Remember that terrain features cannot be placed within 3″ of another terrain feature. Additionally, no terrain features can be placed within the Town Square.

At the end of each round starting with the second, a player scores 1 victory point if he has more models completely in the area of the Town Square than his opponent. Ignore models that are fleeing or out of formation, inert warjacks, and wild warbeasts when determining models in the area of the Town Square.

VICTORY CONDITIONS

A player wins the game when he has 3 victory points or if he has the only remaining warcaster(s) or warlock(s) in play.

MULTIPLAYER GAME

In a three-player game, center the Town Square at a point in the middle of the table 28″ from the west table edge. The Town Square remains centered in the middle of the table in a four-player game.

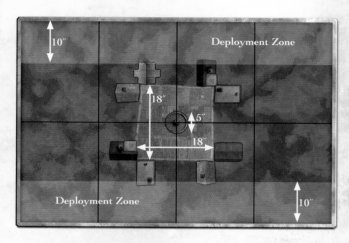

SCORCHED EARTH

Leave no stone standing. It will be as if the elements themselves passed judgment upon our enemies.

—*Krueger the Stormwrath*

DESCRIPTION

This battle fully embraces the spirit of total war. One army defends a fortified base, settlement, or encampment while their enemies attempt to destroy every structure left standing.

SPECIAL RULES

Before placing terrain, players each roll a d6. The high roller chooses whether to be the attacker or the defender.

Before deploying, the defender places five structures within 20″ of the center of the table but not within 5″ of a deployment zone. He must place three of these structures completely on his own side of the table and the other two completely on the attacker's side of the table. The structures cannot be smaller than 3″ × 5″ or larger than 6″ × 8″, are ARM 18, and collapse after taking 100 points of damage.

After the five structures are placed, the defender can place up to three additional terrain features. The attacker can then place up to two terrain features. Remember that a terrain feature cannot be placed within 3″ of another terrain feature, including a structure.

The defender deploys his models first and takes the first turn.

VICTORY CONDITIONS

The attacker wins when three of the structures are collapsed or if he has the only remaining warcaster(s) or warlock(s) in play. The defender wins if at the end of the fifth round three structures remain standing or if he has the only remaining warcaster(s) or warlock(s) in play.

MULTIPLAYER GAME

This scenario is not suitable for multiplayer games.

TREASURE HUNT

If it falls into the wrong hands it could change the course of history...

—*Major Victoria Haley*

DESCRIPTION

It is a race for vast riches, ancient artifacts, or secret lore as rival armies compete to unearth and retrieve hidden treasures.

SPECIAL RULES

Before placing any other terrain features, players take turns each placing two 4″ × 6″ ruins anywhere not within 18″ of the back edge of a deployment zone. These ruins cannot be placed within 5″ of another ruin. After the ruins have been placed, players take turns each placing two additional terrain features.

KEEP YOUR EYES ON THE PRIZE!

Players should strive to keep their forces mobile in this scenario. Going for a warcaster kill may be rewarding in the short term, but the real prize here is the treasure. As ruins are eliminated as hiding places and the potential locations become increasingly limited, you will want to reposition your models to concentrate on those ruins that remain unsearched. It could take quite a while to reveal which ruin contains the treasure, so plan your end game accordingly!

Ruins are rough terrain. A model within the area of a ruin gains cover.

In this scenario, players are competing to locate and retrieve a treasure. To find the treasure, players must have their models search the ruins.

Models cannot begin the game within the area of a ruin.

A player can have one of his warrior models search a ruin if the only models in the ruin are his and the searching model began its activation completely within the ruin. To search the ruin, the model must make a special action while completely within the ruin. When a model makes a special action to search a ruin, roll a d6. On a 6 the treasure has been found. Each ruin can be searched only once. If the treasure has not yet been found when the last ruin is searched, that search automatically results in finding the treasure.

Whether or not the treasure is found, the model's activation ends immediately after the special action is resolved.

Once a model locates the treasure, the treasure will move with that model. It may be helpful to place a marker next to the model currently carrying the treasure.

A friendly warrior model B2B with the model carrying the treasure can make a special action to take the treasure. The treasure can change hands this way only once each turn.

If the model carrying the treasure is destroyed or removed from play, mark the location of the center of the model's base at the time it left play. This is the new location of the treasure. If the model carrying the treasure moves or is placed by any means other than advancing, it drops the treasure, which remains on the table centered on the model's location before moving or being placed.

If the treasure is on the table and not being carried by model, a warrior model in B2B contact with the treasure can perform a special action to pick it up.

VICTORY CONDITIONS

A player wins the game when the treasure is within his deployment zone or if he has the only remaining warcaster(s) or warlock(s) in play.

MULTIPLAYER GAME

In multiplayer games each player places only two ruins. In a four-player game, the ruins can be placed within 22″ of the center of the table.

THEME FORCES

ARTIFICER GENERAL NEMO
LIGHTNING WAR

WARJACKS: Lancers, Cygnar non-character warjacks with Immunity: Electricity, Thunderhead

UNITS: Field Mechaniks, Cygnar units with Immunity: Electricity

SOLOS: Journeyman Warcaster, Cygnar solos with Immunity: Electricity

BATTLE ENGINES: Storm Strider

TIER 1
Requirements: The army can include only the models listed above.

Benefit: Reduce the point cost of Stormguard units by 1.

TIER 2
Requirements: The army includes one or more Stormwall colossals.

Benefit: After deployment but before the start of the game, you can place any number of your Stormwalls' Lightning Pods anywhere within 20″ of the rear edge of your deployment zone.

TIER 3
Requirements: The army includes two or more units.

Benefit: Your deployment zone is extended 2″ forward.

TIER 4
Requirements: The army includes a character warjack with Immunity: Electricity.

Benefit: During your first Control Phase of the game, warjacks in Nemo's battlegroup are each allocated 1 focus point.

INTERCESSOR KREOSS
REVELATIONS OF THE CREATOR

WARJACKS: Protectorate non-character warjacks, Fire of Salvation

UNITS: Choir of Menoth, Exemplar units, Protectorate Cavalry units

SOLOS: Reclaimers, Exemplar solos, Vassal solos

BATTLE ENGINES: Vessel of Judgment

TIER 1
Requirements: The army can include only the models listed above.

Benefit: Increase the FA of non-character cavalry units and solos by 1.

TIER 2
Requirements: The army includes one or more Exemplar Venger units.

Benefit: You gain +1 on your starting roll for the game.

TIER 3
Requirements: Your army includes Fire of Salvation.

Benefit: Reduce the point cost of heavy warjacks without ranged weapons by 1.

TIER 4
Requirements: Your army includes one or more Choir of Menoth units.

Benefit: For each Choir of Menoth unit in the army, one heavy warjack in the army gains Advance Move. (Before the start of the game but after both players have deployed, a model with Advance Move can make a full advance.)

VLADIMIR TZEPESCI, GREAT PRINCE OF UMBREY
CHARGE OF THE HORSELORD

WARJACKS: Khador non-character warjacks, Drago

UNITS: Battle Mechaniks, Khador cavalry units

SOLOS: War Dog, Khador cavalry solos

BATTLE ENGINES: Gun Carriage

TIER 1

Requirements: The army can include only the models listed above.

Benefit: Increase the FA of non-character cavalry solos, units, and battle engines by 1.

TIER 2

Requirements: The army includes two or more cavalry units.

Benefit: Warjacks in this army gain +2 SPD during your first turn of the game.

TIER 3

Requirements: This army includes two or more cavalry solos.

Benefit: You gain +1 on your starting roll for the game.

TIER 4

Requirements: Vladimir's battlegroup includes Drago.

Benefit: Reduce the cost of warjacks in this army by 1.

ASPHYXIOUS THE HELLBRINGER
ORCHESTRATIONS OF ANNIHILATION

WARJACKS: Cryx non-character warjacks, Cankerworm, Malice

UNITS: Bile Thralls, Mechanithralls, Necrosurgeon & Stitch Thralls, Soulhunters, Withershadow Combine

SOLOS: Warwitch Sirens, non-character Undead Cryx solos

BATTLE ENGINES: Wraith Engine

TIER 1

Requirements: The army can include only the models listed above.

Benefit: Add a Necrotech solo free of cost for each helljack or colossal in the army. These solos ignore FA restrictions.

TIER 2

Requirements: The army includes one or more Pistol Wraith solos.

Benefit: Pistol Wraith solos gain Advance Deployment ➤.

TIER 3

Requirements: The army includes three or more units.

Benefit: For each unit in the army, one model can begin the game with a corpse or soul token.

TIER 4

Requirements: The army includes one or more Kraken colossals.

Benefit: Your deployment zone is extended 2″ forward.

VYROS, INCISSAR OF THE DAWNGUARD
GUARDIANS OF THE GATE

WARJACKS: Retribution non-character myrmidons with force field damage boxes

UNITS: Dawnguard units

SOLOS: Arcanists, Dawnguard solos

TIER 1

Requirements: The army can include only the models listed above.

Benefit: Dawnguard Destor units in this army become FA U. Additionally, reduce the point cost of Dawnguard Destor units by 1.

TIER 2

Requirements: The army includes one or more Dawnguard Sentinel units.

Benefit: Dawnguard Sentinel units gain Advance Deployment ▶.

TIER 3

Requirements: The army includes one or more Dawnguard Destor Thanes.

Benefit: Dawnguard Destor units and solos gain +2 SPD during your first turn of the game.

TIER 4

Requirements: Vyros' battlegroup includes one or more heavy warjacks.

Benefit: During your first Control Phase of the game, your warjacks are each allocated 1 focus point.

GENERAL OSSRUM
STATE OF WAR

WARJACKS: Mercenary Rhulic non-character warjacks

SOLOS: Mercenary Rhulic solos

UNITS: Mercenary Rhulic units

TIER 1

Requirements: The army can include only the models listed above.

Benefit: One unit in this army gains Advance Deployment ▶.

TIER 2

Requirements: The army includes two or more units with ranged weapons.

Benefit: For every two units in the army, place one trench template anywhere completely within 20" of the back edge of Ossrum's deployment zone after terrain has been placed but before either player deploys his army. Trench templates cannot be placed within 3" of a terrain feature but can be placed within 3" of each other.

TIER 3

Requirements: The army includes two or more solos.

Benefit: Friendly models/units can begin the game affected by Ossrum's upkeep spells. These spells and their targets must be declared before either player sets up models. Ossrum does not pay focus to upkeep these spells during your first turn.

TIER 4

Requirements: Ossrum's battlegroup includes three or more warjacks.

Benefit: Warjacks in Ossrum's battlegroup gain +2 SPD during your first turn of the game.

CYGNAR
OPENING OLD WOUNDS

CORVIS

The Khadorans had been either unable or unwilling to capitalize on the injuries sustained by General Nemo that had forced him from the field. Perhaps it had been enough that he had succeeded in dismantling the cannon emplacement they had erected to crack Corvis' city walls. Whatever the reason, although the Khadorans remained encamped near the city, they had yet to stage a major assault; it was clear they were holding back. Based on reports from Captain Kraye, Nemo suspected the force arrayed against the city was not as large as it had first appeared. They actually might never have expected to seize Corvis, only to pin down its defenders. If that was their goal, they had succeeded.

While the enemy had not yet committed to a full-on attack, their sporadic artillery fire and limited engagements had exacted a toll, and the city's churches were crowded with beds of the wounded even as its graveyards took in the dead. Corvis' stout walls had been steadily reinforced and outfitted with an array of powerful cannons over the years after the skorne invasion of 603 AR, but the sprawling city was divided into three sections by the junctions of the Dragon's Tongue and Black Rivers, and some areas were more exposed than others to artillery fire. In addition, the population had swelled dramatically since the Llaelese War as refugees had flooded in from the north. Newcomers unable to find a place within the city proper had erected a shantytown outside the walls along the main roads, and these areas were extremely vulnerable. Shells fired at and over the battlements exploded with devastating consequences.

Nemo had ordered his forces to engage whenever Khador violated their perimeter, keenly aware of the range of their bombards and mortars. Though effective, his tactic was reactionary. Nemo knew he was doing precisely what the Khadorans wanted by staying fortified here rather than reinforcing other embattled garrisons along the river. Urgent reports arrived at a steady pace, describing both Khadoran and Cryxian assaults elsewhere. Knowing this did not change Nemo's main priority, however, which was safeguarding Corvis and its inhabitants.

He had no choice but to wait for the enemy to make a critical mistake. When Captain Kraye sent word that the Khadorans had established a small strike force south of the city on the west bank to block the river, he hoped his chance had arrived. The enemy clearly sought to choke the city's vital supply line from Caspia, but to do so they would need to hold—which would give him the opportunity to confront them. Even were he not eager to do so, he could not allow the Khadorans to block the river, and not simply because of his supply lines. What the Khadorans could not know was that the Stormwall colossals were expected to arrive any day, shipped upriver from Caspia. And they would be at their most vulnerable while aboard those riverboats.

As a precaution, he sent a patrol of storm lances to sweep the east bank of the river, but his main army marched from the southern gates on the west. A dozen warjacks strode ahead of quickly widening lines of blue-armored storm knights in turn backed by hundreds of long gunners with readied rifles. Storm Chaser Adept Caitlin Finch stayed by Nemo's side as he sent his mind into his machines. She clearly did not approve of his return to the field so soon after the injuries he had sustained from the Cryxian Stalkers. While he appreciated her concern, he could not afford to be idle. The battle-chaplain had done much to erase his wounds, and they troubled him no more than the constant aches in his joints he had been ignoring for years.

Finch activated the voltaic coils on her back, which glowed blue as they sent spikes of crackling energy to connect with the nearly identical coils on Nemo's warcaster armor. The air around them thrummed with power. Thus linked, she could fine-tune the reaction timing of his warjacks. As she made adjustments to the complex apparatus, she asked sweetly, "Did you ever consider that your new title might be an attempt by King Leto to encourage you to return to your research?"

"I doubt that's what he had in mind," he responded dryly.

After a three-hour march, they saw the Khadorans. Enemy 'jacks had hastily erected cover by hauling several riverboats ashore to create a makeshift wall against the embankment.

A number of smaller field guns and mortar teams took cover behind it, presumably intended to threaten Cygnaran riverboats but now facing Nemo's direction. These soon began to fire, sending explosive shells arcing toward them. West of the boat wall stood a copse of trees from which Winter Guard rifles erupted, taking a toll on the nearest knights. Cygnaran long gunners responded in kind, and Nemo sent a pair of Sentinels in that direction. He planned to focus the rest of his force on the Man-O-War soldiers and heavy 'jacks ahead, the hard center of the Khadoran blockade.

At his urging Defenders hammered shells into the nearest Destroyer, while Stormclads strode to meet the Marauder and Juggernaut already advancing. He could see his storm lances confronting the Khadorans across the river. Winter Guard on that side had been busily securing a heavy iron chain across the water that stretched from a great metal post sunk into the earth. Behind this chain and obstructing the river were a dozen lashed-together boats that served as an improvised bridge—clearly the means by which the Khadorans had crossed the Black River.

Nemo's mind guided his heavy warjacks as they crashed into their opposing counterparts with the screaming of metal and steam engines pushed to their limits. He effortlessly divided his mind among the machines, perceiving them with a clarity that made it easy to react to the smallest enemy motions. He knew his concentration was aided considerably by Storm Chaser Finch's presence; the experimental equipment she bore enabled her to tap into his own connection with the 'jacks and filter the information they fed back to him. By her efforts he found it considerably easier to allocate his attention.

A bullet barely deflected off the flickering surface of his power field, while another clanged into the raised shield of a Sentinel moving protectively ahead of Finch. Two of the nearest Stormguards were less fortunate and fell to precisely aimed head shots. With a flickering thought, Nemo directed one of his Lancers to round the nearest riverboat of the improvised wall as its arc node sparked to life. Seeing through its eyes, he noticed a squad of Widowmakers perched along the upper surface, peering through rifle scopes. Runes manifested around his hand as arcane power flowed across the Lancer's arc node and leaped through the nearest Widowmakers. Lightning leapt from one to the next, causing their bodies to sieze and smoke.

Raising his staff, Nemo sent electricity plunging from the darkening sky to strike among the Winter Guard crewing the nearest mortar. Others rushed to take cover among the half-shattered bulkheads of their fortifications and fire on the approaching Stormguard and Stormblades.

With several blows of its generator blade, one of Nemo's Stormclads reduced the nearest Marauder to scrap. Nemo took charge of its cortex and sent it crashing through the nearest boat in the barricade with an explosion of splintered wood. It laid about with its blade as lightning spilled over to electrify the nearest riflemen. Stormblades followed behind it to carve through the nearest Man-O-War shocktroopers, although several were cut down as they advanced. Finch stepped forward just enough to send additional lightning into the remaining guardsmen.

Nemo turned his attention to the chaotic clash in the nearby stand of trees, where Stormguard and long gunners sought to root out the riflemen. Suddenly he sensed something across the river: the unmistakable presence of an approaching warcaster.

He stepped to the river and peered across its swiftly flowing depths. The Winter Guard manning the chain post had been ruthlessly ridden down by the storm lances. The Cygnarans pulled up short, however, as new arrivals poured over the nearest hills, including Winter Guard, Iron Fang pikemen and uhlans, and additional warjacks. The woman who led them bore a mechanikal scythe, and Nemo recognized her instantly as Forward Kommander Sorscha Kratikoff.

The storm lances fired searing bolts of galvanic power into the front ranks of this new force, but they were massively outnumbered. With a shout the Cygnaran captain attempted to lead his men upriver toward open ground, but Kratikoff was on them in an instant. Pale blue runes surrounded her as a wave of supernatural cold seized the nearest horses in an icy grip. They could do nothing as pikemen charged into them with explosive blasting pikes, blowing apart horse and human flesh with merciless efficiency.

Nemo gritted his teeth, gathering his will. Kratikoff looked up and caught his eye, likely sensing his power. She shouted orders and mortar crews rushed to ready their weapons to fire across the river. Nemo threw a lever on the side of his armor, and its coils surged with blue energy. His armor thrummed as he fed his own power into the customized emitters, pushing them to the verge of overload as the sky above darkened. He raised his tempest staff while stretching out with his will. A swirling vortex of grey energy manifested above the mortar crews, and Nemo triggered the switch on his tempest staff to send forth an outpouring of voltaic power. The clouds buckled and lightning crashed into the Khadoran crewmen, killing several. Shouting in alarm, the Winter Guard drew back. The two warcasters stared at one another with palpable hatred.

With the nearest Khadorans largely neutralized, Nemo's soldiers regrouped near him and took stock of the enemy on the opposite bank. Officers called knights to order and set up a perimeter while long gunners lined up and prepared to fire. Nemo said to the nearest senior officer, "Major, be sure our men stay out of mortar range."

"Yes, General." He conveyed the orders to his subordinates. The mortars outranged them, making retaliation impossible, and the river stood between them.

Storm Chaser Finch asked, "What now?"

"A good question, Adept," Nemo said. "They seem serious about blockading the river." He was glad to have finally drawn out Kratikoff, who had proven elusive in these battles, but the situation was far from ideal. The intervening ship bridge could be destroyed should either side attempt a crossing. "Looks to be a stalemate."

Finch thought a moment. "The only safe crossing we can use to reach them is back at Corvis. Even if we destroy the blockade, the Khadorans might escape into the Marches or find some other way to cross before we can regroup to follow. We'll never catch them."

Nemo nodded, wishing he had brought Captain Kraye to lead his 'jacks and cavalry to confront the enemy on the opposite side of the river. He felt the needless deaths of those storm lances keenly. Kratikoff was singularly dangerous, though; skilled as Kraye was, he might have met his death just as easily.

The fact remained that so long as they were here, the Khadorans threatened the arrival of the colossals. He was just about to order the destruction of the boats blocking the river when another mental twinge indicated the approach of a more familiar warcaster, and soon he heard the sound of hooves. Looking north, he saw Captain Jeremiah Kraye galloping toward him as though summoned by Nemo's stray thought. He was followed closely by a pair each of Hunters, Chargers, and Sentinels, all moving at impressive speed. "Captain Kraye, your arrival is well timed," Nemo greeted him as he neared.

Kraye's steed, Malagant, slowed to a stop with an exhalation of breath, his sweat turning to steam in the cold air. The newly arrived warjacks quickly formed a protective cordon around both of the warcasters, gleaming eyes staring intently at the nearest Khadorans.

Not sparing the enemy a glance, Kraye said, "Before you do anything else, you'll want to read this." He extended a courier satchel bearing the stamp of Lord General Duggan. Kraye apologetically added, "The ranger who brought it killed his horse to get here. I felt obliged to take a look to see if it was worth interrupting your operation."

Nemo's scowl intensified as he opened the satchel and absorbed the contents of the pages it held. The orders were authentic. Any suspicion he might have had was neutralized by the presence of several of the secret code words inserted into all legitimate communications between commanding officers. Nemo cursed explosively—an uncharacteristic outburst that prompted Finch to stare at him, raising an eyebrow. He shook his head, reading the words again before looking across to where the Khadorans were adjusting their lines. "Captain, how much do you know about Forward Kommander Sorscha Kratikoff?"

Malagant pawed the earth and turned at the subtle nudging of the warcaster's legs so Kraye could follow Nemo's gaze. "Conversant with her tactics. Expect you know as much as I do."

Nemo grimaced but did not take his eyes from the other shore. "How likely do you think it that she will honor a flag of truce long enough for me to cross those boats to tell her we are now allies?"

Kraye frowned thoughtfully before saying, "I'd call it fifty-fifty."

Artificer General Nemo cautiously made his way to the small riverboat at the center of the blockade between the two shores, well within range of both armies. If Sorscha Kratikoff joined him, as he hoped, the destruction of the ship beneath them would place them in equal peril. Adept Finch had reminded Nemo just how poorly his voltaic armor and weaponry would respond to immersion in the river.

The Khadorans could simply have ignored Nemo's request to parley and unleashed a hail of mortar and Destroyer fire to erase him from Caen. He was keenly aware of this as he awaited the approach of his counterpart. The intelligence Nemo had on Sorscha Kratikoff did not reassure; while she was highly regarded by her superiors, some of her commendations were for acts of ruthlessness. He suspected killing a Cygnaran general was worth a medal, possibly two.

After a brief delay, however, she crossed alone to meet him, moving with admirable grace and poise across the intervening vessels. The eyes that met his were piercing and unflinching, and it required no empathy to perceive the anger simmering behind them. He could clearly see the volume of ordnance trained on their position and recalled from Kratikoff's CRS files how swiftly she could move if she wished. He was fairly certain they were not both at equal risk.

A brief and halting exchange made it clear that her Cygnaran was better than his Khadoran. "What is the reason behind this parley, General?" she asked with a frown, staring unblinkingly.

Nemo gritted his teeth as he tried to find a way to put it into words. Strange as it had been to read the orders, speaking them aloud was worse. "I've been ordered to cease hostilities," he said, feeling a muscle in his cheek twitch. "Lord General Duggan and Supreme Kommandant Irusk have come to an . . . arrangement."

"What?" she asked in clear disbelief. "How do you mean, arrangement?" As he stared at her, Nemo considered how perfectly Kratikoff embodied the Khadoran ideal of a soldier—someone who had entirely given over her life to become a weapon of war.

"I expect your orders will arrive soon. It seemed prudent to warn you before more needless lives were lost. Duggan and Irusk have arranged for a temporary alliance." He found it hard to say the words with conviction, and perhaps his own discomfort convinced her he spoke truth. "They have plans for our combined forces to join an operation against Cryx in the Thornwood."

He knew it was not from a lack of comprehension that she required him to repeat himself; her face showed her own difficulties digesting this information. Her incredulity was almost reassuring.

She was reluctant to make any lasting agreements until her own orders had arrived but accepted a provisional cease fire. After some tense discussion, they decided to rejoin their respective armies closer to Corvis. With the sun setting in the west, she finally consented to remove the river blockade but agreed to an exchange of the dead for burial before it was dismantled. Nemo recognized several faces among the fallen knights, including a lieutenant whose father had been an old friend from Highgate.

The march back to the city was solemn, with each side ill at ease. Men gripped their rifles closely and glowered at the enemy ranks marching on the other side of the water. Kraye galloped ahead to Corvis to pass the cease-fire orders to the wall garrisons and instructed their officers to strip the battlements of any soldier who was not a veteran. The last thing they needed was accidental fire from a nervous recruit.

The Khadorans on the opposite bank rejoined their legions in the Widower's Wood north of the city. Kraye was able to gain a better sense of their numbers and composition, and his reports told Nemo they represented more soldiers than he had originally credited, perhaps even an entire kommand. Had they committed themselves, they could have made life quite difficult for the besieged. Nemo decided the forward kommander had been buying time until additional forces arrived.

Though welcome, the reprieve from fighting in no way reduced tensions among those manning the walls. Every soldier remained at high alert, having little confidence in the stability of the inexplicable alliance. The next day, Kraye's rangers spotted a Greylord on horseback approaching the Khadoran encampment. Countless eyes watched and waited until Sorscha stepped from her tent alongside the new arrival. At her signal, Winter Guard across the perimeter slung readied rifles and blunderbusses onto their

backs, while artillery crewmen stepped sharply back from their mortars and cannons and stood at attention. Kratikoff left her escort to approach the walls of Corvis alone, and Nemo went to join her.

She did not reveal much of what had been relayed from Irusk, only acknowledged that their orders required cooperation and that they needed to bring in their command staffs to plan their next steps together. After a brief delay the unprecedented council convened: Sorscha, two kommanders, and a half-dozen kovniks standing for Khador; Nemo, General Galt Langworth, and their subordinate commanders for Cygnar. Translators added to their number to facilitate discussions of the logistical issues of advancing together to the rendezvous site. Nemo held reservations about the course of action that had been laid out by Irusk and Lord General Duggan—which were based on limited intelligence on the enemy in addition to lacking King Leto's authorization—but he was careful not to reveal any hesitation to the Khadorans.

> **HE FELT THE NEEDLESS DEATHS OF THOSE STORM LANCES KEENLY. KRATIKOFF WAS SINGULARLY DANGEROUS.**

Duggan and Irusk had instructed them to march immediately into the Thornwood. Forces stationed at Stonebridge would receive identical instructions, meaning that the majority of Cygnar's First Army as well as Khador's 2nd were being sent into the forest to root out Cryx. The idea was as bold as it was terrifying. Nemo had fought Cryx too long to expect the operation to go smoothly, even without the possibility of "friendly" fire between Khadoran and Cygnaran soldiers. The nations had only limited awareness of Cryx's numbers and disposition, and the enemy's extensive use of underground passages would give them a strong local terrain advantage.

Despite his doubts, it was not long before Nemo started to imagine the possibilities of combining their forces against Cryx. Such solidarity was unheard of—even during the Scharde Invasions King Vinter IV had rejected the idea of using diplomacy to involve the other kingdoms along the western coast. Nemo had long regretted this, feeling that the mainland powers working together might have been able to entirely eliminate Cryx as a threat to future generations. At the same time, he knew this particular alliance held great potential for harm. Undoubtedly, the empress would exploit circumstances to her advantage if she saw an opportunity. But he had his orders, Morrow help them all.

Even operating with the utmost urgency, it took some time to muster the 2nd and 5th Divisions out the north gate and make ready for the march. Two days into the process, Nemo received news of a highly anticipated arrival. He and Adept Finch rushed to the largest pier, just north of the city walls on the west bank of the Black River. Cygnaran engineers had recently inspected and reinforced the pier, knowing the reinforcements delivered here would be immediately deployed against enemies to the north. Nemo had planned operations that would secure the area against Khadoran interference during the landing; now such measures were no longer necessary. The Khadorans could observe from their encampment, situated only slightly farther than the Cygnaran divisions preparing to march into the Thornwood.

> ## NEMO FELT OVERWHELMED FOR A MOMENT WITH THE TANGIBLE REALITY OF HIS VISION MADE MANIFEST.

Two enormous military riverboats approached the piers, having made their stately way through Corvis with their escorting gunboats. All the vessels bore prominent Cygnaran Army insignia. Drawn by the sight of the massive boats as they passed, a small crowd of citizens had gathered to watch them. Among the first to disembark once the lead vessel docked was Captain E. Dominic Darius, who strode in his armored, steam-powered rig across the heavy ramps lowered from the ship onto the pier. He offered a salute and a wide smile to Nemo as he approached. "Are you ready, General?" Great pride was obvious in his voice as he said, "I present . . . the Stormwall!"

The boat's own steam-powered cranes maneuvered into position as its large central cargo hold cracked open. A dozen crewmen scrambled to guide dangling hooks from the cranes and attach them to the enormous warjack chassis taking up most of the ship's hold. The great warjack's engine was ignited and smoke poured from its exhaust even as the steam engines that powered the cranes roared to life. The cables went taut as the first Stormwall was pulled from the depths of the hold and carefully maneuvered onto the steel-plated deck of the reinforced pier. Nemo watched with some apprehension, praying that the weighty machine would not crash through.

The pier held—and the first of Cygnar's new colossals stood before him. Nemo felt overwhelmed for a moment with the tangible reality of his vision made manifest. Seeing its specifications drawn on paper was quite different from seeing it in person, and the mighty machine took his breath away. He could hear the sound of its storm chambers cycling up to readiness, drowning out the cheers of the nearest watching Cygnarans. The coils on both shoulders glowed with energy, and its head turned to face him, eyes alight with machine awareness. It opened and clenched its metal hands as if savoring motion after the long journey.

"Magnificent," Nemo breathed. "Fine work, Dominic. Very fine indeed." The second of the larger army transport ships had pulled into its berth along the neighboring pier, and another Stormwall was being hauled onto land.

His face glowing, Darius seemed abashed at this praise. "Your plans made it possible. I never could have dreamed of a machine on this scale if you hadn't shown me the drawings."

Nemo scanned the lines of the machine with a critical eye, making an effort to be analytical and suppress his initial amazement. "I wish we'd been able to implement an entirely storm-driven engine, allowing for more voltaic weaponry. Someday, perhaps. But you were right to recommend the integrated approach and relying on proven weaponry." He took in the heavy cannons and cyclone chain guns affixed to either side of the colossal's central chassis. Sparks played along the Stormwall's coils and flickered along the mechanisms on the backs of its oversized fists. On a purely technical level, the Thunderhead was more advanced, but as an engineering accomplishment, this project went beyond the scope of anything they had ever done.

"With that much mass, steam was the way to go," Darius said. His enthusiasm was evident as he continued, "The steam engines we made for these are simply beautiful— the most efficient large steam engines ever built by human hands. Someday I'll have to show you at the Armory. And with the foundries in place, the cost for repeated production is a fraction of what it would have been with an all-galvanic approach. Never fear, those voltaic fists pack a wallop. And you'll love the lightning pods. We managed to get fifteen extra yards of launching distance, and they work perfectly as voltaic conduits."

Nemo reached out with his mind to touch the machine's cortex, which was of an entirely new design. He could not actually connect, as its locks were sealed around its link with Darius. He remembered the day he had been inspired to initiate this project, when he had touched the cerebral matrix of the demolished colossal lying adjacent to the Temple Garrodh. Upon his recovery from that battle, he had set Darius to work overseeing the construction of the forges and assembly factories in Caspia necessary to see his vision become a reality. It was a tremendous undertaking, one that several times had seemed on the verge of failure. He only wished it had been completed sooner: what should have been the unveiling of a tremendous advantage for Cygnar had become an arms race with its enemies.

He was so caught up in thinking about the Stormwall that he did not realize when they were joined by another. It took Caitlin Finch's surprised intake of breath to tear him from his reverie, then Darius followed her gaze and nodded respectfully toward the arrival. Nemo turned to find Major Victoria Haley stepping onto the pier, dressed in her warcaster armor. She exchanged brief greetings with Darius and Finch, then looked to Nemo.

Her skin had a decided pallor, and he could see shadows under her eyes. He noted the way her living arm trembled as she leaned on her mechanikal spear Echo for support. What troubled him more was how her warcaster presence felt faint, like a flickering candle. "You should be in bed," he said sternly.

She stared back with proud defiance. "I heard about the upcoming operation. I won't be left behind."

Darius sensed the tension and had the good grace to withdraw, trying unsuccessfully to draw Adept Finch with him. Nemo shook his head and said, "Victoria . . ." He realized even as the word left his lips that he almost never used her first name. Her scowl deepened. "You need rest," he continued. "You are in no condition to enter battle."

"You need me there," Haley insisted. "I'm still a warcaster." Her Lancer Thorn stepped forward and spun its spear, a complex move that suggested her guiding will. "You'll need every experienced officer—every warcaster—in the fight ahead."

Nemo stared at her long and hard. Despite her demeanor he sensed fragility behind her harrowed eyes. Excluding her now might do her confidence lasting harm. Pragmatically, she was right. Even without magic her ability to mentally control multiple warjacks combined with extensive combat experience against Cryx made her invaluable. After a long silence he spoke again. "Confer with Vigilant Dolan. I will consider the possibility only if he persuades me it will not affect your recovery."

Her eyes still defiant, she opened her mouth to say something but stopped, perhaps realizing she had achieved a small victory. She swallowed and nodded before saying, "I'll find him at once." She then turned on her heel and left, Thorn following. Nemo could feel Caitlin's eyes upon him and offered a preemptive warning: "Nothing from you."

She ignored him, as always. "She should stay here, and you know it. You're letting sentiment allow you to put one of Cygnar's greatest assets at needless risk. She's *not* your daughter."

"You just crossed a line, Adept. Not another word." His voice was cold, and she finally looked away from his glare. He glanced back at the departing warcaster,

thinking that at times the only way to help some people learn was to let them make their own mistakes. Though Haley had never truly failed, the impending battle would afford ample opportunity.

Sorscha Kratikoff stood rigidly atop a slight hill near the Cygnaran tents, a spyglass set to her eye and her lips tightly compressed. She found herself holding her breath as the machine stepped forward. As the reality of it hit her, she could feel her heart racing.

She had known they were coming; she ranked highly enough to have received news of Khador's own Conquests even now being sent by train toward the war front. Yet it was one thing to read of colossals in the abstract and another to view one with her own eyes. Even from a distance, she could see how small the nearest people looked as they stood at its feet. The shape of the machine, with its rounded silhouette, was typically Cygnaran, but the sense of menace and power was inescapable.

Seeing the storm chambers accumulate power and send ripples of electrical energy along the colossal's coils brought all-too-vivid memories of the recent clash; the smell of ozone and burnt flesh was still fresh in her mind. This was a new and sophisticated engine of death, and she could not help but worry that the Conquests Khador had so hastily built would not be able to stand against them. She was unaccustomed to such doubt, but it was impossible not to be moved by the sight of the colossal. Neither could she avoid the thought that, had things gone differently, she might have sent those boats to the bottom of the river along with their dangerous cargo.

She had to remind herself of her new orders. Cygnar's new colossal would fight at her side against Cryx, and for that she should be grateful. Yet she found only small comfort in the thought, even knowing it was better that the undead should expend themselves against the machine before it was eventually turned on the sons and daughters of the Motherland. Such a prospect was, she knew, inevitable. This alliance would not last. She shivered at the thought of eventually confronting the towering warjack and seeing its chain guns and cannons pointed at her as they roared to life.

ARTIFICER GENERAL NEMO & STORM CHASER ADEPT CAITLIN FINCH
CYGNAR EPIC WARCASTER & CHARACTER SOLO

We are as much remembered in the actions of those we inspire as by our own deeds. You have given us the storm for today and tomorrow.

—King Leto Raelthorne

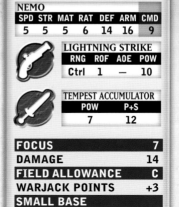

NEMO						
SPD	STR	MAT	RAT	DEF	ARM	CMD
5	5	5	6	14	16	9

LIGHTNING STRIKE			
RNG	ROF	AOE	POW
Ctrl	1	–	10

TEMPEST ACCUMULATOR	
POW	P+S
7	12

FOCUS	7
DAMAGE	14
FIELD ALLOWANCE	C
WARJACK POINTS	+3
SMALL BASE	

FEAT: EYE OF THE STORM

Every storm weapon in Cygnar's arsenal has its roots in the work of Artificer General Nemo, who knows how to push them beyond their normal limits. With an outpouring of power, the artificer general unlocks the governors of every storm chamber in his vicinity to send these weapons into keening overload and unleash a torrent of voltaic destruction.

While in Nemo's control area, friendly models gain an additional die on electrical damage rolls ⚡. Eye of the Storm lasts for one turn.

NEMO

Ⓜ **Immunity: Electricity**

Lightning Field – When lightning arcs as a result of an attack made by a friendly model in this model's control area, ignore models with Immunity: Electricity Ⓜ when determining which model the lightning arcs to.

Overpower – During your Control Phase, after this model replenishes its focus but before it allocates focus, this model can spend focus to increase its control area for one round at 1 focus point for each 1" increase.

LIGHTNING STRIKE

⚡ **Damage Type: Electricity**

Lightning Generator – When a model is hit with this weapon, lightning arcs from that model to d3 consecutive additional models. The lightning arcs to the nearest model it has not already arced to within 4" of the last model it arced to, ignoring this model. Each model the lightning arcs to suffers a POW 10 electrical damage roll ⚡.

TEMPEST ACCUMULATOR

Ⓜ **Magical Weapon**

Ⓡ **Reach**

Disruption – A warjack hit loses its focus points and cannot be allocated focus or channel spells for one round.

SPELLS	COST	RNG	AOE	POW	UP	OFF
CHAIN LIGHTNING	3	10	–	10	NO	YES

A model hit by Chain Lightning suffers a POW 10 electrical damage roll ⚡, and lightning arcs from that model to d6 consecutive additional models. The lightning arcs to the nearest model it has not already arced to within 4" of the last model it arced to, ignoring this model. Each model the lightning arcs to suffers a POW 10 electrical damage roll ⚡.

ELECTRIFY	2	6	–	–	YES	NO

If target friendly model is hit by a melee attack, after the attack is resolved the attacker is pushed d3" directly away from the affected model and suffers an unboostable POW 14 electrical damage roll ⚡, then Electrify expires.

FAIL SAFE	3	6	–	–	YES	NO

Target friendly warjack gains +2 ARM and does not suffer the effects of crippled systems.

FORCE HAMMER	4	10	–	12	NO	YES

Instead of suffering a normal damage roll, a non-incorporeal model Force Hammer hits is slammed d6" directly away from the spell's point of origin regardless of its base size and suffers a POW 12 damage roll. Collateral damage from this slam is POW 12.

LIGHTNING SHROUD	2	6	–	–	YES	NO

Target warjack in this model's battlegroup gains +2 STR and its melee weapons gain Electro Leap. (When a model is hit by a weapon with Electro Leap, you can choose to have lightning arc the nearest model within 4" of the model hit, ignoring the attacking model. The model the lightning arcs to suffers an unboostable POW 10 electrical damage roll ⚡.)

TACTICAL TIPS

CHAIN LIGHTNING, LIGHTNING GENERATOR, and LIGHTNING SHROUD – Damage from lightning arcs is not considered to have come from a hit or by a melee or ranged attack.

ELECTRIFY – If the model that is affected by Electrify is destroyed by the attack, Electrify expires before it is resolved and the attacker does not suffer its effects.

FAIL SAFE – When all its damage boxes have been marked, the warjack is still wrecked as normal.

FORCE HAMMER – Incorporeal models are not slammed. They just suffer a damage roll.

When the present fades into history, Sebastian Nemo will be remembered not only for his military record but also as one of the greatest minds of the Cygnaran people. The efforts he has made to defend his country are myriad and far reaching. He has advanced the arcane science of mechanika more than anyone since Kerwin, and his willingness to put his hypotheses and experimental devices to the test on the battlefield has shattered preconceptions of what is and is not possible. As the war has grown more desperate, King Leto has recognized the necessity of empowering this national hero to do whatever is necessary to improve the Cygnaran Army.

Nemo's contributions to his craft cannot be overstated: all modern weaponry that leverages the storm chamber

and galvanic power derives from his pioneering work. The stormsmiths might not even exist if not for his theories, and the same applies to the storm knights empowered by his inventions. But perhaps his crowning achievement will be the ideas that have led to the modern colossal.

Had Cygnar's leadership met Nemo's visionary Stormwall project with the urgency he demanded, the nation might have made decisive strikes against its enemies before they could field similar machines. In light of this missed opportunity, King Leto and his War Council decided to empower Nemo to act with greater latitude—with the hope that future crucial developments might not be delayed by such laborious bureaucracy. His new title brings with it considerable authority and oversight over the entirety of Cygnar's military industry; further, he is entitled to choose from among the nation's brightest minds to fill the specialized ranks of his army and the workshops where his latest creations take form.

As he contemplates his legacy, Nemo is deeply concerned with the next generation of Cygnar's warcasters. He has mentored and fought alongside many of them over the past half-century. Unfortunately, he has also outlived several of his former students and felt the grief of seeing them fall in battle before reaching their full potential. His uncompromising values and irascible nature have profoundly affected many of these powerful individuals, who often look to him in their times of need; in fact, it can be argued that Nemo has directly molded the ideal of the modern Cygnaran warcaster. He has served as a particular bastion of reason, moral rectitude, and paternal support for Lord Commander Coleman Stryker and Major Victoria Haley, as each traversed difficult trials.

While he has long acted informally in this consultative capacity, Nemo's new title confers direct authority over the stormsmith specialist branch of the Cygnaran

ADEPT

Army. He oversees them by communicating with their ranking storm chasers, the senior-most stormsmith officers engaged in active fieldwork. Storm chasers join major battles to coordinate storm smiths across multiple fronts. One of the finest is also one of the youngest: Adept Caitlin Finch. Nemo quickly recognized Finch as one of the most brilliant minds of her generation when she came to his attention while contributing to the prototype of the Squire. Demonstrating keen insight, she developed a unique mechanikal improvement that greatly improved the mechanism assisting a warcaster with spell targeting. Since Finch was selected to assist Nemo, she has seen her duties expand with the scope of the artificer general's new position.

Finch possesses a reserved nature Nemo has come to respect despite her occasional arrogance. He recognizes her attitude as healthy in an ambitious young arcanist—even if her stubborn adherence to military protocol occasionally irritates the artificer general, who holds no love for bureaucracy. Still, Finch is utterly devoted to Nemo and delights in the opportunities she has to test experimental devices in the field alongside the prestigious warcaster. In battle, the prim and proper storm caller demonstrates great courage, showing no fear of employing her electrical weaponry against the enemy.

With his time split between fighting on the front lines and directing advanced military research, Artificer General Nemo is busier than ever. Nevertheless, he is acutely aware of the limited time he has remaining to pass on what he knows and fulfill his vision for Cygnar. Despite Finch's warnings that he should leave the fighting to younger officers, he continues to wield his power wherever Cygnar faces its most dangerous adversaries. When Nemo fights, he does so drawing on decades of experience and employing the most technologically devastating weaponry ever fielded by Cygnar.

FINCH

Immunity: Electricity

Arcane Assist – If its warcaster is in this model's command range during your Control Phase, the warcaster can upkeep one spell without spending focus.

Arcantrik Tuning – When this model's warcaster allocates 1 or more focus points to a warjack in this model's command range, the warjack is allocated 1 additional focus point.

FINCH						
SPD	STR	MAT	RAT	DEF	ARM	CMD
6	5	5	5	14	12	8

ELECTRICAL BOLT			
RNG	ROF	AOE	POW
10	1	—	10

TUNING FORK	
POW	P+S
5	10

DAMAGE	5
FIELD ALLOWANCE	C
SMALL BASE	

Attached to [Artificer General Nemo] – This model is attached to Artificer General Nemo for the rest of the game. Each warcaster can have only one model attached to it.

Companion [Artificer General Nemo] – This model is included in any army that includes Artificer General Nemo. If Nemo is destroyed or removed from play, remove this model from play. This model is part of Nemo's battlegroup.

ELECTRICAL BOLT

Damage Type: Electricity

Electro Leap – When a model is hit with this weapon, you can have lightning arc to the nearest model within 4" of the model hit, ignoring the attacking model. The model the lightning arcs to suffers an unboostable POW 10 electrical damage roll.

TUNING FORK

Reach

Disruption – A warjack hit loses its focus points and cannot be allocated focus or channel spells for one round.

TACTICAL TIPS

ARCANTRIK TUNING – A warjack cannot exceed normal focus allocation limits as a result of Arcantrik Tuning.

ELECTRO LEAP – Damage from Electro Leap is not considered to have been caused by a hit or by a melee or ranged attack.

STORMWALL

COMMANDER NEMO'S ADDRESS TO KING LETO'S WAR COUNCIL, DOLOVEN 11TH, 606 AR

Your Majesty, Warmaster General, and other lords, thank you for hearing me. You know me to be a soldier. I am not a man of speeches, and I would not come here were the need not great. In recent days it has become clear that our nation is entering into crisis. Only a few months ago I personally bore witness to a battle between the belligerent powers of western Immoren in a clash that might have resulted in consequences too terrible to imagine, had we failed. It was in the midst of that battle, while surrounded by the fiendish weapons of our enemies, I found something unexpected.

Amid Orgoth ruins I saw the wreckage of an ancient weapon, a colossal: a weapon our ancestors forged to defeat their oppressors and free themselves from enslavement and subjugation. Though its machinery had been demolished centuries before, its cerebral matrix was aware. I could feel its drive to fight for those who had built it, an imprint left from whoever had controlled it in battle. It was at that moment I realized we had reached a turning point, that these ancient machines could be relevant to our battles today.

The colossals of old were decommissioned because technology had moved on. They had served their purpose, but the warjack was the superior weapon. Now, the mechanikal innovations of the past centuries demand that we overcome the limitations of old. We must not be afraid to challenge our assumptions. The face of warfare has evolved; as our enemies become more numerous and formidable, we must rise to the challenge or be destroyed.

I know how this can be done. It will not be easy, or come cheaply, but neither do the lives we expend on the battlefield. I am prepared to create a colossal that embodies our strengths and which will exceed anything our enemies can field against it. The supremacy of Cygnaran arms will be achieved, and by it our survival and prosperity will be assured. Allow me to present my plans for the future of Cygnaran warfare: the Stormwall.

STORMWALL & LIGHTNING PODS
CYGNAR COLOSSAL & SOLOS

We are beset on all sides by enemies and traitors, but the squall they have wrought will be washed aside by the storm we command.

—*Commander Adept Sebastian Nemo*

STORMWALL

SPD	STR	MAT	RAT	DEF	ARM	CMD
5	17	6	6	10	19	—

BIG GUN

	RNG	ROF	AOE	POW
L	14	1	—	15

BIG GUN

	RNG	ROF	AOE	POW
R	14	1	—	15

METAL STORM

	RNG	ROF	AOE	POW
L	10	1	—	12

METAL STORM

	RNG	ROF	AOE	POW
R	10	1	—	12

VOLTAIC FIST

	POW	P+S
L	3	20

VOLTAIC FIST

	POW	P+S
R	3	20

FIELD ALLOWANCE	2
POINT COST	19
HUGE BASE	

(A warjack suffering Disruption loses its focus points and cannot be allocated focus or channel spells for one round.)

STORMWALL

Immunity: Electricity

Activate Lightning Pod – Once per activation, after its normal movement, this model can place one Lighting Pod anywhere completely within 10" of this model if there are fewer than three Lightning Pods this model placed currently in play. At the time a Lightning Pod is placed, enemy models whose bases are intersected by a line drawn between the center of the Lightning Pod and the center of this model suffer a POW 10 damage electrical roll. Warjacks damaged by a Lightning Pod damage roll suffer Disruption. The S boxes of this model's damage grid represent its Lightning Pod system. While its Lightning Pod system is crippled, this model cannot use Activate Lightning Pod.

METAL STORM

Covering Fire – Instead of making attacks with this weapon during this model's activation, place a 3" AOE anywhere completely within this weapon's RNG. The center point of the AOE must be in this model's LOS, ignoring intervening models. This model cannot place an AOE for this weapon while it is crippled. A model entering or ending its activation in the AOE suffers a damage roll with POW equal to the POW of this weapon. The AOE remains in play for one round. If this model is destroyed or removed from play, immediately remove the AOE from play.

Rapid Fire [d3] – When you decide to make initial attacks with this weapon at the beginning of this model's combat action, roll a d3. The total rolled is the number of initial attacks this model can make with this weapon during the combat action, ignoring ROF.

VOLTAIC FIST

Open Fist

Electro Leap – When a model is hit with this weapon, you can have lightning arc to the nearest model within 4" of the model hit, ignoring the attacking model. The model the lightning arcs to suffers an unboostable POW 10 electrical damage roll.

LEFT DAMAGE

1	2	3	4	5	6
					□
		□	□		
				S	S
		L	L	S	C
L	L	C	C	C	C
L	C	M	M	M	M

RIGHT DAMAGE

1	2	3	4	5	6
□					
		□	□		
S	S				
C	S	R	R		
C	C	C	C	R	R
M	M	M	M	C	R

TACTICAL TIPS

Activate Lightning Pod – The damage roll is boostable.

Electro Leap – The lightning will still arc to a model with Immunity: Electricity; it just cannot damage that model. Damage from Electro Leap is not considered to have been caused by a hit or by a melee or ranged attack.

Metal Storm – One Metal Storm can be used to make attacks and the other can use the Covering Fire ability.

HEIGHT / WEIGHT: 28´ / 60 TONS

ARMAMENT: LIGHTNING POD LAUNCHER AND VOLTAIC COILS (INTEGRAL), DUAL HEAVY CANNONS (LEFT AND RIGHT CHASSIS), DUAL CYCLONE CHAIN GUNS (LEFT AND RIGHT CHASSIS), TWIN VOLTAIC FISTS (LEFT AND RIGHT ARMS)

FUEL LOAD / BURN USAGE: 1,650 LBS / 10 HRS GENERAL, 110 MINS COMBAT

INITIAL SERVICE DATE: 608 AR

CORTEX MANUFACTURER: CYGNARAN ARMORY/FRATERNAL ORDER OF WIZARDRY

ORIG. CHASSIS DESIGN: CYGNARAN ARMORY (S. NEMO/E.D. DARIUS)

With all the majesty and menace of a looming tempest, the Stormwall towers above Cygnar's enemies. The machine hurls down wrath as a cloudburst, the thunder of its guns and the rumble of its stride punctuated by cracks of lightning that strike Cygnar's foes.

The Stormwall sprang from the genius of Sebastian Nemo. The renowned inventor was inspired while recovering from wounds sustained during the battle at the Temple Garrodh, where he had discovered a functioning cerebral matrix within the shattered hull of a colossal forgotten since the last battles against the Orgoth. Modern mechanikal innovation in warjack fabrication had made great advances since the Corvis Treaties, and Nemo's mind began to imagine the potential of a modern colossal that could exploit them.

After recuperating in Caspia, Nemo made an impassioned plea to the king's war council about his vision. The anticipated cost of the project provoked politicized deliberation among reluctant nobles and bureaucrats in the Royal Assembly. Nemo continued to speak for the project through fervent letters to the king and warmaster general after being recalled to the front.

Even while he pushed for sufficient funding to produce the new colossal, Nemo labored over detailed schematics. Left to oversee the construction of factory infrastructure in Caspia, Captain Dominic Darius reviewed the plans and offered suggestions vital to the final shape of the machine. In particular, Darius saw the benefit of reliable ammunition-fed weapons systems and convinced Nemo to use coal-based steam power rather than storm chambers alone. Nemo turned to collaborating with the Fraternal Order of Wizardry on a cortex capable of controlling multiple weapon systems. His techniques resulted in a new cortex grade, the arcanum supernum, a powerful and very large design that made use of the colossal's cavernous interior.

While the construction of factory infrastructure was delayed, Khadoran agents learned of the nascent colossal project and were able to obtain schematics of several key components, including the cortex. The Khadoran military hierarchy pushed through its own colossal manufacturing plan with astounding alacrity, demonstrating the empress' absolute power. Once they learned this, the Royal

LIGHTNING POD

⟲ Construct

⊛ Immunity: Electricity

Conductor – When a friendly Stormsmith Stormcaller makes a Surge or Triangulation Stormcall, this model is considered to be another friendly Stormsmith Stormcaller.

Immobile – This model has no movement or action and cannot be knocked down or moved. Its front arc extends to 360°. It has no melee range, cannot engage, and is automatically hit by melee attacks.

| LIGHTNING POD | | | | | | |
SPD	STR	MAT	RAT	DEF	ARM	CMD
—	—	—	—	5	15	—

SMALL BASE

TACTICAL TIP

IMMOBILE – This model can be placed.

Assembly's reluctance to provide funding evaporated—though too late to preserve the advantage Cygnar would otherwise have held.

Once production resources were finally committed, the synergy of Nemo's and Darius' designs, particularly the innovative dual power source, was executed brilliantly by Cygnaran Armory mechaniks. The Stormwall's largest moving parts, including its powerful legs, are driven by a central steam engine that stands as the most efficient and powerful Cygnar has ever produced. The electrical weapon systems draw power from sizable galvanic chambers. The combination of the two power sources allows the Stormwall to sustain itself between refueling longer than any Cygnaran heavy warjack save the purely storm-powered Thunderhead.

The Stormwall carries several experimental lightning pods within its central chassis and launches them into battle using powerful explosive charges. The pods open on impact to form a conduit for the destructive energies produced by the Stormwall's own voltaic coils. Even after the pod has discharged its initial fury, it serves as an ongoing strategic electrical asset. Nearby stormcallers can use the pods to triangulate subsequent lightning strikes around each Stormwall.

The Stormwall's more traditional weaponry is equally impressive. The firing rates of its metal storm cannons and powerful main guns require the colossal to carry an enormous amount of ammunition—its interior chassis holds as much as a small garrison. In action, the Stormwall unleashes torrents of infantry-shredding bullets and riddles warjacks with cannon shells, all while summoning the full strength of its voltaic rage before closing with electrified fists.

PROTECTORATE OF MENOTH
SYMBOLS OF AUTHORITY

NEAR IMER

The stench of machine oils mingled with the sweet aroma of burning incense and holy unguents, while the cacophony of workers hammering iron blended with the holy chants and prayers of priests. Feora, Priestess and Protector of the Flame, felt her every sense assaulted even from behind her masked helmet as she and her escort of elite Flameguard followed the heavily robed figure of Visgoth Ark Razek through the recently erected warrens of the Foundry of the Sacred Flame.

"I'm sure you understand it was no small feat to accelerate the construction of the Judicator," Razek said over his shoulder. "Of course, the Caspian mechaniks your Daughters of the Flame captured proved instrumental by providing the technical knowledge necessary to overcome several mechanikal problems. Creating the boiler assembly alone would have been otherwise impossible."

"Your progress has been remarkable, Visgoth. Menoth truly favors your works," Feora said.

They waited for several robed acolytes to open the mighty iron doors that led to the scaffolds behind the foundry. Due to the great size of the Judicator, final assembly had been moved into the field beneath large tents that warded off the blazing desert sun. The harsh conditions coupled with the dangerous pace Razek had demanded from the artificers had resulted in numerous fatalities, Feora knew—an unavoidable price required to answer the Harbinger's vision, which warned them of the terrible machines that would soon be sent against the armies of the Creator. The truly faithful were willing to make such sacrifices, while the faithless deserved nothing more than to spend their last hours ensuring that the great work came to pass. And come to pass it had: the first Judicator had been completed in advance of initial estimates.

Feora tightened her grip on her weapon in anticipation as she stepped in front of Razek and out into the dry desert air. Her breath caught in her throat as she stared at the sight before her. Towering over the sands stood a magnificent testament to Menoth's glory. Its sharp, angled armor shone as it rose into pure white peaks reminiscent of a cathedral. As Feora continued to scan up, she was almost blinded by the radiant reflection of the sun off the delicate gold trim that lined the Judicator's armored form and the mighty steam vents that crested the elegant rocket pods on each titanic shoulder. Just beyond it, she could see the scaffolding and large canvas tents where another Judicator underwent final construction. Given their haste, it would have been understandable had the visgoth sacrificed form for function and forged a less resplendent machine, but it was clear he considered the project an opportunity to honor the Creator.

"With these we shall carry the fire of the Lawgiver to those who hide from his glory, and they shall suffer his wrath." Feora's voice was nearly a whisper.

She walked forward, eager to establish a connection with the colossal's cortex and be the first to command its power. She was vaguely aware of her Flameguard behind her. So fixated was she on the Judicator, she took no notice of the line of Exemplar knights standing guard around the warjack until they refused to make way. She looked at Razek for an explanation but saw by his body language that he was also taken aback. Then she saw approaching from the other side of the field the unmistakable figure of Vice Scrutator Vindictus. He was flanked by two men in elaborate vestments whom she recognized as Visgoths Juviah Rhoven and Var Bodalin, also vice scrutators. Three of such rank working in unison was enough to make even Feora uneasy. Visgoth Bodalin was a particularly ominous figure in the temple hierarchy, the prime curate of the scrutator caste responsible for the rigid training of that inner cabal.

"Priestess," Vindictus said, his voice ringing through his mask, "I am pleased to see you once again."

Feora forced her grip to relax. "And you, Vice Scrutator. Visgoths." She inclined her head toward those flanking the warcaster. Their staging was significant. Politically the visgoths had more authority than Vindictus, yet they were clearly here on his behalf, which did not bode well. Her voice was steady as she addressed the warcaster. "I did not expect you. I thought your place was at the side of the hierarch, overseeing the compliance of the citizens of the northern capital. I trust you have been treated well by our venerable visgoths. I wish they had informed me of your visit; I would have received you properly."

Vindictus waved away her concerns. "I find the unannounced visitor more often witnesses truths his host would prefer to hide." He turned to look back toward the colossal. "I was pleased to learn the first Judicator had been completed ahead of schedule." He turned back to set his withering stare upon her. "I know of no message sent informing His Holiness of this achievement."

Feora tensed. "There is much the hierarch does not see from his northern throne. Cygnar has already completed the first of its own colossals. With their heresy only recently driven from Sul, there is clear need for these great machines to bolster our garrisons."

Vindictus paused, his fingers tightening around the hilt of Lawgiver. "I understand the threat of heresy all too well, Feora. Our hierarch sees and hears more than you suspect. For example, *your* movements and associations are well known—as are promises made beyond your station."

Feora felt the veiled accusation like a slap, and indignant fury filled her. Sensing their mistress' anger, her Flameguard closed around her, causing the Exemplars across from them to adopt a ready stance with relic blades raised. "I protect our sacred lands and temples! It is my garrisons that afford the hierarch the luxury of committing to his Northern Crusade. I will do what I must."

Vindictus' voice rose. "You forget your place, *Priestess*. You are not in a position to make alliances with foreign powers." His words confirmed he knew of her meeting with Vinter Raelthorne IV, although Feora could not fathom how. Vindictus continued, "Such arrangements seem suspiciously like conspiracy. Even treason."

"Speak carefully, Vindictus," Feora said coldly. "Baseless allegations do not frighten me. If I stand accused, say so. I will quietly endure only so much affront."

"I speak for Hierarch Severius in this matter. It has been long since scrutators have been forced to exercise our authority against the highest temple officers, but we are empowered to do so."

Visgoth Bodalin spoke, his dry voice quiet but threatening. "Visgoth Sollers stands with us. His facilities at Tower Judgment remain at our disposal, should we have need of them." Feora could feel the blood leave her face at this, and she reached her mind out to her warjacks beyond the walls.

Vindictus turned to face Razek. "That applies to you as well, Visgoth Razek. Are you complicit in working against your hierarch? We have reports that several of the Synod have been overly eager to act on the priestess' dictates. Your failure to keep us informed is disconcerting."

Razek's expression could not be read behind his own priestly mask, but his eyes darted between Vindictus and the other vice scrutators. "The Synod is united in our support of the hierarch. I sought only to expedite my labors to arm the Great Crusade—"

Vindictus held up a hand. "Under order of the hierarch, I will take custody of this Judicator. This one and the next three you produce shall be delivered to the Northern Crusade. After that, we can discuss the possibility of allocation to the southern garrisons. I am sure the hierarch will be pleased by your success, perhaps even willing to forgive any lapses in communication."

Razek stared for a moment before bowing his head. "I live only to enact Menoth's will," he said.

Forcing down her rage, Feora chose her next words carefully; bloodshed here would gain her nothing. "Vice Scrutator, forgive my outburst," she said, bowing her head slightly. "I assure you my actions come only from my desire to protect the heart of the Protectorate from its enemies. Any arrangements I have made were intended only to advance the glory of Menoth and his chosen hierarch."

Vindictus stepped forward, through the Flameguard and past the knights Exemplar to touch the armored foot of the colossal. Its eyes gleamed with inner fire as its head looked down and its engines rumbled. Feora could do nothing but tighten her lips as the tremendous machine was taken from her, its cortex now connected to Vindictus. Although her own warjacks were nearby, she knew they would never arrive to intercept were the Judicator set upon her, nor would her Flameguard serve as more than a momentary distraction.

He turned to face her, the colossal behind him staring her direction as well. "The hierarch has tasked you with a great responsibility. It is my duty to cleanse those whose faith is found wanting." He paused, and behind him the Judicator took a single step forward. Feora stood her ground but felt the hand that rested on her weapon tremble. "I hope your faith is shown to be as pure as the flame you guard." He continued past her, the great machine following. "Before I leave Imer, submit to me a written summary of your . . . negotiations. Omit nothing—our eyes are upon you."

SOUTH OF LERYN IN LLAEL

Having left his wounded knights at the Menite temple in Rhydden to recover and to ensure its safety and that of the city's other holy sites, Grand Exemplar Mikael Kreoss led the rest of the survivors back toward Leryn. His was a stalwart and uncomplaining brotherhood, but he could sense their need to recuperate physically and spiritually. He did not acknowledge this aloud any more than they would, but he intended to see they attended to prayer and rest.

Evidence of recent conflict was ubiquitous as they crossed the fallow fields and abandoned lands south of Leryn, and Kreoss thought it unfortunate such fertile territory lay unused. He hoped by the next planting season to see the faithful tending these lands. The soil in Llael was richer than any the Protectorate possessed in the south, even those nearest Sul and the Black River. His nation stood to gain much in this northern region, not least the hearts and souls of those brought back to the worship of the Creator.

Any thought of rest vanished when he saw the panoply arrayed outside the walls of the city. What appeared to be a substantial portion of the entire Northern Crusade gleamed in white, gold, and sanguine beneath the waning autumn sun. Warjacks were present in number, each having been recently repaired, sanctified, and polished to the sheen of one newly built. Countless disciplined lines of Temple Flameguard stood arrayed in perfect formation, while deliverers and Sunburst crews attended to their weapons. Even the thousands of zealots looked impressive in their tabards.

> **NEVER BEFORE HAVE SO MANY RAISED SPEARS AND SWORDS IN A SINGLE ARMY OF THE LAWBRINGER.**

Kreoss rode Agon along the outer lines of the gathered army and humbly took in their adoration and praise without acknowledging it. He approached the large platform backed by cloth of gold. A line of choir priests holding staves surrounded it, and just beyond them stood the Knights Exemplar, Order of the Fist allegiants, and Devout warjacks serving as bodyguard to Hierarch Severius, who was bestowing blessings upon the faithful. Positioning himself so Severius could see him, Kreoss dismounted. He knelt in reverence, bowing his head while listening to the hierarch's sonorous words as he concluded a reading from the Canon of the True Law.

Kreoss expected Severius to descend to speak to him discreetly, perhaps at his nearby pavilion, but instead an attending priest directed the grand exemplar to step up onto the platform and present himself to the hierarch before the armed throngs. Severius spoke to them as though Kreoss' arrival had been prearranged. "Grand Exemplar Kreoss has just returned from a trying ordeal to the south, where he fought horrors to preserve our new temples in Rhydden."

Kreoss felt slightly startled at the hierarch's knowledge of what had transpired, as he had yet to deliver that news. "All of us gathered know of his countless victories, his unwavering devotion to the Creator. How can I properly honor such a warrior?"

"I have only done my duty, Your Holiness. That is honor enough." Uncomfortable with the spectacle, he did not attempt to send his voice beyond the platform.

"The grand exemplar seeks no honors, of course," Severius projected in a voice that effortlessly reached the farthest of those gathered. "What I bestow today represents certain responsibilities only he can shoulder. In the ancient days of our faith, the peerless Priest-King Khardovic granted to his greatest champion a special title, one that over the centuries fell out of use. This title brought with it absolute authority to lead armies and stand for the priest-king in armed disputes." Severius reached a hand toward the choir priests behind him, and a senior hierophant stepped forward bearing a weighty rod. The hierophant turned and extended it to Kreoss as Severius continued, "I restore that title now. Grand Exemplar Mikael Kreoss, I name you Intercessor. When fulfilling the orders of the hierarch, you will speak with my voice, and all the martial orders shall bow to you. Let none ignore your commands, lest they defy the Creator."

Kreoss had no choice but to accept the offered emblem of office, which he recognized from depictions in ancient murals. The bundle of crimson rods, nine in number to represent the nine great ancient Menite temples, was banded into a single mace by strips of hammered gold. Its flanged head comprised two Menofixes embedded perpendicularly to one another, while smaller Menofixes appeared where the metal bands crossed along its length. A short spear blade set into its base bore the more modern symbols used to represent Golivant, Khardovic, Cinot, and Sulon. It suggested the crusade's eventual dominion over all the lands of Man, from Caspia to Korsk, connecting past to present. It was a simple symbol, but a potent one.

A great rhythmic clamor erupted as thousands of Temple Flameguard spear hafts struck against shields and Exemplar relic blade cross guards met breastplates. Kreoss saw even the few paladins of the Order of the Wall among the gathering raise their blades in salute, adopting a posture ordinarily reserved for the leader of their order. He found this gesture surprisingly moving.

He reminded himself that whatever his title, his duty and code of obedience were the same. Nothing had changed. He recalled similar thoughts when the death of Bain Hurst had thrust the responsibilities of Grand Exemplar upon him. This presentation reinforced the authority of the hierarch, not his own. Symbols, ceremony, and titles were important, particularly to an army marching to war.

After allowing the assembled soldiers their moment of adoration, Hierarch Severius bid Kreoss stand, and together they departed the platform and walked toward the hierarch's pavilion. The army quickly returned to the work of organizing itself for travel. Kreoss turned to see the attending priest following discreetly, and when the man gestured toward the Rod of the Intercessor, Kreoss handed it to him, glad to let it go. It would be kept secure except when its presentation was formally required.

Severius said, "Our crusade prepares to march. I am pleased you returned before we set forth. I intend you to lead the vanguard, as is your rightful place. I shall lead the rest." Kreoss inclined his head, and Severius continued, "Remove your helmet, Mikael. I would see your face."

The request was unusual, although it had been some time since they had had an opportunity to speak outside the formal audience chamber. Kreoss obediently removed his helmet and faced his hierarch. Severius did not follow suit; scrutators never removed their sacred masks in the company of others. Kreoss asked, "You intend to take to the field personally? I would recommend against it."

"While I appreciate your concern for my safety," Severius said, "my place is in war. When I reluctantly accepted the hierarchy, I made this declaration. Leryn is secure; it is past time for me to rejoin the crusade."

"Why all of this?" He waved vaguely toward the platform.

"The bestowal of your title? It is important. There is every possibility I will die in the course of this crusade, whether in battle or simply due to the toll of years." Kreoss opened his mouth to protest, but Severius raised a hand. "I intend to delay that inevitability. But eventually I will be called to Menoth's side. Certain realities must be faced. For one, each of our martial orders has become strong. We have worked to make it so. Never before have so many raised spears and swords in a single army of the Lawbringer. Traditionally, the leaders of each order were equal in authority while subordinate to the clergy. As each order becomes an army, however, its leader will feel temptation to exercise authority. Speaking more directly, should something befall me, it is imperative the Knights Exemplar and the Temple Flameguard are not set against one another."

"That would not happen," Kreoss said, frowning.

"Can you be so sure?" the hierarch asked. Kreoss knew they both thought of Feora and her undisguised thirst for power. "I have already sent Vindictus south to ensure order. The Protector of the Flame is pious in her own way, and we need her strength and leadership to preserve Imer and Sul in my absence. Yet she sometimes forgets her purpose. Similarly, none of the visgoths is ready to be hierarch. When I die there will be uncertainty. In Khardovic's empire, the intercessor

safeguarded the temple's arms when the priests could not come to an accord. This is how it shall be again. The Synod will govern, but the martial orders will obey you. You will continue the Great Crusades."

"I will do what must be done," Kreoss affirmed.

Severius inclined his head and waved a hand. "Let us speak no more of unpleasant possibilities, but rather of the tasks ahead."

Kreoss began, "I had hoped to tell you of the Cryxian menace throughout Llael. The darkness encountered by the Harbinger the last time she went forth was no isolated incident."

"Yes, it was by her vision I knew you would be victorious in Rhydden. We should not stand idle while our enemies lick their wounds."

Relieved, Kreoss said, "Then we are in agreement. This land will be despoiled if we do not drive Cryx away."

The hierarch made a disappointed noise. "You mistake me. Although scattered undead remain in the countryside, they will be dealt with eventually, by smaller forces. What we require is to broaden the territory we have reclaimed for Menoth. The Khadorans have left their holdings exposed due to the war with Cygnar south of the Thornwood. High Executioner Reznik has brought word that Khador's new fortress at Riversmet is vulnerable. That is where we march."

Kreoss found himself frowning before he disciplined his expression. He bowed and said, "As you command, Your Holiness."

"Hold a moment." Severius' tone was unexpectedly mild. "I named you Intercessor because I value your leadership. You are troubled. Speak your mind."

"Very well," Kreoss said. "Cryx seems the most pressing threat. War and occupation have left the people of this kingdom defenseless, and now horrors set upon them. Their suffering is great. If we lend a shielding hand, they will see proof of the power of the Creator." He struggled to find his words, not wishing to presume to instruct the hierarch. "I admit my thinking may be flawed."

"Your reasoning is sound, but what you must understand is that these people are not ready to truly embrace Menoth. They have not, in fact, suffered *enough*. They abandoned their Creator when they thought it profited them and only now begin to see the consequences. If we save them, their gratitude would be fleeting at best. Through despair and loss they will recognize not only their own sins but also those of their ancestors. The Harbinger has confirmed this crucible of misery is of no consequence in comparison to the fate of their immortal souls. Our first priority is to broaden our reach, and then we can protect those within our dominion."

Kreoss bowed in assent, although inwardly he felt doubt. "Very well; we shall march against Khador. May I make a suggestion?"

"Of course," the hierarch said magnanimously. "I am eager to benefit from your wisdom."

Despite his superior's invitation, Kreoss had to remind himself that Severius was more approachable than Voyle had been. The former hierarch had never seemed open to suggestions from others, and Kreoss had always felt a barrier between them. He said carefully, "I do not believe Riversmet should be the focus of our efforts." He thought of what he knew of that rubble-strewn town, how its civilians were at last attempting to rebuild. It seemed profoundly wrong to strike in the midst of that, while its people honored Menoth by building. He did not speak those words, though. Instead, he said, "That town has yet to be restored, and in taking it we would be adopting Khador's burdens as our own. Let them restore it first, so that their treasury—not ours—erases the damage they inflicted."

> **FIRE OF SALVATION BROUGHT ITS FIRE-SPEWING MACE CRASHING DOWNWARD REPEATEDLY INTO ITS TORSO UNTIL THE LIGHT OF AWARENESS LEFT THE KHADORAN 'JACK'S EYES.**

"Unexpectedly pragmatic," Severius mused. "Where would the intercessor prefer to strike?"

"If Khador is neglecting its garrisons, we should be bold. If you wish to muster the Northern Crusade in its full strength, send us to Merywyn."

At this Severius' eyes gleamed intently through his mask. "That would indeed be bold, and the time may be right. That said, I do not expect Merywyn to fall easily or quickly. Such a siege could take months."

Kreoss was undeterred. "It would be worth the effort, and the gains would be greater than anything Riversmet offers."

Severius nodded and said, "The Khadorans will be forced to commit reinforcements once they learn the city is besieged, of course. But by then additional strength will have arrived from the south to bolster us. Vessels of Judgment and Judicators should return with Vindictus. Merywyn is the seat of Khador's local authority; its war industry, factories, and machine shops would be ours. This could free the crusade from reliance on Imer."

Kreoss was somewhat startled at how readily Severius seemed willing to abandon his previous plan. His eyes narrowed as he observed, "You had already considered this course."

"The idea had occurred to me, but I dismissed it. I thought it more prudent to attack a known point of weakness, based on Reznik's account. But perhaps I have grown too cautious in my waning years. I trust your judgment and your appraisal of our strength. Of course, I will join you in leading the crusade."

"Perhaps with the additional risk, it would be better—"

"No." Severius' voice carried the unmistakable tenor of absolute command. "The Harbinger shall remain here to preserve our stronghold. I will march with you to seize the largest city in Llael. All glory to Menoth!"

"All praise to Menoth," Kreoss responded automatically. He bowed deeply. "We shall see it done."

Few sensations were as glorious as riding alongside his Exemplar brothers on the charge, their steeds' hooves plunging forward and tearing into the earth. With his warcaster armor's power field and shield, he felt invulnerable as Winter Guard bullets fell away like pebbles thrown against a wall. His spear, Conviction, found the perfect point above a pikeman's shield to strike the man's vulnerable throat as if guided by Menoth's own hand. Imbued with holy fire, the riders to his left and right brought their gleaming lances down just before they crashed into the wall of heavy armored Khadorans to deliver annihilation.

Iron Fang armor was crafted of well-forged tempered steel, but Kreoss and his vengers rode through the soldiers and knocked them asunder, igniting their bodies as they went. Conviction pierced through the back of an officer with a spray of blood and lifted him off the ground to slide forward, impaled. Kreoss swung the weapon to the side to shake the corpse free. Agon reared and plunged with deadly hooves, knocking aside several of the nearest enemies before breaking free of them and running clear to prepare for another strike. All was chaos and bloodshed around him as knights Exemplar joined his vengers on foot, wielding relic blades with deadly effect. Fire of Salvation was there amid the knights, breaking through the Khadoran line and seeking vengeance for any of the faithful who fell in its proximity.

Kreoss saw one section of knights falter as Man-O-War demolition corpsmen crashed into them with ice mauls. Through his nearest Revenger the intercessor invoked blessings upon them in a shower of golden runes, a holy ward that would help deflect incoming blows. Through another he opened a crevasse in the earth to swallow Iron Fangs closing on their flank. Crossbow bolts from knights errant tore into several of the pikemen, and then melee was closed.

He charged again with another kick of his heels, even as he compelled Fire of Salvation toward a lingering Devastator. The Khadoran 'jack had already unleashed a deadly explosive torrent that had ripped through the nearest knights and left their battered bodies strewn across the bloodied soil. It had opened its nearly impenetrable shell to deliver the deadly payload, and Kreoss took advantage by sending Conviction crashing into the join between its torso and left arm, severing the limb completely. Fire of Salvation brought its fire-spewing mace crashing downward repeatedly into its torso until the light of awareness left the Khadoran 'jack's eyes.

Wheeling Agon about, Kreoss saw victory was theirs, and even as he sorely felt the loss of every one of his fallen brothers he had to measure its cost as small. They had chosen the battle site well, luring the northernmost of Merywyn's outer garrisons into the field by allowing them to see only the smallest portion of his vanguard, primarily knights errant. He hoped to goad his enemies from their fortifications at least once or twice more before their officers began to see the pattern. The more Khadorans they could draw into the open, the fewer would be left to man their central battlements for the siege. Even the recent Cryxian attacks across the countryside were working in his favor, as the Khadorans had withdrawn many of their patrols and seemed reluctant to commit scouts to the field lest they simply vanish.

That would change once word arrived of knights Exemplar on the city's doorstep, but even in that Kreoss thought he could use what the enemy knew against them. He had allowed some of the survivors of this garrison to flee to Merywyn, where they would give an erroneous sense of his numbers, particularly given that his vanguard was quite far ahead of the main army led by Severius. It was an unfortunate fact of war that an army could move only as quickly as its slowest elements, and the larger army was moving quite slowly indeed. Consequently Kreoss had been sent ahead to begin the clash and prod the Khadorans into fighting on ground of his choosing.

Much would depend on whether the ranking officers in Merywyn had the stomach to march forth against the Northern Crusade. The Black River, which divided the city, complicated any assault against it, allowing defenders to withdraw to the bridges if the outer walls were breached from only a single direction. River crossings outside the city were limited, with several having been destroyed during the war in Llael.

Despite the victory Kreoss felt no particular satisfaction. This garrison he had crushed had guarded several Llaelese villages that until now had been saved from the depredations suffered by those farther from the capital. Should the crusade's siege go poorly, Cryx would exploit whatever harm they inflicted on the garrisons, like buzzard beetles after carrion. His recent battle against Lich Lord Terminus had left Kreoss in a dark mood. He did not believe it had been the slightest setback to Cryx. The force had comprised too many thralls and not enough of the elite undead Cryx favored. Terminus reigned as one of the Nightmare Empire's twelve supreme generals; why had his army not reflected that status? It had to have been an eminently disposable force gathered from the ample battlefields of recent wars.

Around him, the remaining Khadorans were being dealt with. By Kreoss' command, those who surrendered were offered mercy and taken prisoner by his knights. He was surveying the casualties, which seemed fortunately light, when he heard the galloping hooves of a swiftly approaching rider. He looked up to see one of the Idrian horsemen who had volunteered to serve as scouts and messengers with their lean and swift steeds. He had not brought any with his vanguard, but a number were kept busy riding out beyond Severius' army. The sight of this one closing so quickly now had to be an ill omen. Kreoss rode to meet him.

"Grand Exemplar, I bring urgent news!" The horse was lathered, and the Idrian looked as if he had pushed himself hard in the saddle. "We have spotted an army closing on the main crusade from the northwest. By now they may even be upon them."

Kreoss felt a surge of alarm. "An army? Of what sort?" His mind immediately returned to Lich Lord Terminus.

"Khadorans, a very large army of them. Perhaps thirty thousand or more, including at least a thousand heavy horse. They must have marched from Laedry." He described the banners he had seen.

"The garrison in Laedry is not nearly that large, as far as I am aware," Kreoss said. Internally he cursed his lack of more recent intelligence on the disposition of the enemy. He shook his head, deciding it mattered little. Such an army would be a formidable threat, particularly if they were led by an able warcaster, and the descriptions of the banners told him they were probably Umbreans. Vladimir Tzepesci had to be behind this, he was sure. Tzepesci was a man quite used to war and capable of tremendous fortitude. There was every possibility the warcaster had vengeance on his mind after his imprisonment and interrogation at the hands of Vice Scrutator Vindictus. Vindictus was not here, but Hierarch Severius would be an even more tempting target for Tzepesci's unholy wrath—particularly with the hierarch's vanguard of heavy armor nowhere in sight.

Kreoss turned to his nearest venger seneschal and ordered, "Ready the interdiction. We march at once, with all haste, back the direction from which we came. Let no Exemplar rest until we have ensured the hierarch's safety."

INTERCESSOR KREOSS
PROTECTORATE CAVALRY EPIC WARCASTER

The armies of the faithful are his to wield as only a man of his devotion is able.

—Hierarch Severius

KREOSS						
SPD	STR	MAT	RAT	DEF	ARM	CMD
8	6	8	4	14	17	10

CONVICTION		
	POW	P+S
	8	14

MOUNT	
	POW
	12

FOCUS	7
DAMAGE	18
FIELD ALLOWANCE	C
WARJACK POINTS	+5
LARGE BASE	

FEAT: INVOCATIONS OF THE TRUE LAW

The invocations of the True Law as spoken by Intercessor Kreoss linger and resonate in the air as a holy manifestation of the Creator of Man. Before their truth, enemy glyphs and sigils are purged from existence, while allies of the Intercessor are instilled with holy wrath and renewed zeal.

Enemy upkeep spells and animi in Kreoss' control area immediately expire. Then Kreoss can immediately cast each upkeep spell on his card without spending focus points.

KREOSS

Divine Inspiration – This model gains an additional die on melee attack and melee damage rolls. Discard the lowest die of each roll.

Elite Cadre [Exemplar Vengers] – Friendly Exemplar Venger models gain Divine Inspiration.

Imperishable Conviction – When a friendly Faction model in its control area is destroyed by an enemy attack, this model heals 1 damage point.

CONVICTION

 Magical Weapon

Reach

Blessed – When making an attack with this weapon, ignore spell effects that add to a model's ARM or DEF.

Brutal Charge – This model gains +2 to charge attack damage rolls with this weapon.

SPELLS	COST	RNG	AOE	POW	UP	OFF
CREVASSE	3	8	–	12	NO	YES

If Crevasse boxes its original target, you can make a SP 6 attack using the boxed model as the attack's point of origin. Models hit suffer a POW 12 magic damage roll. Models boxed by Crevasse are removed from play.

DEATH SENTENCE	2	8	–	–	YES	YES

When a friendly Faction model misses target enemy model/unit with an attack, it can reroll the attack roll. Each attack roll can be rerolled only once as a result of Death Sentence.

FORCE HAMMER	4	10	–	12	NO	YES

Instead of suffering a normal damage roll, a non-incorporeal model Force Hammer hits is slammed d6" directly away from the spell's point of origin regardless of its base size and suffers a POW 12 damage roll. Collateral damage from this slam is POW 12.

HOLY WARD	2	6	–	–	YES	NO

Target friendly Faction model/unit gains +2 DEF and cannot be targeted by enemy spells or animi.

IGNITE	2	6	–	–	YES	NO

Target friendly model/unit gains +2 to melee attack damage rolls. Affected models gain Critical Fire 🔥 on their normal melee attacks.

WARPATH	2	SELF	CTRL	–	YES	NO

When a friendly Faction model in this model's control area destroys one or more enemy models with a melee or ranged attack during its activation, immediately after the attack is resolved, one warjack in this model's battlegroup that is in its control area can advance up to 3". A warjack can advance only once per turn as a result of Warpath.

TACTICAL TIPS

CREVASSE – Because a boxed model is removed from play before being destroyed, it does not generate a soul or corpse token.

FORCE HAMMER – Incorporeal models are not slammed. They just suffer a damage roll.

IGNITE – When this spell is cast on cavalry models, it affects mount attacks.

There is no greater honor among the faithful than to take part in the Great Crusades, and there is no mightier crusader than Mikael Kreoss. As grand exemplar, he led his order to retake Sul and then bolster the Northern Crusade. As intercessor, he now leads the greatest army of the faithful ever gathered for a single cause.

After the death of Hierarch Voyle, Kreoss answered Severius' call to lead the Northern Crusade in his stead. His unyielding resolve and the compassion with which he carries out his duties have made him a popular figure even beyond his brother knights; common Menites and soldiers also revere him. More importantly, Kreoss' sense of honor has never interfered with his loyalty to the priests of Menoth. Hierarch Severius looks upon the crusading knight as an essential pillar of his rule.

After the grand exemplar's return to Leryn from the defense of Menite temples in Llael, Hierarch Severius gathered the Northern Crusade to witness Kreoss' elevation to intercessor. The ancient title had gone unused for many centuries but demonstrates Severius' implicit trust in Kreoss, who can now act and fight on the hierarch's behalf. Upon Severius' eventual demise, Kreoss is tasked with maintaining the stability of the Protectorate by preventing the martial orders from turning on one another at the behest of ambitious leaders. He also must ensure that the Great Crusades continue and that the theocracy and its army remain unified at any cost.

Even with his unrivaled tactical brilliance, Kreoss prefers to lead his men personally and conducts cavalry actions from atop his great steed, Agon, alongside a hand-picked vanguard of his Exemplar venger brothers. At the onset of conflict he determines the most critical point on the battlefield and rides to confront the faithless there, crushing lesser warriors beneath Agon's hooves as he advances. Bearing his spear, Conviction, Intercessor Kreoss acts as Menoth's rightful judgment made manifest upon the world.

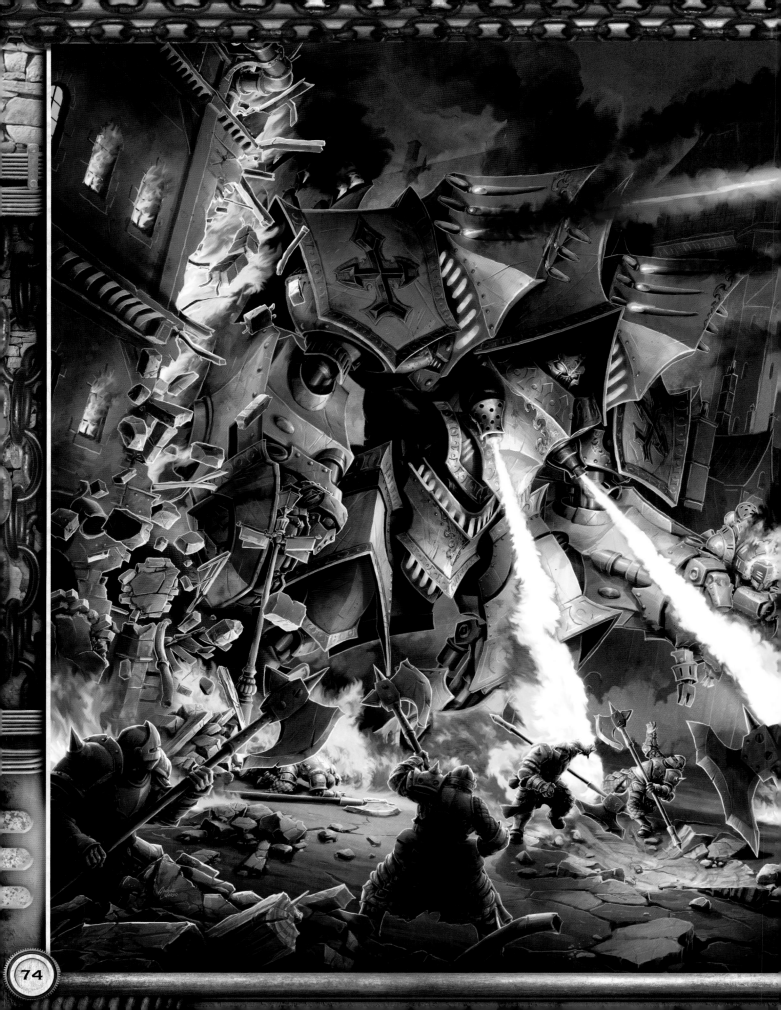

JUDICATOR

FIELD REPORT, EASTWALL CRS, KATESH 3RD, 608 AR

Sir, this is an urgent dispatch and I urge you to hasten it through channels to reach the proper eyes. I have witnessed an extraordinary threat to our nation. The Protectorate of Menoth has crafted a warjack of such size and deadly strength as to be unmatched.

As you know, I have been in the field for the better part of a year, carefully infiltrating the northern reaches of the Protectorate. Recently I discovered a new and costly facility built to the northeast of Imer.

While investigating the site's perimeter I found evidence that a large group had left the facility within the past day. The tracks led in the direction of our small encampment sheltering at Leecliff. I made haste hoping to warn them.

I arrived too late. Through my spyglass I saw a great number of Exemplar errants fanned out in a wide perimeter, presumably to cut down any scouts sent to give word. East of the site dozens of choir acolytes stood around a hulking shrouded form. The shrouds were pulled down to reveal a towering, gleaming warjack. The scale of it seemed impossible: the size of the figures next to it suggested a height of perhaps thirty feet. Missing panels and exposed mechanisms indicated incomplete assembly. A female form in warcaster armor detached from the group. She made broad gestures, as if giving a speech, then pointed at the encampment. The enormous warjack moved forward and systematically annihilated the defenders. It fired more rockets than I could count, making a mockery of what little protection was afforded by the sandbag walls erected around the encampment. When it reached the perimeter it loosed gouts of flame upon the survivors and smashed their warjacks beneath its great fists.

I do not know how else to describe this machine but as a colossal. Seeing the efficiency and speed with which it annihilated our soldiers and warjacks was chilling in the extreme. I will provide a more detailed report upon my imminent return.

Swift Sergeant Weston Cooper

JUDICATOR
PROTECTORATE COLOSSAL

Men come to the Law only through fear and flame.

—*The Harbinger of Menoth*

JUDICATOR						
SPD	STR	MAT	RAT	DEF	ARM	CMD
4	17	6	5	8	19	—

ROCKET POD L			
RNG	ROF	AOE	POW
14	1	3	14

ROCKET POD R			
RNG	ROF	AOE	POW
14	1	3	14

FLAMETHROWER L			
RNG	ROF	AOE	POW
SP 8	1	—	12

FLAMETHROWER R			
RNG	ROF	AOE	POW
SP 8	1	—	12

FIST L	
POW	P+S
3	20

FIST R	
POW	P+S
3	20

FIELD ALLOWANCE	2
POINT COST	18
HUGE BASE	

JUDICATOR

Reliquary – This model is allocated 1 additional focus point during your Control Phase. The S boxes of this model's damage grid represent its Reliquary system. While its Reliquary system is crippled, this model loses the benefits of Reliquary.

ROCKET POD

Inaccurate – This model suffers –4 to attack rolls with this weapon.

Secondary Blast – After determining the point of impact, roll deviation for one additional 3″ AOE from that point. A model hit by the additional AOE suffers a POW 7 blast damage roll.

FLAMETHROWER

🔥 **Continuous Effect: Fire**

🔥 **Damage Type: Fire**

FIST

✊ **Open Fist**

LEFT DAMAGE

	1	2	3	4	5	6
					S	S
			L	L	S	C
L	L	C	C	C	C	
L	C	M	M	M	M	

RIGHT DAMAGE

1	2	3	4	5	6	
S	S					
C	S	R	R			
C	C	C	C	R	R	
M	M	M	M	C	R	

TACTICAL TIP

RELIQUARY – A warjack cannot exceed normal focus allocation limits as a result of Reliquary.

HEIGHT / WEIGHT:	34′ / 75 TONS
ARMAMENT:	DUAL ROCKET LAUNCHERS (LEFT AND RIGHT CHASSIS), DUAL FLAMETHROWERS (LEFT AND RIGHT CHASSIS)
FUEL LOAD / BURN USAGE:	1,984 LBS / 6 HRS GENERAL, 50 MINS COMBAT
INITIAL SERVICE DATE:	608 AR
CORTEX MANUFACTURER:	VASSALS OF MENOTH
ORIG. CHASSIS DESIGN:	SUL-MENITE ARTIFICERS, FOUNDRY OF THE SACRED FLAME

To the Sul-Menites, the Judicator channels Menoth's wrath by delivering the punishment of fire unto heathens; to all others, it is simply a terrifying bringer of death. In support of its holy mission, every inch of the Judicator bears the Creator's favor. Prayers are inscribed upon each armored plate, upon fists and flamethrowers, and upon every rocket—blessings that help sear judgment into the flesh of the faithless. The colossal treads slowly but surely, like Menoth's inevitable reckoning of every man's soul. Its engines and armament roar to the beat of its step and the melodies sung by the great choirs of Menites that follow it into battle.

The vision that led to the creation of the Judicator came to the Harbinger of Menoth in the days after the conquest of Leryn. She foresaw a coming conflict wreathed in smoke and fire, with immense machines bearing the flags and banners of the enemies of the faith. Where they clashed, the earth itself was sundered. She knew those machines would exact a terrible price from the faithful should her nation be caught unprepared.

The Harbinger communicated these dire portents to the hierarch and the visgoths. At first the Synod seemed reluctant to act on her vision, but Hierarch Severius, understanding the seriousness of the warning, brooked no dissent. Efforts to construct the required weapons began at once under the direction of Visgoth Ark Razek and his artificers. Razek reviewed the resources at his disposal and quickly concluded that existing facilities were insufficient for the demands of such a tremendous undertaking. Thus was the Foundry of the Sacred Flame conceived.

Using the endless resources of Protectorate sweat, toil, and faith, the great edifice was erected in the sands east of Imer in mere months. No expense was spared in the construction, though the lives of many laborers were lost in the rush to completion. The manufacture of the Judicator began even as the first choirs arrived to bless the factory, its laborers, and the products of the great work.

The Sul-Menite artificers faced numerous challenges in the design of the Judicator. Lacking the industrial resources of Cygnar or Khador and possessing fewer specialized arcane mechaniks, the artificers found themselves unable to create a colossal-grade cortex similar to either nation's. They turned instead to methods unavailable to the faithless, praying for inspiration to craft a device that would channel the power of the Creator into the finest cortex they could produce.

Drawing upon principles developed during the fabrication of the Vessel of Judgment, they outfitted the Judicator with a holy reliquary containing the interred remains of a favored priest who had died in battle and whose essence would serve as a reservoir for divine energies. These would not be the great priest-kings that empower the Vessels, but humbler servants of the faith whose loyalty to the Creator outlast death. A mechanikal conduit connects this receptacle to the cortex in order to fill the machine with spiritual power and guide its actions in combat. Though the Protectorate still lacks the resources to produce Judicators in great numbers, each can be sent forth to its predestined battles by the guidance of the Harbinger. The success of these efforts is seen as proof that Menoth looks with favor upon such weapons when sent forth on crusades by the righteous.

The Judicator proved too large to be assembled behind closed doors, even at the massive Foundry of the Sacred Flame, and the artificers moved its final stages of construction outdoors. Under the scorching desert sun, expert mechaniks and chanting priests oversaw the assembly as teams of labor 'jacks operated winches and hoists that lifted the massive limbs and armor plating into place. Choirs gathered to sing benedictions as the Judicator's heartfire was stoked for the first time, and the great weapon of the faith took its first steps.

Bearing shoulders filled with dozens of rockets, the colossal can fire withering barrages without concern for precision: the weapons can reduce entire columns of troops to blasted ruin. The machine sprays Menoth's Fury into otherwise unassailable trenches and uses its mighty fists to crush the few who survive. If innocents perish amid the Judicator's unleashed wrath, they will find solace serving Menoth in the City of Man. Those who follow the machine into battle fearlessly chant and pray their devotion, knowing they walk in the footsteps of their god's will.

JUDICATOR CONCEPTUAL DESIGNS

KHADOR
BLOOD WILL TELL

NORTH OF STONEBRIDGE

Orsus Zoktavir had begun to suspect the world had gone mad after the Siege of Fellig. Very little made sense in the following weeks, and for a time he thought existence had narrowed to the endless depths of the forest, where day and night were much the same. Only the presence of his warcaster armor and Lola reassured him he had not died beneath that tree and walked the hellish wilds of Urcaen as penance.

He fed his arcane turbine wood after the coal was gone. When his own hunger became too great he found an animal to slaughter; when he was thirsty, a stream always lay nearby. At the last brook, the laughter of crows had surrounded him, making him scowl and curse Zevanna Agha.

Several times horrors from the forest beset him. Once it was the savage barbarians called Tharn that leapt from the trees with their axes in hand, howling to their dark god. He met them grinning, the blood singing in his veins, and by Lola's blade sent them on to the one they served. Another time it was walking dead with steam-driven fists and blasphemous runes inscribed on pallid flesh. He considered delving into the hole from which they emerged, but it seemed too much like a descent into his grave, so he had plunged back into the trees.

He found a road, and following it gave him some sense of progress, if not direction. After interminable days he came upon a Winter Guard encampment. The soldiers were wan, lean, and desperate. They looked upon him with fear and awe; it had been long since he had been in the company of others or bathed, and his armor was crusted with dried blood. Only Lola was clean.

Claiming an absence of orders and difficulties with supply lines, they had been huddled here like cowards for some time. Their kapitan told him of plans for battle to the south, nearer Stonebridge. They agreed to follow him, reluctantly taking up their weapons. Their hesitation turned his stomach, but he would make use of them. They had an old Juggernaut and a battered Decimator, and Orsus took charge of both. It felt good to reach his will into warjacks again, like putting on a comfortable pair of gauntlets.

Two days into the march a cold wind stirred, and amid the sound of hoofbeats Fenris rode from the mists to greet him. He reared back on his steed and let loose a howl. It put half the Winter Guard into a fright, freezing them in their boots, but Orsus greeted his old friend easily. Fenris made a circling motion with one of his fell blades and rode off again into the trees. The next evening he returned, followed by a dozen doom reavers chained to their weapons. That night Orsus slept well, lulled by the whispering blades. The world had begun to right itself.

The periodic ringing in Orsus' ears had returned, and he hungered for battle again. He felt it less when plunged into in the minds of his warjacks as they marched. At length they arrived at a large clearing off the main road where the forest had been hacked back to make room for Khadoran soldiers in rows of tents. The outer pickets challenged him but then greeted him with more warmth than he was accustomed to once they recognized him.

They escorted him into the main clearing, where there was considerable activity. He had thought to find rear hospitals tending to the wounded and perhaps soldiers ready to march as reinforcements when commanded. Instead, they were packing up gear and preparing wagons. He saw Winter Guard pulling down the support poles of barracks tents. Spotting a thickset kovnik nearby, he strode toward him purposefully and shouted, "You! Kovnik!" The man's face blanched at the sight of the warcaster. "Why are you breaking camp? What news of the battle?"

"Kommander Zoktavir? We had word you were dead!" he exclaimed, stammering slightly. "You should speak with Kommander Leichvich. Our orders have changed; we decamp tomorrow."

Orsus winced at a sharp pain in his head. He saw a blue uniform on the edge of his vision, and he turned with widening eyes to behold Cygnaran soldiers marching into the encampment from the southeast, not thirty yards from him. There was no alarm or agitation among the Khadorans, only a few dirty looks and some grumbling. At the head of the southerners strode a tall, sturdy, dark-skinned man wearing warcaster armor, with a pair of Cygnaran warjacks walking behind him. Orsus recognized Major Markus Brisbane, an infamous enemy of the Motherland. Next to him, talking calmly and earnestly, was an older Khadoran kommander, perhaps Leichvich.

Orsus looked around aghast, but it seemed the encamped Khadorans expected the Cygnarans. He clenched his teeth and felt the red haze start to descend across his vision. This was collusion with the enemy. The pieces came together: the nervous state of the warriors, the breakdown of tents, the shock at his arrival. They were preparing some mission of treachery.

"How much?" he demanded of the kovnik, looming over him menacingly. The Juggernaut and Decimator stepped up, their postures agitated. As the Decimator's rip saw growled, the Winter Guardsmen nearby looked at it in surprise. There was the sound of a horse whinnying and Fenris approached, his doom reavers fanning out to either side, fell blades in hand. Orsus seized the kovnik by the throat and lifted him from the ground, staring into his face. *"How much did they pay you to betray the Motherland?"*

The kovnik gasped, his face turning purple as he struggled uselessly against Orsus' arm. The tendons on his neck strained and he choked out, "Orders! Irusk!"

"You lie!" Several of the nearest soldiers shouted in alarm even as they seized weapons. He threw the kovnik behind him and into the path of his warjacks with a snarl. As his Juggernaut stepped on the treacherous officer, Orsus could feel it as though his own foot crushed the man's chest. He roared, lifting his axe. A lieutenant stepped forward with an angry expression as he raised his blunderbuss to fire. Orsus brought Lola down swiftly. The axe did not slow as it clove the man from crown to groin, spilling innards onto the soil.

Orsus' eyes locked on the Cygnaran warcaster, who was staring at him with widening eyes. The man held up a hand to warn back Kommander Leichvich as a pair of Defenders stepped up to join him, one of them equipped with an assault shield rather than the traditional shock hammer.

Orsus shouted, "Kill them all!" Even as the words left his lips Fenris and the doom reavers charged, unleashing maddened battle howls as they carved into the nearest Winter Guard. His warjacks surged ahead and Orsus ran between them, Lola in hand. Runes surrounded his axe as he drew his power inward, letting it flow through his blood and harden the muscles in his arms and legs.

The first Defender fired straight into his chest, but the heavy shell exploded against his power field in a spray of deflected metal. The second shell hit nearer his waist moments later, penetrating the field but careening off his armor and leaving only a massive dent. His feet ate the ground as he saw Brisbane take a rocket launcher from his back and lower its nose at him. An eruption of blue runes surrounded the Cygnaran warcaster, and Orsus felt foreign energy wash over him and his 'jacks and sink into his armor.

Just as Brisbane fired, the damaged Juggernaut hurled itself in front of him, its steam engine screaming. The rocket impacted the forward armor near its head and exploded. What should have been a trivial blast to the thick armored steel tore through the warjack's chassis as if it were made of wood, severing its right arm and punching through its head, cortex, and steam engine. Orsus did not slow as the machine toppled in front of him but ran across the metal wreckage and leapt from its shoulder to land heavily between the two Cygnaran warjacks.

He let loose a great yell and swung Lola in a wide sideways arc with all his might, the veins in his arms and forehead pulsing visibly. With a crash and the shriek of protesting metal the axe edge carved through pistons and armor, severing the support on the nearest arms of both 'jacks. The shield-bearing Defender's heavy barrel cannon and the other Defender's right arm wielding its shock mace fell with a crash. Before the modified one could raise its shield to bash at him Orsus was swinging again, this time cutting low enough to sever the regular Defender's waist assembly and cut it in two. The heavy body fell with a crash as his swing finished its arc by slashing all the way through the other 'jack's shield and severing its arm in a spray of torn metal and sparks. Dark, oily fluids poured from hoses like arterial spray as the second Defender toppled as well. Orsus stepped past it, leering toward the Cygnaran warcaster.

Several of the Cygnaran soldiers raised their rifles and fired, while others lowered bayonets and charged. As if feeding on the rage of its master, Orsus' Decimator surged forward to drive into their midst with its rip saw, eager for its spinning blade to taste blood. With a galloping of hooves and a great leap Fenris landed nearby to hack down several more as his horse reared and snarled, hooves churning.

Major Brisbane had dropped his rocket launcher and lifted his mechanikal hammer. He gave his own cry as he ran at Orsus, who did not even attempt to dodge as the hammer swung around to connect with tremendous force against the center of his breastplate, where it flashed blue and unleashed a surge of power. Orsus felt the breath knocked out of him as he flew off his feet and backward fifteen feet to crash into a stout tree, half-shattering its trunk. The impact left him gasping while spots filled his vision. Something had cracked in his chest and there was blood on his lips, but he felt no pain.

He chuckled wetly and staggered to his feet to step toward his enemy, adjusting his grip on Lola. Someone was screaming in Khadoran, but Orsus paid no mind. He snarled and charged again, raising the axe above his head and bringing it down. Brisbane scrambled back and raised his hammer to block the blow. There was the high-pitched sound of metal snapping and tearing as Lola chopped through the steel handle and sheared through power field and warcaster armor to open a gash from Brisbane's upper breastplate to his waist. The Cygnaran dropped the broken weapon and tripped to land on his back, raising a hand to his chest as blood began to seep from the wound. Orsus grimaced in self-reproach—it was only a shallow cut, just through the skin.

He stepped forward to finish the work but was blocked by Kommander Leichvich, who waved a piece of paper bearing official seals. He was screaming, ". . . orders, you madman! From Kommandant Irusk! Stop now!"

Keeping his eyes on the other warcaster, Orsus meant to knock Leichvich out of the way, but his axe cut through the man's wrist. The severed hand—still gripping the piece of paper—landed on the ground near where Brisbane struggled to regain his feet. Seeing it there, and hearing the kommander's words, Orsus felt the red haze begin to fade. Unwelcome thoughts were intruding. He was no animal—he obeyed orders. That had been his promise to the empress. His eyes fixed on the paper and not Leichvich, who sat heavily, holding the stump of his arm as it spurted blood. One of his subordinates rushed up with a belt to cinch the flow. Orsus leaned over to take the bloodstained paper and frowned as he read the words.

He stared down at Major Brisbane as the Cygnaran got unsteadily back to his feet, pressing one hand against his chest where blood flowed from the gash. Orsus' hands ached to deliver the final blow, and it seemed to him Lola wanted it just as badly. Instead he said, "You are my prisoner now." He looked around to where battle was still raging. He summoned his Decimator and shouted, "Stop! Enough!" in a ringing voice. Fenris turned his steed away from those he had been killing. Seeing him, the doom reavers also checked themselves, some in mid-swing. Orsus turned to the Winter Guard. "Disarm and bind the Cygnarans. Any that resist, execute."

Leichvich protested feebly, "You can't do this! We are allies now. You'll be court-marshaled for this!"

Orsus said, "Maybe. But I will confirm these orders personally. Your piece of paper means nothing." Meeting Brisbane's stare, he said, "Try anything, and you die. Come."

CENTRAL LLAEL

Vladimir Tzepesci felt considerable pride as he rode his steed Vsada at the fore of his war host. Beneath his banner was an army such as he had never led before: Umbreans, every one, including those who had once lived on Khadoran soil as well as those who had called themselves Llaelese. There were families represented here that had not acknowledged one another in centuries, not since the Orgoth divided them. Empress Ayn Vanar had at last formally bestowed the volozskya that had divided old Umbrey on the Tzepesci family.

Critics of the empress claimed this was bowing to Umbrean dissent, but Vladimir knew its true political meaning. Umbrey now was a sworn territory of the empire, as it should be, and his vows to the empress still held. The empress had shrewdly made it his responsibility to protect the occupied territory, which enabled her to accommodate the High Kommand's desire for the bulk of the Khadoran Army to remain elsewhere. She had given him his family's ancestral lands—but only as they were being ravaged.

The Umbrean force he led, which his liegemen had assembled at great cost and difficulty, had been intended to confront Cryx, to put an end to the bands of roving undead that had been plaguing Llael in recent weeks. But when he had received word of a massive Sul-Menite army marching toward Merywyn, he had known he had no choice but to move to intercept. Count Barak Ushka rode at his side, a hulking man and one of his staunchest allies. A follower of the older drakhun tradition, Ushka rode a massive Karpathian destrier named Grom, necessary due to the tremendous weight of his archaic armor.

Vlad donned his helmet and took his horselord's spear in one hand and his flail in the other as he looked down at their enemy. The tremendous army of Menites stretched out along the flat field to the east of the Black River. Their numbers had swelled far beyond what they had been when Vlad had seen them before the walls of Leryn; it looked to be a substantial portion of the Northern Crusade. Nevertheless Vladimir felt some optimism, as the army comprised mostly Temple Flameguard and zealots and lacked for heavy infantry and cavalry. The Knights Exemplar were conspicuously absent.

The Protectorate army was just entering into a narrower valley ringed by gently sloping hills as the river wound toward the Llaelese capital. They would be forced to spread out into a long column to squeeze through several narrows. He could see places where his vanguard of heavy horse could cross shallower water to strike hard against exposed sections of the column.

"Good ground for us," Ushka said enthusiastically in his deep voice.

"Yes. I could not ask for better," Vladimir agreed. He pointed southeast, ahead of the army's intended path, to where the road narrowed at a bluff ridging the valley's terminus. "Our infantry will hold the choke point, and encamp just beyond, to block the easiest road to Merywyn. Meanwhile we will strike repeatedly to hinder their advance. There, and there." He chopped with his armored glove at their best river crossing and a tributary beyond it, which would aid their withdrawal while hindering forces on foot. "We must avoid entangling our pikemen prematurely. If we make this advance costly enough, Severius will be forced to withdraw to Leryn. Leave the northern route open to facilitate this."

He could not help but imagine the streams of blood that would flow from the clash of the armies to stain the Black River. An unfortunate loss of life, as he knew this was not his true enemy. Before even the crows could properly feast on the slain, Cryx's necrotechs would descend. It seemed as though all his efforts to forestall catastrophe in the region were to be undone by the fanatic obstinacy of the Northern Crusade. The Old Witch's warning was heavy on his mind. First Vice Scrutator Vindictus had prevented his meeting with the hierarch, and now this army marched toward Merywyn. Khador had invested heavily in the city's factories and railway, which sped reinforcements and warjacks to the front line. Vladimir knew he could not allow the city to fall.

Before he could rule Umbrey, he had to protect it. He had already sent messengers to the nearest Khadoran garrisons, including Kommander Harkevich at Riversmet, but he did not anticipate reinforcement. What he anticipated was a long, bloody battle.

Vsada plowed through the water of the tributary and surged up onto the far bank as Vladimir dug spurs into his sides. More uhlans crossed with him to strike deep into the ranks of the Temple Flameguard, scattering bodies and sending shattered shields and spears flying. Vlad wielded his spear and flail with murderous precision. His favored 'jack Drago was beside him, hewing through any enemy foolish enough to close. They barreled through the side of the column and deep into the Menite army, throwing the surrounding forces into reactive confusion. The Menites had been scrambling to secure several of the higher hills to position artillery capable of firing across the river. Vladimir and his vanguard had repeatedly driven into points of weakness, using speed to exploit the inability of the larger army to reposition itself easily.

Down the bank from the great prince, Ushka fought with the strength of a gorax. He shattered his cavalry lance into a Crusader on the initial charge and then drew an oversized axe to pound the 'jack into scrap while Grom shattered the skulls of several zealots with his hooves. A Man-O-

War drakhun joined Vlad and used his annihilator blade to sweep through an intervening wall of additional spear-wielding Flameguard, sending the line into chaos.

The men parted as additional Berserkers rushed across at Vlad's urging and lay into the Menites, leaving crushed and dismembered bodies behind them. His Destroyers fired from the opposite bank before making their own crossing. The smell of burnt flesh and smoke choked the air as zealot fire bombs erupted. Vladimir saw the nearest uhlan scream and fall from his horse as the flames from one consumed him. With a cry, Vlad rallied the uhlans and charged the zealots before they could ready additional bombs. He had reached his immediate objective—the highest point of the hill the Menites had been hoping to hold to defend the river crossing. From here Vlad intended to carve a bloody path through the shifting Protectorate forces and neutralize a deliverer-held hill that had been menacing his infantry where they had succeeded in seizing the southern choke point.

THE SMELL OF BURNT FLESH AND SMOKE CHOKED THE AIR AS ZEALOT FIRE BOMBS ERUPTED

Already the main army was reacting to their strike. The warjacks and bastions protecting Hierarch Severius loomed in the near distance. Severius' warjacks occasionally came against his forces, and his holy prayers filled his soldiers with strength and warded them from harm, but the hierarch kept his distance. Vladimir's initial attempts to signal for a parley had been ignored, which was not surprising. Severius and his army were set on their course, and it seemed too late for words to have an impact.

Over two days of bitter fighting, Vlad's plans had unfolded as intended, with his army encamped along the main route to the capital and inflicting heavy casualties on any Sul-Menite forces seeking to push south. Vlad and his vanguard had fought ceaselessly to interfere with the ordered disposition of Severius' sprawling masses, but despite his efforts the Northern Crusade was beginning to force engagements across the southern end of the valley. The casualties would only escalate, as despite the limits of his force composition, Severius was every bit as skilled at directing his forces as Vladimir expected. Vlad's own army had its weaknesses, and he sorely wished he had even a few kompanies of Winter Guard to provide artillery and small arms support.

Despite having secured the southern valley opening, the Umbreans saw the sheer numbers of the Northern Crusade take their toll. His cavalry did not have inexhaustible reserves of stamina, and Vlad had been relying on them heavily. His pikemen were holding strong—just the day before they had tied up an assault by Flameguard long enough for Vladimir to execute a devastating charge into the midst of the enemy Redeemers and Sunburst ballistae situated on the high ground north of their position, severely gutting their ranged support before it could disrupt his forward lines.

Even as Vlad gathered his horsemen to make their next move, a bright glimmer from the south caught his eye. Peering that way, Vlad saw something that made his blood run cold—the gleam of gold and white in the valleys behind them. To the southwest, where the river wound its way toward the capital, his sharp eyes soon identified the source: another Protectorate army. Hundreds of Exemplar Vengers galloped in their direction, and behind them rank upon rank of gleaming knights on foot were closing on the rear of the Umbrean encampments. The Menite knights and cavalry, whose absence had been puzzling him, had revealed themselves at last, inexplicably approaching from closer to Merywyn! At their fore astride a heavy steed was a gleaming knight Vladimir knew had to be Grand Exemplar Kreoss.

> **VLADIMIR FELT HIS HEART RACE AS HE CONSIDERED HOW DRASTICALLY THEIR SITUATION HAD SUDDENLY CHANGED**

Vladimir felt his heart race as he considered how drastically their situation had suddenly changed. His main army was now in danger of being encircled. Attacked on two sides, with one foe superior numerically and the other a stalwart force of knights including heavy cavalry, they would be crushed between. He considered attempting to confront Kreoss—that might buy him time to deal with Severius' more ponderous army—but such a course risked squandering the bulk of his strength. Kreoss and his Exemplars would not fall easily.

He looked back to the north and observed a section of the main Protectorate army pushing his way. The Sul-Menites had also seen the approach of the grand exemplar and rushed to force Vladimir's hand. His eyes narrowed when he saw Hierarch Severius advancing as well. It was the first time in the engagement the hierarch had risked venturing so close. Within the closing vice of the enemy forces, Vladimir saw a desperate possibility. He could force his way to the hierarch and either parley or end the Protectorate leader's life and in a single stroke break the crusading army's morale.

Count Ushka rode over to him and raised his lance in salute. "Shall we ride to face them?" He inclined his head toward the Exemplars.

Vladimir shook his head. "I have unfinished business with the hierarch." The count's eyes widened, and he looked back to the nearest hill, where Severius and his honor guard had joined the artillery already there to gain a better view of the imminent clash. Vlad ordered, "Take the 4th and 5th Uhlans and any pikeman reserves remaining in our encampment and delay the Exemplars as long as possible. Protect our flanks."

Ushka nodded and closed the faceplate on his helmet as he turned Grom south. Vlad held his spear high and called to his horse captains. His warjacks were already forming up into a line, and at his mental signal they ran north as quickly as their smoke-bellowing steam engines would push them, churning the rain-soaked earth with every stride. Vlad rode near the Berserker closest to Drago and extended a hand, invoking runes along its frame. Drawing on dark powers inherited from his ancestors, he instilled in the machine's cortex a ravenous ferocity and hunger for battle.

The enemy clearly had not expected him to turn north, toward the main mass of their army. Rows of Temple Flameguard ran forward to set shields. The entire Menite army seemed to pulse like a living thing as its soldiers rushed into position: Flameguard in front, zealots next, and a thin row of Deliverers behind them. These last were already opening fire, and several rockets impacted harmlessly against the nearest warjacks. His Destroyers slowed to fire bombards, sending explosive shells amid the packed Menite ranks. Both Redeemers and Reckoners retaliated with their own ordnance.

Vladimir summoned a wall of swirling wind around him that deflected the nearest enemy ordnance, but he saw several of his uhlans thrown from their steeds by explosions. He pointed past the line of his warjacks and screamed to his captains, "Charge past and wheel left beyond the line! Only engage on my call!"

The warjacks crashed into the Flameguard with devastating impact. Berserker axes whirled through shield and armor as spearmen sought to hold their line, but it collapsed utterly as Drago carved through men, steam engine screaming in rage. Augmented by Vladimir's enchantment, the other Berserker similarly hacked through soldiers while its steam engine screamed like a living thing, sending survivors fleeing in terror. Spriggans and Kodiaks closed on the Protectorate warjacks behind them. One of the Berserkers Vlad had sent toward the highest-ranking Flameguard officer began to smoke as its unstable cortex overloaded. It exploded in an inferno of energy, sending shrapnel through the nearest Flameguard.

Vladimir urged his 'jacks onward, hoping to use them to drive toward Severius' bodyguard, Exemplar bastions advancing toward the fray. The hierarch had yet to commit his heavy warjacks, somewhat to Vladimir's puzzlement, while a trio of Revengers ran forward instead. He leaned forward on Vsada, pushing the steed to full gallop, and drew on his power to invoke runes across his closest cavalry to augment their pace as well. The Flameguard had sought to intercept, and their line had been drawn out of formation as they followed raggedly behind, yet still his cavalry raced perpendicular to the main line, veering inward once they reached its end. Their mounts thundered through men and trampled them as they surged up the hill. His uhlans crashed into the nearest Revenger with their explosive lances, crippling the massive machine.

Even as he whirled on his rearing steed, laying about him with flail and spear, his mind joined his machines and he saw the Revengers close. The tactic made no sense to him, yet he felt apprehension; Severius was no fool. His unease grew when he saw that where each warjack's arc node should be was strapped a similar but unfamiliar apparatus that emitted a strange orange light. Atop the hill Severius raised his hands, and golden runes surrounded him as he invoked his holy power. The devices suddenly erupted in flame, and from them pulsed a wave of light. As it struck the Khadoran warjacks Vladimir felt his mind suddenly hurled loose, as if each of their cortexes had extinguished. The machines froze, several—including Drago—in mid-strike. Impossible as it seemed, Severius had somehow breached their cortex locks and paralyzed his 'jacks. He immediately intuited Vindictus somehow had a hand in this.

Vladimir gritted his teeth at his sudden peril. Without his 'jacks on the left flank, and with the Flameguard rushing to close the gap behind him, he was considerably overextended. The Umbreans had torn a hole through the outer Protectorate line, but additional zealots were rushing forward. Those uhlans that had been bogged down by Flameguard slashed with the bladed ends of their reversed lances, but thrusting spears jabbed at them and pierced several.

He looked to Severius, who was staring down the hill at the inert Khadoran warjacks. "To me!" Vladimir shouted, rallying his nearest captains. *"For Umbrey!"*

He spurred Vsada up the hill, giving forth all his sorcerous will to fill his own mount and those around him with his power, to speed their hooves and ward away enemy blows. They surged upward as a line imperishable, wheeling around or trampling through those who would engage them. Vladimir drove his spear into the Devout that tried to stand against him, crippling its hip assembly before then shattering its halberd arm with a mighty blow of Huntsman.

Vsada danced away, bringing him close enough to shatter the helmet and skull of an Exemplar bastion. He could feel the fire of his ancestors rising in his veins with every kill, as blood sprayed his horse and his crimson armor. He and the steed felt like one flesh as they surged forward and then sideways, and with every thrust of his spear or swing of his flail, another Menite died.

More of his uhlans fell, but they took with them the bastions that had formed Severius' inner guard. Dozens of battered and bloodied uhlans rallied to their great prince, hurling their mounts up the hill and wheeling about as they reloaded their blasting lances and readied to deal with the Flameguard closing ranks behind them. Ahead of Vladimir stood Hierarch Severius, and at his side a heavily ornamented Revenger crouched with shield and halberd ready. The hill was almost empty of other Menites; those who had been with Severius had perished in their attempt to intercept Vladimir's charge. More Flameguard and zealots were racing toward the hill from behind, but they would not arrive in time. The hierarch's face could not be seen behind his mask, but his posture suggested no alarm. Elsewhere the battle continued as Flameguard fought the main Umbrean army and Count Ushka's force confronted the Exemplars, but here there was a moment of calm.

Vladimir lowered his spear point toward the hierarch, who intoned in a sonorous voice, "I could say but a word, and your horsemen would turn on you, awakened to the will of the Lawgiver. Are you here to surrender? I am ready to hear your pleas."

The great prince stared back from beneath his helm, unwavering. "Whatever tricks you manage, they will only slow your death. I am within striking distance, and nothing could save you from my wrath, not even the hand of the Creator."

"We will have to add that to your list of blasphemies, Vladimir Tzepesci," Severius said.

"Vindictus violated the Law of Envoys to keep me from speaking to you once before. I would like nothing better than to end your life in repayment. But first, we have more important matters to discuss." Beneath him, Vsada pawed the earth and snorted, eager to charge, his muscles tensed. "Will you listen? Or are you eager for death?"

VLADIMIR TZEPESCI, GREAT PRINCE OF UMBREY
KHADOR CAVALRY EPIC WARCASTER

Neither war nor destiny wait for any man, yet instead hound his steps and will not be denied.

—Drago Tzepesci

VLADIMIR						
SPD	STR	MAT	RAT	DEF	ARM	CMD
8	6	7	5	15	17	9

HORSE LORD'S SPEAR

POW	P+S
6	12

HUNTSMAN

POW	P+S
7	13

MOUNT

POW
12

FOCUS	7
DAMAGE	18
FIELD ALLOWANCE	C
WARJACK POINTS	+5
LARGE BASE	

FEAT: CHARGE OF THE HORSE LORDS

When Vladimir Tzepesci calls his host the ground shakes beneath the countless hooves of warhorses and the heavy tread of warjacks on the charge. Cavalry and machines alike crash into the enemy and leave broken lines behind them as they wheel away to position for another strike.

While in Vladimir's control area, friendly Faction warjacks and cavalry models gain Side Step and Sprint. Charge of the Horse Lords lasts for one turn. (When a model with Side Step hits an enemy model with an initial melee attack or a non-power attack special attack, after the attack is resolved it can advance 2″. A model with Side Step cannot be targeted by free strikes during this movement.) (At the end of its activation, if it destroyed one or more enemy models with melee attacks during its activation, a model with Sprint can make a full advance.)

VLADIMIR

Blood-Quenched – This model gains a cumulative +1 STR and ARM for each living enemy model it destroys with a melee attack during its activation. This bonus lasts for one round.

Combat Rider – During a combat action it did not make a charge attack, this model can make one melee attack with its Mount.

Relentless Charge – This model gains Pathfinder during activations it charges.

HORSE LORD'S SPEAR

⊘ **Magical Weapon**

⊘ **Reach**

Brutal Charge – This model gains +2 to charge attack damage rolls with this weapon.

HUNTSMAN

⊘ **Magical Weapon**

Chain Weapon – This attack ignores the Buckler and Shield weapon qualities and Shield Wall.

MOUNT

Critical Knockdown – On a critical hit, the model hit is knocked down.

SPELLS	COST	RNG	AOE	POW	UP	OFF
DASH	2	SELF	CTRL	–	NO	NO

While in this model's control area, friendly Faction warrior models cannot be targeted by free strikes. This model and friendly Faction warrior models activating in its control area gain +1 SPD. Dash lasts for one turn.

FLASHING BLADE	1	SELF	–	–	NO	NO

This model immediately makes one normal attack with one of its melee weapons against each enemy model in its LOS that is in the weapon's melee range. These attacks are simultaneous.

HAND OF FATE	2	6	–	–	YES	NO

Target friendly Faction model/unit gains an additional die on attack and damage rolls. Discard the low die in each roll.

INFERNAL MACHINE	2	6	–	–	YES	NO

Target warjack in this model's battlegroup gains Terror ☠ and +2 MAT and SPD.

RAZOR WIND	2	10	–	12	NO	YES

A blade of wind slices through the target model.

WIND WALL	3	SELF	–	–	NO	NO

This model cannot make ranged attacks, and non-magical ranged attacks targeting it automatically miss. While completely within 3″ of this model, models cannot make ranged attacks and non-magical ranged attacks targeting them automatically miss. Wind Wall lasts for one round.

While the Umbrean lands have been under Khadoran rule since the empire conquered Llael, their fate had remained uncertain. Many among the nobles and kayazy sought to claim them, but driven by a greater purpose, Vladimir persisted even as he fought in the empress' name. He steadily won the loyalty of all Umbreans who gathered to his banner, whether Khadoran or former Llaelese.

Proving her political prowess, Empress Vanar declared that any noble who would be considered for the lands of Umbrey must fight to defend them against external enemies. Amid escalating Cryxian and Sul-Menite assaults, only Vladimir was willing to risk his life for the Umbrean people. By the empress' decree, the two smaller volozkya and single Llaelese duchy that had once been Umbrey were joined into a single massive volozkya beholden to Great Prince Tzepesci.

The great prince was left to defend Umbrey virtually on his own; should he fail, the shame will fall on him alone. He has gathered his vassals and a great Umbrean host for this task, his soldiers knowing they fight for their destiny as well as to protect their families and ancestral lands.

Vladimir Tzepesci rides his warhorse, Vsada, at the head of an elite guard of heavy cavalry and wields the weapons of his ancient namesake, who usurped the throne and united Umbrey four centuries ago. Carrying the spear in one hand and the mace Huntsman in the other, Vladimir lashes out with dark sorceries while his blood sings in battle, lending him the strength to secure his ancient birthright.

For the first time in generations, the people and lands of Umbrey stand united beneath their rightful lord. Reclaiming the birthright denied his family for centuries, Great Prince Vladimir Tzepesci rides into battle wielding weapons of the ancient Tzepesci horselords and leading the people of Umbrey to seize their destiny.

CONQUEST

KORSK, 608 AR

It was an unseasonably cold day in the capital, but the people of Korsk lined the streets with an enthusiasm undimmed by the weather. Winter Guard lined the thoroughfare leading from the industrial quarter to the massive central railway station. The spirited Korskites in the crowd welcomed the opportunity for a military parade and particularly the chance to catch a glimpse of their beloved empress. The anticipation in the air was sharper than usual, as the crowd awaited a legend reborn in Khadoran steel.

Ordinarily the empress stood atop the great walls of Stasikov Palace to watch processions passing far below, but on this occasion her balcony was modest, jutting from one of the ordinary buildings along the thoroughfare. Even the High Kommand's booth opposite was grander, with bunting and pennants along the rails surrounding the senior officers, each resplendent in their uniforms and medals. Her placement suggested Empress Vanar was proclaiming she was not the center of attention this day, merely an observer like her people.

With them she watched the arrival of the first regiments. Thousands of Winter Guard marched in lockstep, shouldering their weapons in perfect discipline. They turned their heads to face the empress as they passed, and she inclined her head in greeting. Then they turned smartly to face the High Kommand, who also offered them honor. Anticipation only grew as a great dull sound began to echo over the din of marching men: the roar of powerful engines and the tread of massive machines.

The sound grew louder, and the people turned to look down the avenue where a great cloud of coal smoke was visible from round the corner, suggesting some great conflagration. A regiment of highly decorated soldiers appeared, pairs of Spriggans escorting them with lances raised high, and behind them a mountain walked.

An awed hush fell over the gathered civilians and soldiers alike as a colossal in Khadoran colors strode forth like a memory torn from the pages of history, the first to grace the capital in three hundred years. Its mighty engines exhaled plumes of smoke that briefly obscured the polished barrels of its enormous cannons. As it came to the empress' place of honor, it paused and turned to her in salute, its blazing eyes meeting hers. The empress returned the salute, and the crowd cheered wildly, giving voice to the fierce pride they felt in beholding a monument to conquest they had bought with coal once set aside to heat their homes.

CONQUEST
KHADOR COLOSSAL

Khadoran supremacy is meted out in the steel of our singular will.

—Grand Vizier Simonyev Blaustavya

CONQUEST						
SPD	STR	MAT	RAT	DEF	ARM	CMD
4	18	6	4	4	7	20	—

MAIN GUNS			
RNG	ROF	AOE	POW
15	1	4	15

SECONDARY BATTERY			
RNG	ROF	AOE	POW
12	1	3	12

SECONDARY BATTERY			
RNG	ROF	AOE	POW
12	1	3	12

FIST	
POW	P+S
4	22

FIST	
POW	P+S
4	22

FIELD ALLOWANCE	2
POINT COST	19
HUGE BASE	

MAIN GUNS

Critical Devastation – On a critical hit, instead of suffering a normal damage roll, each model in the AOE is thrown d6″ directly away from the attacker regardless of its base size. Move models farthest from the attacker first. The model directly hit by the attack suffers a POW 15 damage roll. Other models hit by the attack suffer a POW 8 damage roll. The POW of collateral damage is equal to the POW of the damage roll suffered by the thrown model.

SECONDARY BATTERY

Creeping Barrage – Instead of attacking with this weapon during this model's activation, if it is not currently crippled you can place two 3″ AOEs anywhere completely within this weapon's RNG, centered on points in this model's LOS, ignoring intervening models. The AOEs must be placed within 1″ of each other. A model entering or ending its activation in one or more of the AOEs suffers an unboostable POW 6 blast damage roll. The AOEs remain in play for one round. If this model is destroyed or removed from play, immediately remove the AOEs from play.

Linked Guns – When this model makes an initial attack with this weapon, after the initial attack has been resolved it can immediately make one additional attack against the target of the initial attack. This additional attack ignores this weapon's ROF.

FIST
✊ Open Fist

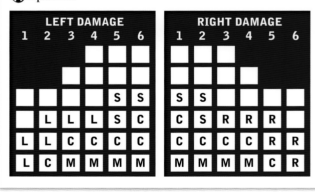

TACTICAL TIP

SECONDARY BATTERY – One Secondary Battery can be used to make attacks and the other can use the Creeping Barrage ability.

HEIGHT / WEIGHT:	31′ / 100.8 TONS
ARMAMENT:	MAIN GUNS TURRET (INTEGRAL), DUAL SECONDARY BATTERIES (LEFT AND RIGHT CHASSIS)
FUEL LOAD / BURN USAGE:	3,150 LBS / 6 HRS GENERAL, 45 MINS COMBAT
INITIAL SERVICE DATE:	608 AR
CORTEX MANUFACTURER:	GREYLORDS COVENANT
ORIG. CHASSIS DESIGN:	KHADORAN MECHANIKS ASSEMBLY

Among the proudest expressions of Khadoran martial determination, the Conquest is a walking mountain of steel bristling with some of the most powerful weapons ever used on the battlefields of the Iron Kingdoms. It advances slowly but inexorably, weighed down by impenetrable armor and boasting the firepower of a mobile artillery battery. The deafening roar of the colossal's steam-fed engine is punctuated by the staggering percussion of its devastating guns, which unleash a punishing hail of shells able to reduce warjacks to slag and render the ground impassable.

The Conquest began as a triumph of espionage by the Prikaz Chancellery of the Greylords Covenant. Agents within Caspia in the employ of the chancellery discovered a massive project underway there that involved tremendous shifts in mechaniks and other laborers. By the heroic efforts of highly skilled patriots, a number of detailed schematics were secured and eventually brought to industrialist Grand Vizier Simonyev Blaustavya, who discerned the impending birth of a new colossal—and a grave threat to Khador. It took little effort for Blaustavya and the supreme kommandants to convince Empress Vanar to meet the new danger with a colossal of their own. The empress decreed that not only would the Motherland field her own colossals, but the machines would be completed before Cygnar's. This was the challenge set before the nation.

Plans for the Conquest were laid out in a matter of weeks. Both the empress and the grand vizier used their formidable presence and political clout to quash all potential opposition, transforming the cost and challenge of the project into a mechanism for gaining favor and prestige. The Greylords Covenant, Khadoran Mechaniks Assembly, and numerous kayazy soon vied for recognition. Though all groups received credit for the effort to one extent or another, the KMA was ultimately recognized as the primary architect of the Conquest due in large part to the political currency and immutable vision of Simonyev Blaustavya.

Given the difficult task of completing the project ahead of Cygnar, Blaustavya quickly arranged for the colossal's components to be fabricated in numerous factories and workshops across several major cities, particularly Ohk, Khardov, and Korsk. He also modified the arcanum supernum cortex from its Cygnaran schematics to account for his country's dearth of several vital rare minerals including those required for its refined metal alloys. This Khadoran variant cortex was ultimately less sophisticated, but it could be built quickly and more cheaply. The engineers and mechaniks tasked with designing the Conquest rose to the challenge of devising weapons powerful enough to be worthy of the colossal without requiring the same degree of cortex supervision.

Ultimately, they looked to the massive guns of the Khadoran Navy's ironhull warships, whose enormous turrets boasted cannons designed to be fired in tandem, the recoil of one being used to reload the other. This principle proved crucial to the design of the Conquest's primary guns, as it prevented the need for its cortex to regulate reloading. The main guns were supplemented by two sets of twin-linked cannons. Mounted in the colossal's shoulders, these guns can lay down an impressive barrage with their high rate of fire.

As work progressed, it became clear that the raw materials needed to build the Conquest would be a burden, but the leadership indulged no compromises. Thousands of citizens in Korsk and Khardov went without coal for a winter, and hundreds froze to death—an unfortunate but necessary sacrifice made to fuel the foundries required to smelt ore for the Conquest's hull. During production, laborers worked in shifts around the clock, and many died of exhaustion or in accidents brought on by fatigue.

The combined efforts and concessions resulted in a resounding victory. The first operational Conquest paraded through the Khadoran capital for the benefit of the people and the empress weeks before the Cygnaran Stormwall debuted. With such a symbol of their unrivaled superiority, the Khadorans unleashed the first Conquests upon those who would deny them their right to empire.

Deployed to the front lines, the Conquest brings unrivaled firepower to Khadoran battlegroups. The tremendous amount of energy needed to operate a machine the size of the Conquest requires an equally impressive amount of coal and water, though, and often entire villages see their fuel supplies requisitioned by passing Khadoran forces. It is a small price to pay for the assurance of dominance under the guns of the Conquest.

CONQUEST CONCEPTUAL DESIGNS

CRYX
DEALS MADE IN SHADOW

LLAEL, BETWEEN LAEDRY AND MERYWYN

Goreshade found something satisfying about placing himself where none of his myriad enemies would dream he might be found. He remembered invading the Morrowan cathedral in the Khadoran capital in pursuit of Nyssor's vault and the keen gratification that had come with defiling holy ground. His thoughts returned to that as he crouched in the shadows of the cargo car near the rear of a Khadoran train. He could hear the slats clacking as the train pushed on, its engine occasionally letting loose a whistle of steam. He had never ridden a train, and the sense of speed as it passed between Laedry and Merywyn was an interesting novelty.

Scaverous had been instrumental in discovering his target's plans, information wrested from the memories of recently killed associates, but it had been his own cunning that had enabled him to sneak aboard the train unseen. It was filled with his enemies, and he was far from any Cryxian support. He had to conclude his business before they reached Merywyn, but he was prepared for this. He remained calm and still, awaiting the response to the note he had sent before beginning this journey. He harbored no doubt she would come. Clandestine activity was meat and drink to her.

There was rattling at the connecting access door as someone dealt with the locks and then it slid open, briefly increasing the noise of the tracks rushing by below. She had arrived. In one hand she held something that emitted a cold blue light, and after a moment he saw it was her sword. Her peculiar Orgoth talisman was in the other. He heard her cough at the reek in the air from the necrotite in his armor's turbine.

"Aleksandra Zerkova," he said, standing to his full height. He had positioned himself to be visible but difficult to reach immediately, behind several low stacks of ammunition and weapons crates. He sensed with some disappointment the Torch was not with her. Things would have been simpler had it been. Her eyes widened and she sucked in a gasp, already drawing on her power. He held up a hand. "This is

not an assassination. Quite the contrary." The note he had sent her had opened with, *"I know your greatest secret. You will never recover what has been lost without me."*

To her credit she stepped forward and stared at him with her good eye, showing no fear. "Speak quickly, eldritch, before I have you destroyed."

"It is a simple matter. I seek a temporary partnership, to our mutual benefit."

Her eyes narrowed and she said, "I have no reason to risk dealing with you even for a moment."

He laughed and said, "I think you do! You lost the frozen vault, and even now chase it. You seek to get ahead of those who stole it from you. Thanks to this conveyance," he gestured to the car around them, "you may succeed. Covering ground is more difficult for the Iosans, who must travel overland and avoid patrols with their unwieldy burden. You know where they must take it: to Ios, which requires them to pass through occupied Llael."

She was adept at controlling her expression and gave him only an icy stare, but that was no matter. He could predict the thoughts that must be passing through her mind, the questions. The hungry look in her eyes told him the mystery of the vault and its contents haunted her. She said, "I have no need of you. I will reclaim the vault on my own—and destroy you if you interfere."

"Perhaps," he allowed. "You kept the Torch of Khazarak, I hope? Yes, that is the key, the only one. Know this: you will never make it work. It lights only for me." At last he saw a flicker of some emotion on her face, a widening of the eyes. She felt vindicated; she had expected that relic must be important, and he had confirmed her theories. She did not want to believe him, but he had planted the seed. "We can come to an equitable arrangement. You have the soldiers required to intercept the vault, but without me your key will never fit the lock."

He sat back slightly and was silent, allowing his words to creep into her mind like pernicious weeds. It was a delicate balancing act of manipulation. What he had not told Zerkova was that despite his words, he had accepted that he had missed his chance to seize Nyssor. As soon as the vault fell into Ossyan's hands, he had known the Retribution of Scyrah would succeed in their goal. Their sect was, if nothing else, persistent and unwavering. Nyssor's return to Ios was inevitable. Zerkova clung to false hopes, but he was willing to use that to his advantage.

Goreshade had opted to play a deeper game, to enact contingencies requiring certain pieces set in motion with tremendous precision. Zerkova was one. She had secured the Torch, and Goreshade lacked the armed might to take it from her at this moment. Even if he could, Nyssor's vault would soon be in Ios, secured at one of the Iosan fanes. Goreshade had no choice but to return to his former homeland. He had long ago prepared the means by which this could be facilitated, knowing it was the only way he could reach Scyrah. There were eldritch in Eversael who would do his bidding. What he required now was a means to get the Torch of Kharazak into Ios as well, lest Nyssor remain frozen and unassailable.

He could never succeed in carrying such a powerful profaned relic past the borders undetected. The route by which he would enter that nation could not be the same as the Torch. His plan would work only if the Retribution brought it, willingly, believing it represented their salvation. Even better if they felt compelled to safeguard it by keeping it near Nyssor's vault. Staring at Zerkova, he could see she had already reached the decision to play along—until she could betray him.

THE THORNWOOD

Deneghra managed the retreat from Point Bourne smoothly, yet she took little satisfaction in this. That city had been intended to be the staging area to demonstrate perfect coordination and planning, including the smooth transfer of Lich Lord Venethrax and his prize to the protection of Skarre Ravenmane. It seemed to her that any aspect of the plan she had not personally overseen had been rife with mistakes. Not that Venethrax's absence could have been foreseen, but it rankled that her careful orchestration had gone to waste.

Skarre had been irate with the notion of lingering behind unsupported to await Venethrax and had confronted Asphyxious directly. When their argument escalated, Deneghra had been forced to intervene in order to prevent violence between the two. Ordinarily she would have taken pleasure from seeing Asphyxious put the pirate queen in her place, but she knew Ravenmane would then poison Venethrax to their cause in their absence, and it was vital to their ambitions that he praised Asphyxious' role in the athanc's recovery to Lord Toruk.

Despite the fact that they had needed to withdraw from Point Bourne, significant gains had been made there. They had lost the thralls left behind to forestall their enemies, of course, but they had reaped a wealth of new war material, including a harvest of fresh souls. The capture of Karchev the Terrible was a point of particular pride, and she savored imagining his fate. Though the revelation of his capture did not immediately spur his comrades to foolish acts of heroism, she knew it would goad them into pursuit. The Khadorans and Cygnarans together had followed eagerly into the forest and pressed north, gathering strength as they were joined by others formerly stationed along the Dragon's Tongue.

Indeed, the alacrity with which the enemies were gathering their might had begun to alarm Deneghra. Her initial plan had been to linger back with a small force to nip at their heels as they advanced, thereby disrupting and stalling them. Asphyxious had irritably insisted such measures were unnecessary and forbade her. He was content to leave behind only those peripheral facilities created over the last year to stand as obstacles and enticements to the advancing armies. These sites had served their primary purposes, such as extracting necrotite and remains from ancient battlefields, but their defenses remained, including thralls emplaced to secure them. He insisted that sacrificing these sites to the enemy would lull them into a false sense of accomplishment. In Deneghra's mind, such efforts were paltry and too few against the considerable armed force the Cygnarans and Khadorans were beginning to raise against them. While it had been her suggestion to lure them into the Thornwood, not once did she underestimate the threat those nations posed to Cryx. She worried Asphyxious had become overconfident.

Regular reports of the disposition of the allied armies began to arrive from her spectral scouts, confirming their rapid progress. Added to this, she had to deal with cephalyx emissaries who complained about the destruction of a section of their tunnel network in the northwestern forest. She pacified them and reminded them of the abundant harvest of drudges recently provided them in the sack of Point Bourne.

The collapse they spoke of was the same one that had nearly thwarted Lich Lord Venethrax and the athanc he sought to recover. The blackclad druids were behind this, just as they had sunk the Temple Garrodh two years earlier. What was the cost to perform such rituals? In the face of such a threat, she had to wonder if the Thornwood Central Necrofactorium was secure. When she had brought the matter to Asphyxious' attention, he had become wroth, dismissing the power of the blackclads as insignificant. It was clear he did not wish to hear anything further on that topic. With each passing day he became more temperamental about any suggestion of potential vulnerability to his great work.

As soon as they reached the necrofactorium she set about preparing their defenses, knowing they had little time. A number of the measures they planned to implement in defense of the facility had yet to be completed, and she did what she could to expedite them. She also personally supervised securing Karchev within the heart of the necrofactorium's occult laboratories.

Returning to Asphyxious, she was surprised to find him not also working to improve their fortifications but rather occupied at his forge. Several of the complex's most skilled necrotechs were laboring on refinements to his armored frame while he crafted a new weapon from his old. He had taken the essence of Daeamortus and transferred it to a broad-bladed sword. Deneghra watched him with irritation, wondering why he would pick such a time for this task. At the same time, she could not help but admire his skill at these arts, so far beyond her own capabilities. In the fabrication of occult weaponry, Asphyxious had few equals.

> **"AT THIS MOMENT IT REQUIRES MORE EFFORT *NOT* TO KILL THEE AND TAKE THY SOUL."**

"I call it Daimonion," he said to her, raising the weapon before him. He returned to inscribing runes on its length as he asked, "Art thou pleased to be home?"

"Of course. But there is much to do, and our enemies come closer with each passing hour." Until recently she had at least felt a sense of invulnerability and safety within the heart of Asphyxious' power, but that was no longer true. The disquieting encounter with Malathrax, the confrontation with the Old Witch, and the reports of the cave collapse atop Venethrax—all had stripped away her belief that this place was inviolable. "I thought you might have the chance to attend to Karchev, now that we are here."

Asphyxious waved a clawed hand dismissively. "In due time. Thou hast the impatience of the living! Another matter is at hand." She was uncertain what he meant until the door to the chamber opened and a slender woman in revealing leathers strode in, her head hooded and masked. Deneghra blinked, for a moment taken aback to recognize Helleana, of the Witch Coven of Garlghast. The young witch strode forward and gave Asphyxious a bow carefully measured to provide just the barest respect.

Turning away from his work to face her, Asphyxious did not speak for a long moment, staring at her in silence. Finally he asked, "Which one are you, and where are your sisters?"

"Helleana, my lord. The others were needed elsewhere," she said evasively. Asphyxious faced her more fully at this, and while others may have found it difficult to perceive emotions behind the iron frame, Deneghra knew from his posture that his temper was close to flaring at this blatant disrespect. The Coven should have come to speak with him as one.

The witch continued, uncaring. "Lord Terminus has need of war supplies, including additional thralls; the forces allocated to him have proven inadequate. I will convey his demands to you."

Asphyxious soared down from the elevated platform of his forge with frightful speed and was upon Helleana before she could blink. Just as quickly she found the heavy scalloped edge of his new blade against the side of her throat. It made a slight keening noise and seemed to push into her living flesh of its own accord, and the eye inhabiting the blade stared hungrily at her. She froze and the blood drained from her face as she stared at Asphyxious as if transfixed. "At this moment it requires more effort *not* to kill thee and take thy soul," he hissed.

"My lord—" she began, but she stopped as the sword bit, sending a trickle of blood down her neck. Deneghra eyed this exchange with some alarm, wondering if Asphyxious had lost all self-control. The Witch Coven were no friends of hers, but she could see no benefit in Helleana's execution.

Asphyxious continued, "*Inadequate?* My armies? He would make *demands?* I think not! Tell thy master that if he needs to beg my assistance, he can do so in person. Now begone!" She had the sense to do as bid. In theory the Coven enjoyed the protection of Lich Lord Terminus, but Asphyxious had made it clear how little that mattered to him. Deneghra felt profound relief when Helleana rushed from the chamber.

After the metal doors closed, Asphyxious examined his newly forged blade, staring at the drops of blood upon it. He said, "I almost thought she would give me an excuse to test its edge."

Deneghra chose her words carefully. "I would have expected you might be eager to demonstrate how much Terminus relies upon you by letting him become indebted."

Asphyxious turned toward her, his eye gleaming. "He seeks to insult me, sending an emissary. Since I seized Morbus' domain, I have anticipated the prospect of seeing Terminus come begging for my scraps. Let him be the one to govern his words and swallow his pride as he grovels before me."

Deneghra shook her head and said, "He has his own pride. He will not grovel but will approach armed and ready for battle. We can ill afford to fight him with two armies approaching!" She realized she had said too much. He stepped toward her with a look that she found deeply unsettling, as though he was considering her no different from the witch he had sent fleeing the chamber.

"Let him come! I welcome such a conflict! He is cut off from his own army, and his strength is pitiful at best. I will destroy him and the Cygnarans and Khadorans all at once if need be! Dost thou disagree? Dost thou think me incapable of this feat?" His voice sounded deeply suspicious.

"Of course not," she said. Deneghra knew better than to argue with him when he was in this sort of mood and quickly took her leave, concealing how greatly his words disturbed her. Perhaps his ego had outstripped his reason. The last thing they needed was a renewal of the feud with Terminus. The timing of such a potential conflict could not have been worse. Even lacking a proper army, Lich Lord Terminus was as formidable a being as existed in Cryx. Lesser thralls were built to obey the lich lords and were not necessarily discriminating; there could be no guarantees that many of Asphyxious' minions would not turn on him should Terminus command it. The army Deneghra had worked to accumulate could be divided to consume itself, just as the mortal armies converged.

She felt turmoil deep in the core of her being, a sensation of powerfully conflicted emotions. She was bound to Asphyxious, body and soul, and the thought of acting against him prompted almost physical pain. Yet he had charged her with administrating his dominion. It was her responsibility to do what she must to preserve his power, even if that meant going beyond his orders. It was her place to be cunning enough to comprehend when his ambitions made him his own worst enemy. She had failed to advise him when he had invoked the power of the Temple Garrodh, and he had nearly been destroyed.

For his own good, she must act. She strode quickly from the complex, transforming into a wraith to pass through the intervening walls until she reached a passage Helleana would need to take on her more circuitous route out.

She kept hidden and followed the witch as she left the necrofactorium and rejoined a pair of Stalker bonejacks. It had become second nature to Deneghra to hide the otherwise telltale signs of her presence from other warcasters. Were circumstances otherwise she might have enjoyed toying with Helleana, but that was not her mission. She stepped forth and became substantial in front of Helleana. The witch stopped abruptly, her hand going to the dagger at her waist. Her Stalkers tensed as well, their blades quivering with readiness. Deneghra said, "Helleana, you should have come to me first rather than approaching my lord. You know better."

Helleana's expression adopted its familiar look of disdain, but one hand instinctively reached to touch the cut on her neck. She said, "I did as *my* lord instructed. He will not be pleased when he learns Asphyxious intends to withhold."

Deneghra said sincerely, "Please, forget my lord's demeanor; he was in a foul temper. I have been empowered to make arrangements for our necrofactorium."

Helleana was clearly skeptical. "Asphyxious seemed firm on the matter."

Deneghra sensed new arrivals before they stepped from the trees, although they were very close before she could feel them: Morgaen and Selene, bringing the Coven to completion. The Egregore floated silently between, forever oozing its flows of spectral darkness. Since her death and rebirth, Deneghra had found the entity even more disquieting, as she could feel its alien mind pressing against her own when it was near. The air between the sisters held tremendous potency. She turned to greet them. "I did not expect to find you here. I thought you occupied in Llael."

Selene shrugged and said, "Efforts there are ongoing, but there were setbacks." Deneghra could see a livid scar on her exposed side, what must have been the puckered remnant of a ghastly wound. The Coven healed quickly, so that injury must have been nearly fatal. "Lord Terminus sends us as a courtesy. If you refuse us, he will take what he needs. Tell that to your master."

"I am here on my own," Deneghra said. "But I believe I can provide what you require."

Morgaen laughed lightly. "That is difficult to believe. You are Asphyxious' puppet. What game is this?"

Deneghra glared back. "I am no puppet, and the stakes are too high to fight among ourselves. The endeavor for which we all labor is at a crucial juncture. Each of us has done our part to return Toruk's athanc, but new obstacles have arisen. Khador and Cygnar have allied and send their armies here to root us out. We will need all the forces we have gathered to stand against them."

Helleana said, "Lord Terminus will not accept such excuses."

"Listen to my words," Deneghra said firmly. "I will arrange for helljacks, bonejacks, and thralls to be delivered to Lord Terminus. Not as many as he would like, I am sure, but we can reach an accommodation. But there is a condition. Two, in fact."

Selene scoffed, "You would place conditions on a lich lord?"

"First," Deneghra continued as if she had not been interrupted, "you should know that Lord Venethrax has been delayed and lacks adequate support to protect the athanc. This means our shared endeavor is in peril. I will for weapons to be delivered to Terminus, but only if he will use them to assist Venethrax in taking the athanc south. Your master should have no disagreements with this."

"If Lord Venethrax is so much on your mind, why not intercede personally?" Morgaen asked.

"The allied armies I mentioned are marching here. We antagonized them deliberately to lure them, so that all eyes will be on us and not Venethrax. Our hands will be full battling Cygnarans and Khadorans."

Helleana seemed to accept this and asked, "Your second condition?"

"Simple." Deneghra smiled again. "Asphyxious is to hear nothing of this arrangement. I do what I must to aid Cryx, to serve Toruk, but keep this matter between us." The sisters shared a look and nodded as one before turning to depart, the Egregore trailing behind.

Unknown to all of them, this meeting had an audience of one. Hovering in the deeper darkness not far from their position was a spectral creature, a wraith with a knack for remaining unseen and an equally vital talent for being in the right place at the right time. In life he had been Thomas Ketchum, and he had learned how to make himself invaluable to his superior officers. Ketchum had put that identity well behind him. He had not, however, abandoned his skills and cunning. He had risen in Deneghra's favor, a task that required nothing more than doing what was asked of him, and doing it competently.

He had been set on this task by his true master, and it had been so long since he had received a summons that Ketchum had almost begun to forget his original orders. His memory was not what it once had been. Several times in recent weeks he had wondered if he should risk returning early to his master, but his instincts had held him back. The little kernels of information he had gathered seemed insufficient. Now the time had come. Malathrax would want to know of this meeting. *Yes*, he thought, *this was just the sort of thing I was waiting for.* He drifted off to the west, passing as a ghost through tree and underbrush

At last the tirelessly laboring thralls had cleared a wide enough opening to escape the collapsed tunnel, although Venethrax mistrusted the improvised struts and supports the necrotechs had placed to shore up the earthworks. The creatures were brilliant in their way with machinery, but their overall engineering expertise was dubious. It fell to his helljacks to haul the damaged athanc-containment conveyance forth, a slow and tedious process. He needed to inspect the enormous mechanism, something that would be possible only when it was fully extracted from the half-collapsed tunnel. Thus far, though, the containment seemed intact.

He did not understand the peculiar and ancient mechanism, but it seemed the Rhulfolk's skill at crafting durable machinery predated the modern era; the worst of the damage had been to the Cryxian-made elements of the transport, specifically the undercarriage and the great wheels. The necrotechs reported three of the steam engines powering the machine had been crushed and disabled, yet clearly it had been built with considerable redundancy, as the metal bands that created the mystical barrier within which the athanc was secured still spun in their arcs emitting their powerful and inexplicable energies. However this mechanism somehow preserved the long-defeated dragon's athanc, he had to trust that item was still intact. Inch by inch the enormous wagon and its load was pulled forth from the rubble and into the broader tunnel. It would not be long before the necrotechs could reach and hopefully repair its undercarriage.

Leaving the thralls and helljacks momentarily to their labor, Venethrax climbed up out of the tunnel and into the dark forest through the exit they had carved after the tunnel collapse. He had lost much during that disaster and now possessed only a barely adequate escort. This had greatly occupied his mind, yet no act of will would speed the slow process of extraction.

Lich Lord Malathrax stood at the edge of the improvised clearing in whispered communication with a ghostly pistol wraith. Malathrax's tall but slender frame was hidden beneath the flowing lengths of black robes set with metal plates, each inscribed with occult sigils. Shifting lumps could be seen wriggling beneath the cloth, evidence of Malathrax's peculiar spiderlike necromechanikal minions. Otherwise the lich's most notable feature was his ever-shifting metallic face, an intricate mechanism of mosaic panels that created a variety of masks. Venethrax eyed him warily; the circumstances around the discovery of the athanc were still exceedingly suspicious. Malathrax had always seemed loyal to Lord Toruk but in recent centuries had become increasingly reluctant to dispense the information that was ostensibly his primary function and area of oversight. There was also the timing of the disappearances of both Goreshade and Lord Exhumator Scaverous, who had gone on some unspecified errand before the column entered the tunnels. The Cryxian spymaster protested ignorance, but Venethrax did not believe him.

Seeing Venethrax emerge, Malathrax made a gesture and the pistol wraith inclined its head and moved back into the trees. It was not uncommon for Malathrax to receive regular ghostly apparitions bringing morsels of information. Turning to Venethrax, Malathrax asked, "How goes the work below?" The panels of his masked metal face folded back and reformed into the guise of a goat-like beast with small curved horns.

"Slow, but we will have it free soon. Have you learned anything of the tunnel collapse?"

"No more than before. The cause was organized and supernatural; we both felt the manifestations. Blackclads, I am sure, but there is no sign of them yet. I am perturbed they were able to pinpoint our location. If they know they failed to destroy us, I expect we will be visited by them soon enough." His mask clicked over to resemble a cherubic childlike visage.

Sudden movement behind Malathrax caught Venethrax's attention. He raised Wyrmbane and began to summon his inner fire. A large, eyeless, bat-like creature flew into the clearing. Venethrax raised a metal-clawed hand as green flame manifested in his palm, preparing to hurl it at the beast. He was a moment too slow. Malathrax had not moved or even turned to face the winged thing, but a pattern of runes erupted like a crown around his head, and a dark nimbus that crackled like thunder appeared around the creature. The thing contorted, turning inside out as its skeleton split from its flesh and fell as individual bones down into the undergrowth along with its its blood, tissues, and organs. Malathrax turned and peered at the gore impassively. "Ah. Dragonspawn. It seems we have been found."

Venethrax strode forward and prodded at the remains, irritated Malathrax had left so little to identify to creature. Still, he had already recognized it as a harrier, the flying counterpart to the akriel, described in ancient texts of Morrdh. "Everblight."

"Yes," Malathrax said. "Not long ago Mortenebra had a run-in with a number of similar spawn to the southeast. I have sent feelers out among my contacts seeking additional information on them. They are behaving in a way that is not at all in keeping with known lore on dragonspawn. I suspect you know this already."

Venethrax was barely listening as he scanned the trees around them. "This creature may have been a lone scout. But we should prepare against imminent attack, as others will likely follow." He summoned several of his helljacks from below, leaving the rest to their task of hauling the transport from the rubble. Through their eyes he saw they had gotten it partially clear, enough for two of his necrotechs to begin working on it. The rear portion was still inaccessible.

The silver mosaic layers of Malathrax's mask clicked over to create a leering fiend. "That is one course we could take. But I think we need to consider the necessity of removing the athanc from its containment and securing it elsewhere until more reinforcements can gather. I have several secure locations that might serve—"

"No," Venethrax interrupted. "That will not be happening."

Malathrax shrugged as his mask turned cherubic. "I was just informed by one of my subordinates that we may be receiving aid from Terminus soon, although he has sought reinforcements from Asphyxious, who is being troublesome as always. I expect we will be on our own if we need wait for those two to come to agreement."

> **THE THING CONTORTED, TURNING INSIDE OUT AS ITS SKELETON SPLIT FROM ITS FLESH AND FELL AS INDIVIDUAL BONES.**

Venethrax glowered at the spymaster and finally said, "Make yourself useful and go ensure reinforcements are incoming. Find Terminus and tell him time is of the essence. We have no time for Asphyxious' games."

The other lich lord's fingers twitched as if agitated and he said, "Surely my place should be here, with the athanc. What if you are attacked while I am away?"

"I will manage," Venethrax said through his teeth.

"Of course," Malathrax said. "I am, as ever, pleased to be of assistance, and it is true combat is not my forte." He sounded apologetic as he looked down again at the pile of gore that had been a dragonspawn and then stepped into the shadows.

ASPHYXIOUS THE HELLBRINGER & VOCIFERON
CRYX EPIC WARCASTER & CHARACTER SOLO

Where his shadow falls, hell follows.

—Wraith Witch Deneghra

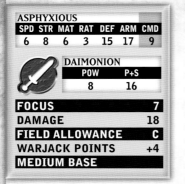

ASPHYXIOUS						
SPD	STR	MAT	RAT	DEF	ARM	CMD
6	8	6	3	15	17	9

DAIMONION		
	POW	P+S
	8	16

FOCUS	7
DAMAGE	18
FIELD ALLOWANCE	C
WARJACK POINTS	+4
MEDIUM BASE	

FEAT: RITES OF SHADOW

When the time is right, Asphyxious the Hellbringer invokes the Rites of Shadow to enfold the battlefield in a spiritual darkness of his own design. Amid this flickering landscape, the magic of his enemies is tainted. With every incantation his iron frame is mended, while the restless souls of the slaughtered rise only to be harvested to fuel the Hellbringer's powers.

When an enemy model is forced, casts a spell, and/or spends 1 or more focus or fury points while in Asphyxious' control area, Asphyxious heals d3 damage points and gains one soul token. Rites of Shadow lasts for one round.

ASPHYXIOUS

 Terror

 Undead

Cull Soul – This model gains one soul token for each living enemy model destroyed within 2″ of it. When this model replenishes its focus during your next Control Phase, replace each soul token on it with 1 focus point.

DAIMONION

 Magical Weapon

Reach

Blood Boon – Once per activation, immediately after resolving an attack in which it destroyed a living enemy model with this weapon, this model can cast a spell with COST 3 or less without spending focus.

TACTICAL TIPS

BONE SHAKER – Because a boxed model is removed from play before being destroyed, it does not generate a soul or corpse token.

CULL SOUL – A model can have more focus points than its FOCUS as a result of Cull Soul.

HEX BLAST – Because they expire immediately, upkeep spells and animi that had an effect when the model/unit was hit or damaged will have no effect.

RITES OF SHADOW – Cull Soul converts tokens gained from Rites of Shadow into focus points. If a model casts a spell by spending focus or fury, Rites of Shadow triggers only once.

SPELLS	COST	RNG	AOE	POW	UP	OFF
ASHEN VEIL	2	6	–	–	YES	NO

Target friendly model/unit gains concealment. Living enemy models suffer –2 to attack rolls while within 2″ of an affected model.

BONE SHAKER	2	8	–	12	NO	YES

When this spell boxes a living or undead non-warcaster, non-warlock enemy warrior model, you can immediately make a full advance with the enemy model followed by a normal melee attack, then the boxed model is removed from play. The boxed model cannot be targeted by free strikes during this movement.

CARNAGE	3	SELF	CTRL	–	NO	NO

Friendly Faction models gain +2 to melee attack rolls against enemy models in this model's control area. Carnage lasts for one turn.

HEX BLAST	3	10	3	13	NO	YES

Enemy upkeep spells and animi on the model/unit directly hit by Hex Blast immediately expire.

MOBILITY	2	SELF	CTRL	–	NO	NO

Models in this model's battlegroup currently in its control area gain +2 SPD and Pathfinder for one turn.

SCYTHING TOUCH	2	6	–	–	YES	NO

Target friendly model/unit gains +2 to melee attack damage rolls. Affected models gain Critical Corrosion on their normal melee attacks.

More than one thousand years of preparation, intrigue, and nested contingencies have brought Asphyxious closer than ever to his goal of rising above the other lich lords to stand as Toruk's most invaluable general. He has carved out a subterranean empire filled with necromechanikal terrors, having built a ghastly army that stands ready to answer his every command. Even those Cryxian lords who despise him and deem themselves his equal have been forced to turn to him for aid, as he alone holds the key to unleashing the vast might of the Nightmare Empire.

Since the moment the druid who would eventually become a lich lord chose to leap to his death as a sign of commitment to the Dragonfather and rose again in undeath, Asphyxious has chosen a path meant to ensure his eternal status as Toruk's most favored servant. Whereas once he was deemed merely a useful minion in the arsenal of Lich Lord Daeamortus, little more than a skilled scavenger feeding on the periphery of mainland wars, he has since risen to change the very shape of Cryxian leadership. Even his failures and defeats have ultimately advanced his position, as he has the tenacity as well as the ability and desire to adapt and exploit every possible advantage. In recent years his plans have begun to unfold with exponential speed. Even serious setbacks like the destruction of the Temple of Garrodh have prepared the Thornwood for its one and true master.

Asphyxious' greatest accomplishment is undoubtedly the great necrofactorium that sprawls beneath the Thornwood. Only the deathless city of Skell, capital of the Cryxian

Empire, can rival this immense creation of his. Leveraging dark pacts made with the enigmatic cephalyx, Asphyxious has directed the extensive excavation beneath the soil of the Thornwood for years, guiding the work that now connects the upper reaches of a vast cavern with a network of tunnels that have never been seen by any surface dweller. Only a mind as devious and ancient as Asphyxious' could have hoped to parley with such strange allies. What payment he promised them for their cooperation—beyond the provision of countless living slaves—remains unknown to any but the iron lich and the Cephalyx themselves. Whatever the cost, he gained invaluable access to their subterranean facilities and ongoing aid.

Once the tunnels were established, Asphyxious set about installing a vast abattoir and factory complex within, making use of the plentiful product of battle: both those corpses his forces gathered in their own quiet raids and those bodies harvested from the ongoing conflicts between the petty nations of mankind. Asphyxious removed one obstacle after another, ensuring the preeminence of his work in the great war he knew was not long to come. The latest of these obstacles was the overseer of Cryxian war industry, Lich Lord Morbus, who arrived on the mainland to urge patience and advocate slow growth. When Morbus threatened to seize control of the Thornwood necrofactoriums and impede progress, Asphyxious encouraged Deneghra's scheme to lure the lich lord to his destruction while obfuscating the conspiracy by allowing Cygnar to deal the fatal blow. Consequently, Asphyxious at last firmly established himself as the master of Cryxian war industry.

Asphyxious is willing to make any sacrifice to advance his schemes. As far as he is concerned, eliminating Cryxians too inept or incautious to protect themselves only serves to strengthen the armies of the Dragonfather. Ultimately, his work has culminated in the production of several of the mighty Krakens he will unleash just when his enemies think he is simply cornered in his lair. Asphyxious has spent years overseeing the labor that has produced countless necromechanikal terrors, a rising tide of death waiting to be unleashed. Their time has arrived.

As Toruk's war on his progeny rapidly approaches, the other lich lords must make obeisance to Asphyxious if they wish to avail themselves of the war resources he now controls, which they need to supply their own discrete armies. The forces that have begun to emerge from beneath the Thornwood are no mere raiding parties or even battalions; rather, they are the great hosts Lord Toruk intends his lich lords to use to weaken his draconic progeny so he can consume them. Should Caen be razed in the passage of these hosts, it is of no consequence. Those few souls fortunate enough to have escaped the brief Cryxian occupation of Point Bourne have had a glimpse of the world Asphyxious would leave behind him: a charnel land of inescapable death where souls are nothing but fuel for the Dragonfather and his machinations.

To aid him in his great work Asphyxious has crafted Vociferon, a skarlock of special cunning that he has perfectly equipped to serve as a conduit for souls. Created from carefully prepared materials and bathed in blighted energies, Vociferon benefits from Asphyxious' artistic and impressive mastery of thrall runes. It carries a battle standard of death and discord that resonates with unholy

ASPHYXIOUS

VOCIFERON

- ✠ Arc Node
- ✪ Commander
- ☠ Undead

VOCIFERON						
SPD	STR	MAT	RAT	DEF	ARM	CMD
6	5	5	3	13	16	9

CLAWS		
	POW	P+S
	3	8

DAMAGE	5
FIELD ALLOWANCE	C
SMALL BASE	

Arcane Extension [Asphyxious the Hellbringer] – During your Control Phase, while this model is in Asphyxious the Hellbringer's control area Asphyxious the Hellbringer can allocate focus to warjacks in his battlegroup that are in this model's command range.

Attached to [Asphyxious the Hellbringer] – This model is attached to Asphyxious the Hellbringer for the rest of the game. Each warcaster can have only one model attached to it.

Companion [Asphyxious the Hellbringer] – This model is included in any army that includes Asphyxious the Hellbringer. If Asphyxious is destroyed or removed from play, remove this model from play. This model is part of Asphyxious' battlegroup.

Death Harvest – If this model is in its warcaster's control range during your Maintenance Phase, you can take any number of soul tokens from this model and place them on the warcaster.

Ghost Shield – This model gains +1 ARM for each soul token currently on it.

Soul Collector – This model gains one soul token when a living enemy model is destroyed in its command range. This model can have up to three soul tokens at a time. During its activation, this model can spend soul tokens to gain additional attacks or to boost attack or damage rolls at one token per attack or boost.

TACTICAL TIP

DEATH HARVEST – Cull Soul converts tokens gained from Death Harvest into focus points.

intent, for it was made to collect the essences of all who perish within its reach. Going about its soul harvests with nefarious intellect, Vociferon has sanction to speak with the lich lord's voice and direct lesser minions.

Ready to unleash his host upon western Immoren and demonstrate his imperishable convictions, Asphyxious faces the prospect of upcoming battles with keen anticipation. He intends to play a key role in bringing Lord Toruk the victories the dragon hungers for—and thus elevate himself above all others. All that lives shall look upon his armies and tremble as the world is reduced to ashen waste and its people become no more than howling souls in the clutches of Asphyxious the Hellbringer.

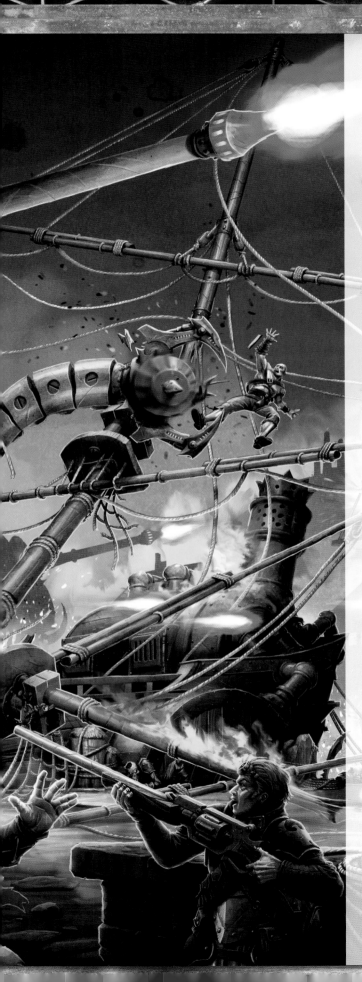

KRAKEN

THE BROKEN COAST, 585 AR

At first, assigning a ship of the line to ferry a few Cygnaran academics from Ceryl to Mercir had seemed a waste of naval resources to First Mate Boors, but now he regretted they were out on the seas at all. A black tentacle swept past him to knock three men from the rigging to the deck below, and he could only grit his teeth and climb toward the crow's nest.

Only moments before, the night sea off the coast of Cygnar had been calm. Captain Kilkenny had set double watches against the threat of attack by Cryxian raiders, but the *HMS Benewic* had had not seen action in weeks.

At the first great thud shaking the deck planks he thought that they had run against some unseen rock or shoal, and he heard the captain yelled orders to turn hard to port. Shouts had died in their throats as a second impact struck the hull from the opposite side, this time with greater violence, throwing several seamen from the deck into the water. Boors had looked down to see the water churning white as a great black shape emerged. His eyes widened at the sight of what must be a beast of the ocean depths—something from stories told to frighten children.

He hauled himself higher, watching in shock as a pair of massive tentacles punched through the ship's side and then up through its deck. One wrapped around a Buccaneer and pulled the 'jack into the sea along with two crew members trying to reload a nearby cannon. The other tendril swept the deck clear and hurled men indiscriminately over the rails. Sailors screamed and the water churned red as they were smashed against wreckage that had been pulled free of the listing ship.

As the terrified crew and passengers poured onto the deck, the great bulk of the beast emerged from the waves. A tentacle shot up from the foaming chaos of the water to snatch up a cabin boy, then tossed him aside in favor of a Cygnaran university professor. The old man screamed as the tendril pulled him into a gaping opening in the side of the creature's body before it vanished once more below the churning water.

Boors climbed higher still, knowing the *Benewic* was lost. He hoped only that the creature was sated, a thought that was interrupted when a great black tentacle shot up from the water and wrapped itself around him despite his screams. As Boors was thrust into the yawning hole, he smelled the scent of blood mixed with iron and knew that this was no beast, but a machine that would be his tomb.

KRAKEN
CRYX COLOSSAL

The most exaggerated tale of terror beneath the waves does not begin to describe the shadow of the Kraken.

—Skarre, Queen of the Broken Coast

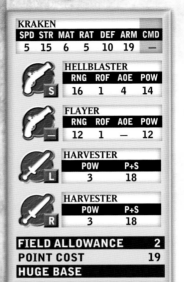

KRAKEN						
SPD	STR	MAT	RAT	DEF	ARM	CMD
5	15	6	5	10	19	—

HELLBLASTER (S)

RNG	ROF	AOE	POW
16	1	4	14

FLAYER

RNG	ROF	AOE	POW
12	1	—	12

HARVESTER (L)

POW	P+S
3	18

HARVESTER (R)

POW	P+S
3	18

FIELD ALLOWANCE	2
POINT COST	19
HUGE BASE	

KRAKEN

Amphibious – This model ignores the effects of deep and shallow water and can move through them without penalty. While completely in deep water, it cannot be targeted by ranged or magic attacks and can make attacks only against other models in deep water. While completely in deep water, this model does not block LOS.

Collector – If this model has fewer than three corpse tokens when it boxes a living enemy model as the result of a melee attack, remove the boxed model from play and give this model a corpse token. During your Control Phase, you can spend up to three corpse tokens to allocate this model 1 focus point for each corpse token spent.

Kill Shot – Once per activation, when a living enemy model is destroyed or removed from play as a result of a melee attack made by this model during its activation, immediately after that attack is resolved this model can make one normal ranged attack ignoring ROF.

Meat-Fueled – This model gains +1 STR for each corpse token on it.

HELLBLASTER

Doom Driver – For each corpse token on this model, this weapon gains +1 to damage rolls.

FLAYER

Rapid Fire [d3+1] – When you decide to make initial attacks with this weapon at the beginning of this model's combat action, roll d3+1. The total rolled is the number of initial attacks this model can make with this weapon during the combat action, ignoring ROF.

HARVESTER

(F) **Open Fist**

Chain Strike – This weapon has a 4″ melee range during this model's activation.

Chain Weapon – This attack ignores the Buckler and Shield weapon qualities and Shield Wall.

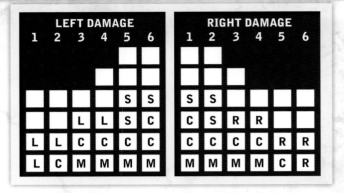

LEFT DAMAGE					
1	2	3	4	5	6
				S	S
		L	L	S	C
L	L	C	C	C	C
L	C	M	M	M	M

RIGHT DAMAGE					
1	2	3	4	5	6
S	S				
C	S	R	R		
C	C	C	C	R	R
M	M	M	M	C	R

TACTICAL TIPS

Amphibious – This model can attack other models that are in deep water.

Chain Weapon – Chain weapon does not modify the melee range of power attacks made by this model.

Collector – Because a boxed model is removed from play before being destroyed, it does not generate a soul token. This model cannot exceed its focus allocation limit as a result of Collector.

HEIGHT / WEIGHT: 27Đ / 85 TONS
ARMAMENT: HELLBLASTER CANNON (INTEGRAL), FLAYER CANNON (INTEGRAL), TWIN HARVESTERS (LEFT AND RIGHT ARMS)
FUEL LOAD / BURN USAGE: UNKNOWN
INITIAL SERVICE DATE: UNKNOWN
CORTEX MANUFACTURER: UNKNOWN
ORIG. CHASSIS DESIGN: UNKNOWN

The Kraken ranks among the most terrifying necromechanikal fabrications ever loosed upon the mortals of the Iron Kingdoms. Lashing out with grasping tentacles, it snatches up men and stuffs them within the grease-slicked orifices of its shell. The captured have but a moment of terror to consider their lightless environs before their life energies are extracted and their bodies consumed by a necromantic furnace that fuels the Kraken's engines and armament. The Kraken was conceived as the perfect Cryxian engine of death—a machine that could strike from below with overwhelming force, devour its victims, refuel itself on their carcasses, and then vanish beneath the waves.

Cryx has held the colossal in reserve for centuries, using it only sparingly and in secret. The first Kraken was built in the decades following the last defeat of the Orgoth. Having observed the strengths and weaknesses of the mighty machines fielded by Khador and Cygnar in the Colossal War fought between 250–257 AR, Cryxian agents raided the graves of the mainland's most brilliant inventors, arcanists, and mechanikal engineers and interrogated the remains for their genius. In some cases, their very essences were used to produce the effects their insights had inspired.

The necrotechs of Skell immediately set about refining the designs of those great machines. Well aware of the shortcomings of the first colossals, Cryx designed its version to be smaller, more agile, and able to traverse a broad range of terrain—innovations centuries ahead of the mechanikal achievements of the mainland. The use of necrotite to power the Kraken's engines further reduced the weight of the machine, making it shockingly fast for such a large construct.

For centuries, the lich lords tightly controlled the use of Krakens. They intended to use them as secret weapons for a later stage of a long-term plan to subjugate the mainland and advance on Lord Toruk's progeny. Lich Lord Scopulous, responsible for Cryx's reserve army, was particularly loath to employ the colossals abroad and consented to dispatch them only for the utter destruction of isolated targets such as remote shoreline villages and lone ships carrying items or individuals of great value. In these instances, the Kraken received support from other Cryxian forces to ensure that any hapless survivors would not live to describe them. More than a few vessels thought to have been swallowed up by the storms of the Meredius were in fact dragged beneath the waves, their prized passengers taken by the Kraken's harvesting tendrils and brought back to Cryx. A few witnesses lived to speak of what they had seen, but their stories of great sea monsters were either dismissed as the ravings of madmen or thought to describe beasts of the deep unassociated with Cryx.

With several lich lords now leading armies deep inside enemy mainland territories and other colossals being fabricated in mortal forges, the time has come for Cryx to unveil its diabolical machines. Lich Lord Asphyxious, eager to support his armies independent of the Cryxian islands, has crafted additional Krakens within the depths of his vast necrofactorium under the Thornwood. Pressured by his peers, Scopulous has also relented and made the previously built Krakens available to the other generals and war witches of Cryx.

The Kraken will soon demonstrate its lethal worth to a wider audience. With an agility and speed surprising for a machine of its size, a Kraken can quickly maneuver to take advantage of any situation on the battlefield, while its hellblaster cannon delivers deadly payloads. Even as detonations from this cannon tear holes in enemy formations, bursts from its flayer cannon cut down any foe brave enough to launch counterattacks. The Kraken surges into the ranks of the living to glut its endless appetite for slaughter. Its long tendrils, shockingly adroit, erupt like serpents in the midst of formations, tearing apart warjacks and grasping victims to fuel its vile hunger. The screams of those pulled into harvesting apertures are accented by ripples of cannon fire. Not every victim snatched by a Kraken immediately perishes, however; some unlucky few are kept alive and brought back to the machine's masters for further horrors.

KRAKEN CONCEPTUAL DESIGNS

RETRIBUTION OF SCYRAH
THE LONG ROAD HOME

OCCUPIED LLAEL, NORTH OF ELSINBERG, 608 AR

Lord Arcanist Ossyan's face was grim and pale as he surveyed the still-smoldering ruins of the Retribution safe house. Trying to imagine how the battle had unfolded slightly distanced him from the horror of the violence, but not entirely. Perhaps he should have been grateful the corpses had been left behind, a departure from the usual Cryxian methods, but the removal of the heads and inscriptions in blood suggested some deeper desecration.

"So many lost . . ." Nyshyl's voice trailed away as she choked back both rage and anguish.

"I knew Ghyrrshyld would not surrender his ambitions to recover Nyssor's vault, but I thought he would confront us directly. Not like this." Ossyan's voice was hollow, and he did not realize his footsteps were faltering until the mage hunter took his arm to steady him.

Her face was similarly wan, and concerned, and she looked down to his side. "You have not given your wound a chance to heal."

"We have no time," he answered vaguely, fighting off the sensation of weakness and pain. "That has not changed." They had bound the injury dealt him by Goreshade, but it was a deep wound and would require rest to mend, even once he was able to accept the ministrations of those trained in such matters. What troubled him more than the injury itself was how difficult it had become for him to perceive the strands of fate since that confrontation. He hoped it was simply the daunting weight of Nyssor's proximity, as the god possessed a fated destiny as pervasive and occluding as a moon during an eclipse. Some part of him feared his divinatory ability had been permanently diminished or torn from him, but only time would tell.

Since he had seized the winter god's vault in Skirov, Ossyan had been making haste back toward Ios as enemies closed in on him. An unavoidable skirmish with Khadorans as they crossed the border of occupied Llael had cost them more lives than he could easily spare as well as his Arcantrik Force Generator. Even after evading the Khadorans, he

could not rest; he knew Goreshade had not simply crept away to lick his own wounds. The eldritch's undead flesh lacked the limitations of his own living body.

Even before Ossyan had committed to their attack on Skirov, Nyshyl had sent word back to the rest of the Retribution of their discovery. With the sect's forces dispersed throughout Khador, it would take time before anyone else could reach him. Despite his wound, he had pressed on. When they had entered Llael he had hoped they might buy enough time by holing up in a safe house to allow the nearest Retribution forces to catch up. The carnage he had found at the first of these refuges several days ago had been a vivid reminder that danger was closer than ever, but he had hoped the worst was now past.

"We need to move," Nyshyl warned. "No doubt his agents have spotted us here." They had not seen the eldritch himself, but several times smaller Cryxian groups had harassed them, killing a few of Ossyan's men before melting into the shadows. The senior mage hunter had advised against trying another safe house after they had discovered the first compromised. Now he saw she had been right: they must presume there was nowhere safe outside Ios' own borders.

Ossyan grimaced against the pain in his side as they climbed the stairs back to the surface. He said, "He is herding us. But I did not come all this way to fail."

Nyshyl agreed, "We push on." She signaled to the other mage hunters and they spread out with crossbows ready to check for threats. Ossyan stepped toward the wagon that traveled amid his myrmidons and steadily diminishing houseguard escort. To his mystical sight the frozen vault held an almost irresistible aura of mystical gravity, a sense that its very weight seemed to impinge upon and alter the world itself, and he had to tear his eyes away.

He looked back at the breached opening of the Retribution base and said, "There will be a reckoning with that monster." Nyshyl nodded grimly, clearly taking his vow to heart.

The Black River flowed high and fast ahead, swollen from recent heavy rainfall. His group was thirty miles south by southwest of Riversmet, in the region where Khadoran-occupied Llael gave way to lands contested by the Northern Crusade of the Protectorate of Menoth. There were limited options for crossing the river, particularly with the water this high, and it was the last major geographical obstacle before Ios. Approaching it, Ossyan felt exposed, though they had already neutralized what seemed to be the main Khadoran armed patrol in the vicinity.

Recent Cryxian attacks in the region had worked to their advantage, as the Khadorans had abandoned most outposts to consolidate at larger garrisons. He had still expected this bridge to be guarded, but there was no evidence of Khadorans. Adding to his disquietude were signs of recent violence, including several toppled and burnt wagons together with spilled crates on both sides of the bridge, still sending plumes of smoke into the sky. It looked as though some caravan had been intercepted during a crossing. He saw no corpses, but this had been common at battle sites in the area, likely as a result of Cryxian opportunism. Ossyan sought to enter the trance whereby he could gain insight into the immediate future and saw the wisps of his fate stretching tentatively toward the river and the bridge but then wavering and dispersing. A headache overwhelmed him and he returned to his normal sight, troubled.

He mentally reached out to look instead through the eyes of Hypnos where the myrmidon advanced at the fore of his houseguard. The bridge looked very old and was likely a relic from the Thousand Cities era, its double-arched stone construction weathered and pocked over time. It was just wide enough for four men to cross abreast—barely sufficient to accommodate the wagon bearing the vault. Getting everyone across would take time, so he sent his Daemon across first, followed by his houseguard of halberdiers and riflemen, to establish a defensive position. He remained behind with the wagon that carried Nyssor's vault. Hypnos was at a state of high alert, scanning their surroundings repeatedly.

He extended his supernaturally augmented senses to see if he could detect Nyshyl and her strike force, who had gone ahead earlier to take up positions in the trees near the bridge and cover their crossing. Allowing his consciousness to comb their surroundings, he could sense nothing but the hum of his myrmidons. Once again, he was impressed at the skill of Nyshyl and her fellow mage hunters.

Even as the last of the houseguard finished crossing, he squinted at the smoke rising from the toppled wagons. Oddly, it seemed to be increasing rather than decreasing. It was then he felt the unmistakable sensation of another warcaster extending mental control to nearby warjack cortexes.

Before Ossyan could react, Hypnos' power nodes flared to life. With a loud shriek it shot a mystically charged metal sphere from its phase gun to explode the nearest smoking wagon, revealing a metal shape striding out from beneath. Shouts of alarm went up from his soldiers as the other toppled wagons and piles of crates erupted and identical shapes emerged. The smoke of the wagons had provided cover for that of warjacks behind the wreckage, where they had crouched in shallow holes dug out beneath to conceal their bulk. The machines looked well built, at least by human standards, with gently curved armored plates. Each wielded a crescent-bladed polearm in its left hand and carried a thick tower shield with small cannon barrels protruding from the center with its right hand: Llaelese Vanguards, painted in the red and black of Khador.

There were three on the near side of the bridge, two on the other, with one of those immediately moving to block the far landing and firing its cannon point-blank into a houseguard rifleman among the last squad moving across. The other charged toward the nearest riflemen that had been forming into lines just past the bridge, sweeping into them with its guisarme. Dark-garbed assassins burst from the cover of the trees across the river to rush the halberdiers at the fore of the houseguard, followed shortly by a number of Greylords that were already invoking their freezing ice magic.

Ossyan felt some immediate disdain for his foes as they sprang forth; he could see that despite being well laid the ambush would be insufficient to stop him. He divided his consciousness among his warjacks, urging them to engage different threats. First he urged his Daemon on the other side to whirl around to confront the Vanguard tearing through his riflemen. Simultaneously he directed Hypnos to fire its cannon into the nearest enemy warjack, buckling the armor plating on its freshly painted red shield. Ossyan raised his chronophage cannon and added his own powerful blast of energy and managing to sunder its shield arm entirely. The disruptive fields of both his weapon and Hypnos' projectile left that warjack severely damaged, slowing its movements and interfering with its cortex. Leaving it to Hypnos, he impelled his Sphinx to rush the remaining two Vanguards on his side of the river, trusting in the myrmidon's weight and arcanikal weaponry to help it triumph over the lighter opponents.

As the air filled with the sound of weapons crashing into steel armor, Ossyan summoned his power to gather glowing runes around himself as he shifted his perception of reality and time, gaining clarity as events around him slowed. Each strike of the brawling machines could be observed in sequence. For light 'jacks the Vanguards were surprisingly durable, and his Sphinx lost one of its arms before crumpling the first one to scrap.

He saw his soldiers reacting with well-drilled professionalism. The halberdiers had suffered losses from the rushing assassins as well as blasts of freezing cold from the Greylords but reformed their line and were using their weapons to advantage. One of the flanking squads had fallen back to engage the Vanguard blocking the bridge, surrounding it. Riflemen on the bridge had backed up and were firing from cover, while the others on the far bank took aim at the Greylords, taking down one and wounding another.

Widowmaker sniper fire sounded in retaliation, with precise shots delivered from the nearest copse of trees on Ossyan's side of the river. He heard screams from the trees where the shots had originated and realized Nyshyl and her mage hunters had joined the fight. He saw no sight of them amid the trees but left those enemies to them. Suddenly he became aware of a new cortex signature on the periphery. He spotted a Berserker breaking from the trees behind the Greylords, its engine howling.

> "I HAD THE GOOD GRACE TO LEAVE YOU WITH ONE EYE AND STILL YOU ARE BLIND TO A SIMPLE TRUTH: I AM OUR PEOPLE'S ONLY HOPE OF SALVATION."

Ossyan's divinatory awareness returned enough to see mystical lines forecasting what the warjack would do, but with little chance to stop it. He had his Daemon pull away from the damaged Vanguard to intercept. It complied, taking a swipe from the Vanguard's polearm, but the ancient Khadoran heavy had built up steam and smashed into the lighter myrmidon to knock it flying back and into the river. The Berserker hardly slowed as it ran into the midst of the riflemen atop the bridge. Before it could swing its axes it vanished amid blinding light and roaring fire as a massive explosion deafened everyone nearby.

Berserkers possessed notoriously unstable cortexes prone to catastrophic explosions when pushed by warcasters. After the spots faded from his vision, Ossyan saw the extensive damage wrought by the blast. The Berserker and riflemen were nowhere to be seen, and the far half of the stone bridge had collapsed into the river. Ossyan and the wagon bearing the vault were effectively cut off from the houseguard on the other side.

The lord arcanist lent arcane might to Hypnos and his Sphinx as they finished off the last of the Vanguards on his side. He then urged them to step up to the river and join him in firing across on the Greylords and other enemy forces on the opposite side, trying to defend his remaining houseguard. A shot from Hypnos exploded among the Greylords, taking several down, but the others summoned swirling snow and wind to obscure themselves and moved to cover behind large stones lining the opposite riverbank. He fired his chronophage cannon but missed his mark, and its energies harmlessly dissipated against stone.

Ossyan was so focused watching across the river he was unaware of new arrivals until Hypnos sent an urgent mental warning. Augmented by his time-dilating perception, he stepped to the side even as a blade of wind sliced through the air where he had been. The quick motion prompted a spike of agony through his injured side as his wound opened. He grimaced and drew Locus as he turned toward the new foes. The world began to slow and he sucked in a breath, recognizing the convergence of a crisis point event— one that threatened his very mission.

Advancing behind several snow-veiled Greylords was a woman holding a mechanikal sword in one hand and a peculiar occult relic in the other. He knew this must be the warcaster coordinating the ambush, and from descriptions he had heard from the initial strike to secure Nyssor's vault, he knew it was Kommander Zerkova. Two Juggernauts flanked her, their ice axes gleaming a cold blue as they strode forward.

"You have something that belongs to me," she said while glaring at him with her good eye.

"It *belongs* in Ios," Ossyan retorted. He redirected his myrmidons to fire on this new threat as he raised his arm-mounted cannon. Their shots were joined by several crossbow bolts from behind: Nyshyl and her mage hunters had joined them. They had rushed forth to support him after having dealt with the Widowmakers.

Zerkova opened her arms and in a surge of power summoned around herself an unnatural howling gale stronger than any northern blizzard. The whipping winds made it impossible to aim properly, and every Iosan shot went astray. The great wind swept against Ossyan, his myrmidons, and the mage hunters with a force that made it difficult to even breathe, let alone advance.

The Khadoran warcaster pointed her sword at him as her warjacks broke into a run, unhindered by the gale. Their heavy footsteps sounded like pounding war drums. Runes surrounded Zerkova's blade. He was forced to step behind his damaged Sphinx as she unleashed another burst of frozen wind, and the gale sliced into its armor instead. Too late he saw his peril as the Juggernaut in the lead worked up to full speed, lowered its shoulder, and hammered into the Sphinx he was using as shelter. He tried to leap aside as the myrmidon flew back off its feet, but it hit him with a glancing impact as it toppled and slid. Pain again exploded from his side as he fell onto the grass, and his vision went black.

Dawnlord Vyros gritted his teeth as he thundered across the Llaelese countryside toward the Black River astride his powerful warhorse Solarys. Behind him rode a company of one hundred handpicked destors, and together they were making all haste to catch up with Ossyan and Nyssor's vault. With him were two Griffons, the only myrmidons swift enough to keep pace with the fast-moving mounted force.

Vyros had reluctantly left the rest of his myrmidons and his larger Dawnguard force with Adeptis Rahn after they had received the message relating the incredible find made by Lord Arcanist Ossyan of House Vyre. Now, Vyros knew, the fool from House Vyre was rushing toward Ios nearly alone. Had he any wisdom, Ossyan would have gone the other direction, seeking Retribution reinforcement first so the full strength of an Iosan army might ensure his return.

With such a large distance to cover and little time to spare, Vyros had forged ahead with his cohort of destors. Word had come of a hornet's nest stirred up among the Khadorans at Skirov, in addition to whomever else the lord arcanist's actions may have alerted. His brazen attack on a major Khadoran city without coordinating with the sect was proof of his inexperience, although clearly in this case his luck had been with him. Vyros was determined to be the one to restore the vault of Nyssor to Ios, before this upstart opportunist lost it as quickly as he had found it.

Vyros released his hunting hawk, Jyren, to scout the area ahead. Through her elevated vantage, he could see the Black River and the faint outline of Ossyan's forces massing on one side of the river. He felt relief flood through him even as he spurred his steed to a gallop. As he entered the forest and the light of the sun was blotted out by the dark trees that surrounded the road, Vyros heard a shriek of wounded animals and turned to see dark shapes springing from the undergrowth into the column: Cryxian Stalkers.

In a quick and practiced motion, he unslung his greatsword, Justicar, and pressed his horse's left flank just in time to avoid another of the black bonejacks leaping from the darkness. Still galloping at full tilt, Vyros could not prevent one Stalker from tearing apart two destors just behind him. He reached out through his mental link and commanded one of the Griffons to engage it. Other destors had brought their horses around to confront the bonejacks.

Looking down through Jyren's eyes, he saw black-armored banes ahead, their grinning skulls glowing a pale green and brutal weaponry poised to cut down any destors who survived the Stalker onslaught. At their back was an even larger figure whose warcaster armor belched sickly black smoke and who wielded a long and strangely elegant curved blade veiled in frozen air. Vyros felt dark rage as he looked into the creature's eyes and recognized the desiccated face.

"Ghyrrshyld!" he shouted and spurred Solarys forward, his other Griffon with him. Vyros braced himself as his steed smashed into the front line, crushing armor and skulls beneath armored hooves. Vyros felt the momentum of his charge slow as the banes absorbed his deadly stampede, even as the remainder of his men crashed into the Cryxian line. He swung Justicar to both sides in one hand, putting an end to the bane thralls nearest to him, and sent his Griffon to sweep through several others. He let his power field surge to full strength, and it deflected several axe blows as he battled through. There was the report of several lance cannons, fired expertly to open a path to where Goreshade waited, blade raised in a visible nimbus of cold.

He kicked hard into Solarys' flanks and sent the horse forward before the banes could close the gap. Just as he was almost to Goreshade, a tremendous impact knocked him from his saddle and sent white-hot pain through his side. Solarys managed to shake loose from the Stalker and bolted, blood trailing from slices along his flanks. Even a well-trained warhorse was prone to flight once deprived of its rider, but Vyros knew his steed would return.

He pulled himself to his feet, hefted Justicar, and charged the infernal machine even as it turned on him. Vyros' first strike severed the bonejack's left arm, and the back strike drove through head and torso, piercing the machine's vile cortex. The bonejack shuddered and fell in a heap.

He heard low, rumbling laughter behind him. "Dawnlord Vyros Nyarr. A reunion at last."

Vyros turned, his features drawn into a dark frown that caused the scar that ran down his face to tighten. Around them the destors and banes still fought, but for the moment the two warcasters were untouched by the conflict. Remembering the horrors of the War of the Houses, Vyros felt his hatred rise. He sought to control his anger, gathering his arcane power but holding it in reserve. "I dealt you a mortal wound once," he said, "and am prepared to finish that work."

Goreshade seemed unfazed. "I had the good grace to leave you with one eye and still you are blind to a simple truth: I am our people's only hope of salvation. In seeking my death, you only hasten your own."

Vyros laughed derisively. "Your madness is equaled only by your hubris."

The eldritch's eyes flared. "Do not play the noble hero, Vyros. You seek the title I once claimed, and your attachment to the Retribution is purely pragmatic. You are no more than a parasite."

Fast as a viper, Goreshade struck, but Vyros was ready. He parried the blow, knocking the elegant blade away and delivering a riposte that slid through Goreshade's power field and drove sparks off his warcaster armor as it opened a rent. Even as he pressed forward, something about the eldritch's blade troubled him. He felt cold seeping into his hands and arms despite his gauntlets.

A second blow caught Goreshade's sword, and for a moment Vyros found himself staring into the unfathomable blackness of the undead warcaster's eyes. Goreshade said, "You used rumors of me to incite your people to war. It was *I* who spared your 'Angel of Retribution' and sent her running with word of Nyssor's vault. *I* opened what was sealed, saw the Father of Winter with my own eyes, and spoke to him. *I alone* know the futility of your quest. What will you do when you have him? Seal him away in those tombs you call fanes? Useless."

Vyros tried to ignore the words, knowing the eldritch was prone to lies, but just enough matched reports he had heard that it gave him pause. He sneered as their blades locked again and said, "No god would speak to you."

"I had the Torch of Khazarak," Goreshade taunted him with a smile, "a Menite relic whose flame even his cold cannot endure. I bear Nyssor's curse as proof, and I wield his sword, taken from his hand. With its edge I shall end his life, freeing him to return to the Veld."

> THERE WAS A THUNDERING SOUND, AND IT SEEMED THE GROUND SHOOK UNDERFOOT. ZERKOVA TURNED TO LOOK TO THE WEST AND HER FACE PALED.

The sun caught on the silvered edge of Goreshade's blade, and Vyros beheld it clearly for the first time. He saw the Aeric runes, the perfect lines, the metal that shone unmarred. The sight of it broke through his doubt, and for a moment he was consumed by shock. With a mighty heave, Goreshade knocked Vyros back before he could respond, and numbing cold seeped into the dawnlord's body, tightening his muscles. As the eldritch struck again, Vyros lifted Justicar through supreme effort of will. When the blades met, he watched in horror as Justicar shattered beneath the blow and shards of its metal deflected off his power field. Goreshade then clove through both the field and the armor of his shoulder, biting the flesh beneath. It was a shallow wound, but numbness and icy cold seized him and Vyros found he could not move.

Goreshade stepped back from his immobilized opponent and looked up to see destors closing, having dealt with his banes. He smiled at Vyros again. "The Khadoran witch keeps the Torch of Khazarak, and without it your victory is meaningless." With that he turned and disappeared into greasy smoke and shadow even as the destors fired on his position and rode to surround their lord. Vyros felt warmth begin to return to his limbs and found he could move again. He quickly mounted a horse that had been deprived of its rider and together with his escort raced after the wisps of smoke indicating Goreshade's direction. He had little hope of catching him, but his eyes narrowed as through the trees he saw what looked to be a heavily laden supply wagon in Khadoran colors surrounded by an escort of Winter Guard. Perhaps he could gain something from this encounter after all.

An explosion sounded in the distance and Vyros turned his head in that direction. He wondered if Goreshade's true purpose had been to delay him from reaching Ossyan and the vault. Making a snap judgment, he used hand gestures to signal one squad of his destors to secure the wagon ahead, while the rest wheeled with him to hasten east.

Ossyan fought to emerge from the encroaching blackness. He felt along the ground for his blade, then finally grasped it and pulled himself to his feet. He had blacked out for only a moment, but to his surprise Nyshyl and her mage hunters had swept forward to intervene, several surrounding the Juggernaut that had smashed his Sphinx aside. He could sense nothing from his warjack's cortex and saw the damage from what had to be a finishing strike of an ice axe.

The mage hunters were experts at fighting such machines, but against Khadoran armor even their practiced strikes rarely landed a damaging blow, only occasionally dislodging connective piping or hammering at exposed joints. Compared to their nimble movements the Juggernaut's swings seemed ponderous, but its axe ripped through the air with such weight that the slightest contact could prove fatal. Battling the other Juggernaut, Hypnos landed punishing blows with its fists that prompted the Khadoran warjack's cruder internal mechanisms to seize up and freeze.

The rest of the mage hunters, including Nyshyl, had closed on Zerkova and her Greylords with blades drawn, demonstrating foolish bravery. Ossyan gritted his teeth and staggered toward them. He fired his cannon at the nearest Greylord, watching with satisfaction as blazing light pierced the bearded Khadoran's chest. Zerkova cut the throat of one mage hunter and obliterated another with razored air. Ossyan extended a hand to bestow augmented perception and increased speed on the strike force, eager to prevent their slaughter.

Zerkova's eyes flashed and he could feel her readying her power. His vision swam, and he felt blood leaking steadily down his wounded side. The Juggernaut that had been enduring the blades of the mage hunters swatted one aside and turned both its baleful gaze and its ice axe in his direction.

There was a thundering sound, and it seemed the ground shook underfoot. Ossyan thought at first the pounding was his heart, but then Zerkova turned to look to the west and her face paled. She called her Juggernaut back to her and withdrew, sending whirling vortexes of wind against the nearest mage hunters as she went. Ossyan realized he had fallen to his knees, but Nyshyl was there, helping him stand, and he was relieved to see she had not thrown her life away.

Ossyan looked back and saw dozens of Dawnguard destor cavalry rushing toward them, led by none other than Dawnlord Vyros, his hawk flying above his head. They galloped across the intervening soil toward Zerkova's retreating forces like an avenging flood, firing lance cannons in a booming announcement of their presence. The Khadoran unleashed a tempest that shredded apart one of the lead riders but was then forced to abandon her Juggernaut by sending it as a diversion into the path of those following. They hammered its armored chassis with their lances in turn, each wheeling away after impact to make room for the next. It managed to hack through two riders before it collapsed. Other destors fired on Greylords trying to reach the tree line and managed to kill several before the rest reached cover.

Vyros and those destors not already committed to chasing the retreating enemy rode up to him. He could tell from their ragged lines and signs of injury that they, too, had seen recent battle. A number of their horses in destor barding carried empty saddles.

"Dawnlord, you are a glad sight," Ossyan said. He felt slightly unsteady and leaned on Nyshyl for support, but at least he was standing.

"Lord Arcanist," Vyros said as he dismounted. He began to relay orders to his destors. "Secure that vault! And check the perimeter for additional forces." He looked back to Ossyan. "I heard an explosion. Was the vault harmed? I need to inspect it."

"Of course," Ossyan said. "The vault is safe; the explosion was to the bridge." Looking that direction, he was glad to see that some of his houseguard on the other side of the river had survived.

Ignoring Nyshyl's concerned look, Ossyan led Vyros toward the wagon where the frozen god awaited. He swayed a bit, feeling as if his control of events was suddenly evaporating. Perhaps that was not altogether a bad thing. Finally

receiving support to ensure their return to Ios brought a profound sense of relief. "So," Vyros said in a hushed voice as he reached a hand toward the smooth marble of the vault with its silver Aeric runes. He seemed to think better of touching it and stopped. "Within rests the fruit of all our labors." He stepped back suddenly with a frown; Ossyan expected he could feel the tremendous unnatural cold seeping from the vault.

Their pondering was interrupted as additional destors leading a heavy wagon in Khadoran colors approached. Ossyan looked at it and asked, "Spoils of war?"

Vyros ignored the question and moved to inspect the wagon before waving its escort to move it to the midst of his forces. Ossyan observed with interest the marks of the Greylords Covenant visible on the crates carefully stacked in the back of the wagon, including one banded in bronze and marked with mystical sigils. Vyros was clearly pleased to see it, and his eyes looked triumphant as he turned back. "Lord Arcanist, how long until that bridge can be restored?"

Ossyan's vision wavered, and he sensed some great darkness enveloping that metal-banded box. As the wagon neared the vault of Nyssor he caught his breath: a strange, shadowy resonance in the warped lines of fate swirled like smoke between the two wagons. When he finally tore his eyes away, he realized the dawnlord was waiting for an answer.

"The bridge?" He frowned and peered ahead, considering that he could direct Hypnos to assist in dragging some of the nearby detritus and debris in order to shore up the missing section and assist their crossing, helped by his houseguard on the far side. "I think I can have us underway by nightfall," he said. The words had just left his lips when he saw a reassuring flicker of his future destiny now weaving steadily to the east, toward home.

VYROS, INCISSAR OF THE DAWNGUARD
RETRIBUTION CAVALRY EPIC WARCASTER

Destiny is but another word for perseverance. We must grasp victory with our own hands.

—Incissar Vyros

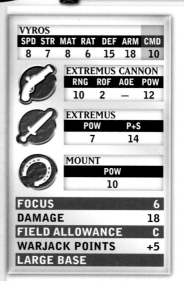

VYROS						
SPD	STR	MAT	RAT	DEF	ARM	CMD
8	7	8	6	15	18	10

EXTREMUS CANNON			
RNG	ROF	AOE	POW
10	2	–	12

EXTREMUS	
POW	P+S
7	14

MOUNT
POW
10

FOCUS	6
DAMAGE	18
FIELD ALLOWANCE	C
WARJACK POINTS	+5
LARGE BASE	

FEAT: TIDE OF WAR

Vyros, Incissar of the Dawnguard is famed for his tactical brilliance and the fluid adaptability of his army. Every loss becomes an opportunity as his forces react to close gaps in their lines or advance to fix the enemy in place. The more determined the opposition, the more Vyros turns the ground to his own advantage.

When a friendly Faction model is destroyed by an enemy attack while in Vyros' control area anytime except while advancing, immediately after the attack is resolved a friendly Faction model in Vyros' control area can make a full advance. A model can advance only once as a result of Tide of War. Tide of War lasts for one round.

VYROS

Bird's Eye – While in this model's control area, models in its battlegroup extend their front arcs 360° and when determining LOS ignore cloud effects, forest terrain, and intervening models.

Inspiration [Dawnguard] – Friendly Dawnguard models/units in this model's command range never flee and immediately rally.

Quick Work – When this model destroys one or more enemy models with a melee attack during its combat action, immediately after that attack is resolved this model can make one normal ranged attack. Attacks gained from Quick Work do not count against a weapon's ROF.

EXTREMUS CANNON

⊘ Magical Weapon

EXTREMUS

⊘ Magical Weapon

⊘ Reach

SPELLS	COST	RNG	AOE	POW	UP	OFF
EASY RIDER	3	SELF	CTRL	–	NO	NO

Friendly Faction models beginning their activations in this model's control area gain Pathfinder (🏃). Easy Rider lasts for one turn.

DEFLECTION	2	SELF	CTRL	–	NO	NO

While in this model's control area, friendly Faction warrior models gain +2 ARM against ranged and magic attack damage rolls. Deflection lasts for one round.

LOCK THE TARGET	2	10	–	10	NO	YES

A model damaged by Lock the Target cannot run, charge, or be placed for one round.

SYNERGY	2	SELF	CTRL	–	YES	NO

While in its control area, models in this model's battlegroup gain a +1 cumulative bonus on melee attack and melee damage rolls for each other model in the battlegroup that hit an enemy model with a melee attack this turn while in this model's control area.

TWISTER	2	10	3	10	NO	YES

The AOE is a cloud effect that remains in play for one round.

TACTICAL TIPS

LOCK THE TARGET – If a model cannot charge it also cannot make slam or trample power attacks.

QUICK WORK – This model cannot make the additional attack if it is still in melee.

Vyros has given his people both the greatest victory in the history of Ios and the gift of renewed hope. The conquering general has punished those who would defile their gods and freed an Iosan deity from their grasp, downplaying the contributions of Ossyan of House Vyre. Ios has accepted this omission with equanimity; the leader of the Dawnguard is their hero of the hour.

The hallytyr granted Vyros the honor of presiding over the rites interring the reclaimed god Nyssor within the fane beneath Iryss, Scyrah's original fane. Precisely what the god's return means is uncertain, but it is proof that the Retribution of Scyrah can deliver on its promises and that the sect has no greater military leader than Vyros of House Nyarr.

Recognizing the achievements of the Dawnlord, Consul Calcyr Nyarr has formalized Vyros' standing by giving up all claims to military leadership of his house. The consul has stepped back to focus entirely on his roles in the Consulate Court and among the Nine Voices of the Retribution, giving Vyros unfettered command over the house's military assets. Given that Vyros was already serving in this capacity, the act is largely symbolic, but it represents his continued rise within his house and Ios in general.

Vyros' growing political clout among the people facilitates his advancement of the Retribution's aggressive agenda; in fact, he has already begun formulating the strategies by which he will strike the next blow. That the Retribution has brazenly added the Hyperions to its arsenal is due to Vyros' status as well as to the level of cooperation between Houses Nyarr and Shyeel. The formidable colossals, previously held in reserve to defend Ios' borders, now prepare to march against enemies abroad.

Comprising the core of Vyros' military elite, the Dawnguard increasingly enjoy standing as the backbone heavy infantry of the Retribution's armies. Incissar Vyros commands them from his mighty destrier, Solarys, with the assurance that the tides of war are his to command. He has proven that victory is his to take—whether by political maneuvering or at the point of a blade.

HYPERION

IRYSS, 583 AR

Dearest Tenae,

I am not given to letters, as well you know, but today I must share what I have seen.

We have made slow progress in Iryss. The fighting has been more vicious than any of us expected. Inspired by their power-mad and self-proclaimed narcissar, Ghyrrshyld, House Vyre's soldiers make us pay a heavy price for every foot we gain, and more than once their myrmidons have retaken ground we had previously won. Our victory has been inevitable for months, but at a high cost in lives. Against the advice of many, the hallytyr has authorized the deployment of Hyperions within Issyr. I know you feel the same dread as I at this.

We both know the forces harnessed—I do not say controlled—within the Hyperion. Much of our arcane research was in the theoretical pursuit of those forces. The starburst effect was designed to protect Ios from the most terrible threats imaginable, such as being threatened by another dragon. We never dreamed of its use in our own city streets. When I was ordered to gather my men and protect the first Hyperion deployed, I almost resigned my commission on the spot. But like a coward, I obeyed. Scyrah help me.

Command was given to Adeptis Rahn. We followed him at a fast pace through the streets of the southern wards of Iryss, towards a heavily barricaded Vyre position. Their house guards had entrenched themselves at this alley for days, and we'd lost half a dozen lives in our attempts to dislodge them. The Hyperion turned the corner and was upon them in a few swift strides.

Adeptis Rahn had the Hyperion discharge its starburst cannon repeatedly upon the barricaded position, minimizing time spent in conflict. Once one has committed to an action, no matter how terrible, one must see it completed. The Vyre forces were erased from Caen. Only a rough crater filled with fine ash remained where the starburst had struck. Several adjacent buildings were annihilated or left with walls missing as if sliced from reality. We did not bother to search for survivors.

We have unleashed the greatest potential our people have ever known, a force of limitless energy and endless death. That the Hyperion would be first employed against our own kinsmen is sickening enough without considering its weapon is only the initial expression of the forces with which we tamper. I have resigned my commission and will be home within the month. What follows then, I know not.

Your Loving Brother Nygyll

HYPERION
RETRIBUTION COLOSSAL

The sun brought down from the heavens, searing our path to victory.

—Incissar Vyros

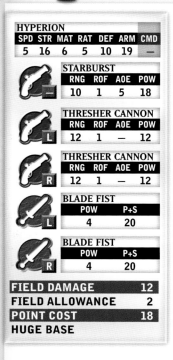

HYPERION						
SPD	STR	MAT	RAT	DEF	ARM	CMD
5	16	6	5	10	19	—

STARBURST			
RNG	ROF	AOE	POW
10	1	5	18

THRESHER CANNON			
RNG	ROF	AOE	POW
12	1	—	12

THRESHER CANNON			
RNG	ROF	AOE	POW
12	1	—	12

BLADE FIST	
POW	P+S
4	20

BLADE FIST	
POW	P+S
4	20

FIELD DAMAGE	12
FIELD ALLOWANCE	2
POINT COST	18
HUGE BASE	

HYPERION

Field Dependent – While its Field Generator system is crippled, this model cannot make Starburst attacks.

STARBURST

⚡ **Magical Weapon**

Critical Consume – On a critical hit, if the attack hit a small-based non-warlock/warcaster model the model hit is removed from play.

THRESHER CANNON

Auto Fire [d3] – Make d3 ranged attacks targeting a primary target and any number of secondary targets within 2" of the first target. Ignore intervening models when declaring secondary targets. A secondary target cannot be targeted by more attacks than the primary target. Auto Fire counts as one attack for ROF.

BLADE FIST

✊ **Open Fist**

LEFT DAMAGE

1	2	3	4	5	6
			□	□	
	□		G	G	G
	L	L	G	C	C
L	L	C	C	C	C
L	C	M	M	M	M

RIGHT DAMAGE

1	2	3	4	5	6
	□	□			
G	G	G			
C	C	G	R	R	
C	C	C	C	R	R
M	M	M	M	C	R

Towering over the vanguard of Retribution forces, the Hyperion carries with it the fury of the Iosan people—and the most powerful weapon ever built. Its thresher cannons and bladed fists first clear a path to the most heavily armored and entrenched enemy position. Enemies who have lived to describe what comes next speak in hushed voices of the hair-raising sensation that accompanies the eerie sound of its field generator gathering power. Just before the starburst weapon emits its charge, all ambient sound is swallowed by an ominous silence. Suddenly, a discharge of warped energy emanates from channels within the colossal's chassis, too quickly to be observed. The resulting blinding sphere eventually fades to reveal a zone of utter annihilation: stone, steel, and flesh erased from existence with the surety of the Retribution's cause.

The Hyperion and its armament were created by the Iosans centuries ago, in response to an indisputably dire threat. The Iosans were appalled by the staggering casualties inflicted by the dragon Ethrunbal when he arose from beneath the city of Issyrah. Thousands of civilians were slaughtered before military forces succeeded in subduing the dragon and extracting his athanc, and in the end, the city of Issyrah was reduced to rubble and abandoned. Looking upon the catastrophe, the artificers of House Shyeel saw it as their duty to craft a weapon powerful enough to confront threats as dreadful as that which besieged Issyrah.

The finest minds of House Shyeel began countless experiments in the realm of unconventional energies. They eventually discovered that the fundamental forces of nature could be altered to produce an incomprehensible force related to the energies with which the gods had forged the stars. Their earliest successes required mechanisms too large to be housed within even the largest myrmidon. It took decades more to design smaller constructs that could channel such energy. After the first test of their terrible creation, one of the principal architects is said to have been so shaken that he suggested the entire project be abandoned. He was quietly retired from public view while others in House Shyeel continued his work.

The Hyperion's chassis and hull were built in tandem with the final stages of starburst development. The colossal's infrastructure had to be large enough to accommodate the oversized generators necessary to power the machine itself and to create the starburst effect as a function of its protective energy fields. Given how completely the powerful weapon monopolized the Hyperion's energy output, Iosan engineers decided to outfit the colossal with an independent secondary weapon system. These thresher cannons, unlike other Shyeel weapons, fire kinetic projectiles similar to the firearms used by some Iosan infantry.

House Shyeel built several Hyperions but kept them in reserve against major threats from outside Ios. The colossals, however, would see their first deployment under circumstances much different than originally intended. In the final days of the War of the Houses, the allied hallytyr met heavy resistance from the powerful and enormous myrmidons of House Vyre—machines employing unorthodox and dangerous energies. Fearing a prolonged siege against Ghyrrshyld and his house and hoping to prevent greater loss of civilian life in a protracted battle, the hallytyr urged House Shyeel to deploy the Hyperions.

The colossals inarguably brought the Iosan civil war to a swift conclusion, but at great cost: many ancient buildings were annihilated, and hundreds of civilians perished. The few to survive exposure to the puissant energy were left crippled, as any flesh caught within the blasts simply ceased to exist. After House Vyre quickly and prudently dismantled its greatest war constructs, the hallytyr unanimously moved to prohibit the use of the Hyperion or anything related to starburst technology within any Iosan city. In accordance, House Shyeel deployed its Hyperions along the Iosan border.

Now that the Retribution of Scyrah is on the rise, with its extreme politics and its alliances with Houses Shyeel and Nyarr, old legal shackles have begun to fall away. Fresh from his victories abroad, Incissar Vyros brazenly pulled the Hyperions from the borders to add them to the Retribution's arsenal. Hallytyr consuls were forced to stifle their objections lest they be seen as impeding Ios' only hope for a brighter future. The liberation of Nyssor has given the Retribution all the clout it requires to arm itself with the most formidable construct ever developed on Iosan soil. Hyperions now march alongside the Dawnguard, thrumming with barely restrained power as they prepare to eradicate any enemy the Retribution deems deserving of their attention.

HYPERION CONCEPTUAL DESIGNS

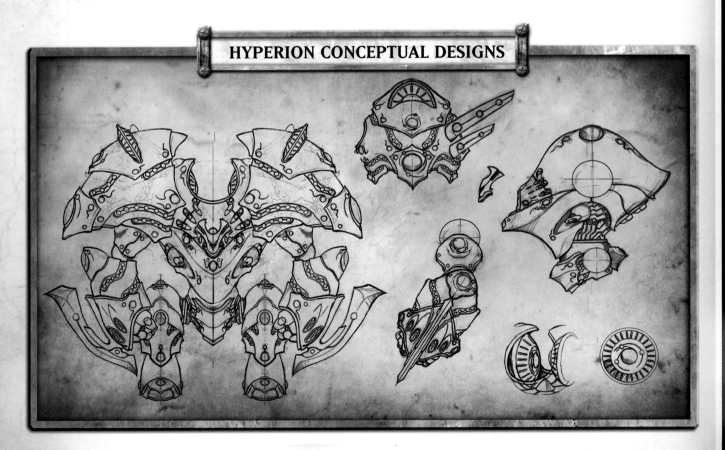

MERCENARIES
NOTHING GOOD COMES CHEAP

THE THORNWOOD

General Ossrum Durgh made his way down the long line of armored troops and machines, two heavy Rhulic warjacks with him. The column had halted along the winding road running through the tangled forest. Ossrum was growing tired of the constant delays; this expedition was painful even compared to negotiating the twisting passes of the Glass Peaks. To keep his men sharp he had been ensuring they were using the time properly—cleaning weapons, checking armor and ammunition, and maintaining warjacks and other equipment.

Most of his troops were from Hammerfall Fortress: four full companies of High Shield Gun Corps, four platoons of Assault Corps, and nearly a dozen warjacks, half heavy and half light. Added to this was a company of Forge Guard from Horgenhold. He saw the force not as a host of sell-swords but as a professional army held to the standards of Clan Durgh.

He had accepted a large sum of Khadoran gold to safeguard a special convoy. As he neared the center of the column, the brown and gray of Rhulic uniforms gave way to the crimson and black of the Khadorans. Among them, three Khadoran Conquests towered over the treetops, more than thirty feet tall and nearly as wide, hulls bristling with weaponry. They lacked the refinement and reliable efficiency of the Rhulic colossals, but there was something to be said for sheer battlefield presence.

As he neared the small Khadoran force surrounding the Conquests, he raised his hand in greeting to the young warcaster in charge. "Kovnik," he said in Khadoran. "No major difficulties, I trust?"

Kovnik Andrei Malakov stood at the foot of one of the colossals, consulting with a Man-O-War mechanik. Malakov's impeccable red warcaster armor gleamed as new and unscarred as the skin on his hairless cheeks. To Ossrum, he looked shockingly young, clearly a fresh graduate from the Druzhina, Khador's military academy. "Routine maintenance and refueling, General," the Khadoran said. "We will be in motion again soon." The youth looked at him with a perpetual air of restrained disapproval. Ossrum was uncertain if this was due to him being a mercenary, or Rhulic, or both.

Ossrum accepted this and walked on. One sign that the Conquests had not been built by Rhulic hands was how frequently they required attention. He had his doubts about Malakov as well. The man was apparently a rising military star, but entrusting such a command to someone so young seemed foolish. He suspected politics had played a part, as he had overheard Khadorans in their escort mention Malakov's well-connected family. This opportunity to deliver new weapons to the supreme kommandant would have been a rare honor.

Ossrum continued down the column, checking the wagons. The supply train was huge, as it had to support not only hundreds of soldiers and their warjacks but also the Conquests and their gluttonous appetite for fuel. The Khadorans had sent the colossals as far as possible by train, but the unavoidable barrier of the Thornwood required they make the remainder of the journey on foot.

His experience suggested this supply train was their greatest vulnerability, particularly with the forest infested by Cryxians. He had done what he could to ensure it was protected, but the terms of his contract specified the bulk of his army be deployed near the Conquests. Ossrum had positioned some of his best troops at the rearguard, including the Assault Corps led by his most trusted subordinate, First Sergeant Kargul Shatterhaft.

When he reached the rearguard, he found Kargul kneeling on the grassy sward next to the tree line, reassembling a battle cannon. The ogrun and dwarves around him were checking their gear and running through weapon drills, while others were on watch along the tree line. The sergeants who saw Ossrum acknowledged him respectfully. His rapport with the men was good, as most of the force had served with him for years now. He did not take their trust for granted.

"Glad to see everyone's busy, Sergeant," Ossrum said as he approached.

Kargul raised his head and gave a casual salute. "Anything to avoid your 'an idle soldier is an unprepared soldier' lecture." Ossrum grinned; after decades fighting together, he allowed the sergeant some leeway with military formality. The ogrun slammed the breach of the battle cannon closed and stood, towering almost four feet above his korune. "Doesn't that lad realize how vulnerable we are every time we stop? I've never seen machines so hungry for coal."

"We can't exactly leave them behind," Ossrum replied. "I'm sure the Khadorans would prefer the front line to be situated more conveniently."

"Hostiles! From the east!" a dwarven voice bellowed from that side of their column.

Ossrum found his axe Oathkeeper in his right hand before he even thought to take it from his belt. Likewise, Kargul had drawn his hand axe in his left hand. He streadied his battle cannon in the other using the supporting strap buckled to his right shoulder. The staccato crackle of small arms fire sounded from the tree line, and Ossrum saw where two ranks of High Shield Gun Corps had taken up position, bracing carbines on their shields, to fire volleys into the forest.

"Gun Corps right and left!" Kargul shouted. "Assault Corps behind!" At his orders, the remaining High Shield corpsmen positioned themselves on either side of the road, keeping the supply wagons between them. The Assault Corps ogrun stood behind the dwarves, ready to fire their cannons over the front line. Ossrum mentally reached out to the two warjacks with him—a reliable old Avalancher he called Zenith and a freshly rebuilt Wroughthammer Rockram he'd named Breacher—and sent one to either flank as he took a position next to Kargul.

A ragged line of muscular humanoids in enclosed metal helmets rushed from the trees into the Rhulic defenders. Ossrum could see their arms ended in mechanikal swords and saw blades. "Drudges," he said under his breath with disgust. The cephalyx and their enslaved warriors were well known in Rhul, where they occasionally menaced deep mining operations.

The first wave of drudges fell to gun corps carbines, while those behind them received an explosive barrage of battle cannon shells and the heavier ordnance delivered by Ossrum's warjacks. As more drudges replaced the fallen, Ossrum saw the thin, spidery forms of cephalyx mind slavers lurking behind them. Peering through Zenith's eyes, he drew a bead on the closest slaver with the warjack's cannon and then poured his will into the weapon. The shell struck true, obliterating the cephalyx and a few drudges nearby.

The drudges had made it into melee range with the gun corps, and the dwarven troops abandoned their carbines

for short-hafted war axes. Here the Rhulfolk were at a disadvantage, and the drudges hacked into their ranks with whirring saws and keen swords.

Ossrum shouted over the din, "Sergeant Kargul! Buy us some breathing room!" Kargul and a dozen ogrun with hand axes charged forward to bolster the collapsing line, the drudges no match for their bulk and fury.

The flow of drudges from the forest slowed to a trickle, but Ossrum could no longer see the shadowy forms of cephalyx behind them. He felt a sudden dread and looked back toward the south in time to see a burst of sickly green light blossom over the center of the column, followed by the desperate screams of men and dwarves in agony.

"Sergeant!" Ossrum shouted over the fading notes of gunfire as they finished the remaining drudges. "You're with me!" He broke into a run, followed by his warjacks and the remaining Assault Corps.

Ossrum clenched his teeth. It was not like Cryx to attack the strongest point in an enemy army. Their priority must be the Conquests themselves, with the strike at the rear meant to divert resources. He summoned his power and poured his will into the warjacks and ogrun around him. Their pace quickened considerably, and the rough ground flowed easily beneath them.

At the center of the column, the gun corps troopers had formed up ranks in front of the Conquests, creating a buffer between themselves and the Khadorans. A solid mass of drudges, hundreds strong, charged them from the trees. Behind the advancing wall of mind-controlled slaves a dozen or more bloat thralls squatted amid the trees on spider-like legs, firing bile cannons up and over the attackers. The corrosive fluid melted armor, flesh, and bone with appalling speed.

Immediately seeing that the bloat thralls were unassailable while in the forest behind the wall of drudges, Ossrum urged his two warjacks to add their firepower to that of the Rhulic troops. He knew it wasn't going to be enough. The bloat thralls would inflict horrible casualties before his troops could close.

Kovnik Malakov had positioned his two Demolishers at the flanks of the dwarven lines. Armed with two shoulder-mounted cannons each, the 'jacks blasted into the advancing drudges, but there were far too many.

Above Ossrum, the Conquests suddenly shuddered to life with a blast of smoke and steam, and then the world dissolved into an explosion of sound and light as they fired their primary and secondary guns in rippling salvos. Gargantuan shells shrieked into the massed drudges, leaving only smoking craters where they struck.

Ossrum was impressed at the efficient and well-directed firing salvo from the young kovnik, but he immediately perceived a potential vulnerability. Focused on the drudges and bloat thralls, all the central column defenders had pulled onto one side to create a buffer before the invaluable colossals. They were ignoring the dark forest behind them.

He reached out to every Rhulic warjack in mental range, taking control of an additional pair of Avalanchers and several Gunners he had left with the central column and urging them to move toward the forest behind the Conquests. Startled by their withdrawal, Malakov shouted indignantly, "What are you doing?"

"Saving your gods-be-damned machines!" Ossrum roared. He directed Kargul and the Assault Corps toward a slight rise where they would have an open firing lane on the vulnerable area.

Another salvo from the Conquests obliterated the trees and reduced the drudges to a field of shattered body parts. Two hundred rifles went off in unison, supported by the pounding barrage of Khadoran warjacks, and the exposed bloat thralls were quickly torn to pieces. Another wave of drudges supported by their cephalyx masters pushed forward, but with less cover from the blasted clearing. Ossrum's Forge Guard charged them, wielding their hammers to intercept the enemy.

Suddenly hulking shadows burst from the trees on the opposite side of the column: at least two dozen helljacks, including Slayers as well as crab-like Harrowers and Leviathans. The hovering form of a cephalyx overlord and a pair of slavers moved behind the advancing wall of blackened steel. The helljacks surged forward, some firing volleys of jagged metal spikes and blasts of ghostly necrotic fire into the Khadorans as they closed on the nearest Conquest.

Ossrum sent his warjacks barreling into the path of the Cryxian machines, firing as they went, in a desperate attempt to blunt their charge. He empowered his 'jacks with his sorcery, creating shimmering walls of force around each that pushed the enemy back as it neared—a temporary measure.

Too late, Kovnik Malakov saw the peril and diverted his Demolishers, but the Conquests themselves blocked the path to the enemy. Ossrum's machines were horribly outnumbered, and in the first seconds of battle he felt Zenith's hull buckle beneath a Leviathan's crushing claw. The old 'jack retaliated with its assault shield, but he knew it would not endure. Breacher fared only slightly better.

He rushed to where Malakov stood near his trio of Conquests, backing them away from the helljacks while firing, a tactic that would never work given their relative speeds. Ossrum shouted, "Kovnik! Send the Conquests *forward*! Into the fray!"

A shadow of anger flickered across Malakov's youthful face. "Unacceptable, General! The Conquests must reach Kommandant Irusk undamaged!"

"The only way to protect them is to smash those bloody helljacks!" Ossrum shot back. When Malakov hesitated, he added, "My 'jacks are down—you need to attack! Try to disengage and I guarantee we'll have nothing but wreckage at the end of this."

Malakov glared at him, but Ossrum could see he had gotten through. The Khadoran focused his will to force the Conquests to reverse. Their engines roared. The earth shook underfoot as they built up momentum on a counter-charge. Ossrum took advantage of their noisy distraction to close on his own target: the cephalyx overlord. He drew his hand cannon as he ran, aiming it at one of the intervening cephalyx slavers, and it bucked as it discharged. The will-guided bullet struck the cephalyx in its leather-clad torso, slamming it to the ground as its spidery blades clattered in its death throes.

Out of the corner of his eye, he saw one Conquest bring a huge, armored fist down on top of a Leviathan, crushing it to pieces. The effect was disturbingly similar to bringing a boot down on a spider. He was certain even Khadoran heavy armor would have been torn to pieces by this many helljacks if they had confronted only one colossal at a time, but the three Conquests fighting side by side obliterated one helljack after the next with punishing impacts of their great fists.

The overlord floated slightly above the ground ahead, with a mentally enslaved dwarven gun corps soldier standing protectively in front of it. As Ossrum neared, the cephalyx turned its bizarre multi-eyed head toward him and something flared against his power field. His ears rang from the psychic assault, but he continued to set one foot in front of the other. Again invisible force hammered into his brain, but he gritted his teeth against the pain and moved closer.

The Rhulic slave rushed forward, axe in hand, his eyes tormented. Ossrum fired. The heavy ball struck the dwarf in his left knee, shattering the joint, and he dropped to the ground in a heap.

Ossrum was within a dozen feet of the overlord now. Again it blasted him with psychic energy, slowly moving backward as it hurled shards of mental agony at him. He managed to aim and fire his hand cannon. The shot struck the cephalyx high on its right shoulder, spinning it around. The psychic pressure on his brain ceased, his vision cleared, and he closed the remaining gap. The overlord's spidery blades jabbed down into his power field, penetrating it in numerous places and drawing a line of burning fire across his face. Ossrum lashed out with Oathkeeper and drove its edge deep into the cephalyx's flesh with a satisfying crunch, and his head echoed with psychic dying screams.

He jerked Oathkeeper from the corpse and drew a deep breath. His ears were ringing, but he realized the sounds of battle were fading. The Conquests waited nearby, relatively quiet now that they had annihilated the Cryxians sent against them. Of his own men, Ossrum counted thirty dead and twice that number wounded. Among the injured was Kargul, who had taken a Leviathan spike through one thick leg before finishing the helljack with his battle cannon. The ogrun sergeant was still shouting orders to his men as they placed him on one of the medical wagons.

Ossrum had lost all his warjacks except Breacher and two Gunners in the battle, and he saw the Khadoran had lost one of his Demolishers. All three Conquests showed signs of battle damage, heaviest along the lower portions of their legs. The one at the fore had one leg badly torn, and its dangling right arm suggested more serious damage. Kovnik Malakov broke away from his senior mechaniks when Ossrum approached.

"One suffered badly," the Khadoran said in an accusatory tone.

"At least you can repair it. Could have been far worse."

"True," he allowed. It was obvious the kovnik was unaccustomed to being wrong. "Committing the Conquests was the right thing to do. My condolences for your casualties. Your men fought bravely."

"Thank you, Kovnik," Ossrum said with a nod. He offered the young warcaster a grim smile. "You can tell Supreme Kommandant Irusk his Conquests are fully battle tested now. Consider it a bonus."

CLOCKERS COVE

Bartolo Montador stepped off his skiff and onto the well-worn dock, his heavy mechanikal blade Rip Tide at his hip. His destination loomed at the end of the pier, an immense warehouse fronting a smoke-bellowing factory complex within a tangle of dockside buildings. Once a major shipwright, Black Anchor Heavy Industries was not only the largest foundry in Clocker's Cove but also the largest privately owned warjack foundry in western Immoren.

Montador offered his hand to a slim, dark-haired woman still in the skiff. Her black and purple warcaster armor bore the triple arrows of Thamar, leaving no mistake about her identity. Fiona the Black accepted his assistance with a bemused smile and then moved ahead of him onto the pier, balancing her three-pronged spear Viper over one shoulder as she scanned for potential threats. Behind her came the stout, grease-stained woman called Dirty Meg,

toting a sizable wrench, and his master gunner, Dougal MacNaile, whose belt supported a sheathed cutlass and a holstered quad iron.

The captain led his crew toward the foundry, a smug smile on his bearded face. The last time he had felt such eager anticipation had been on visiting Black Anchor almost ten years ago, after the foundry had refitted the *Calamitas* with steam engines and added to its considerable firepower. It was time to add a similarly impressive weapon to his arsenal.

A dozen yards from the warehouse they heard the rumble and shriek of a steam-driven mechanikal apparatus, and the building's huge double doors, over thirty feet high, began to slide open. At first they saw only the glare of blazing forges within the cavernous space, but then a massive shadow fell across the pier.

"Thamar's teeth!" Dougal MacNaile exclaimed. "Look at the size of it!"

> SUDDENLY HULKING SHADOWS BURST FROM THE TREES ON THE OPPOSITE SIDE OF THE COLUMN.

The Galleon seemed to shimmer, backlit by the brilliance of the forges, which cast a radiance across its heavy steel plates. The highest of its three towering smokestacks nearly brushed the lintel of the gargantuan doors. Its head sat low on its torso, fitted with a single eye. Its left arm terminated in an enormous toothed claw that looked equally ideal for lifting heavy cargo into a ship's hold or crushing an enemy warjack into scrap. Its right arm was taken up by a three-pronged trident, easily as big as a ship's anchor. Cannons protruded from gun ports on its chest, three to a side.

Montador grinned and clapped his hands together. "See, old man?" he said to Dougal. "With enough money you can make nearly any fantasy a reality."

A group of men emerged from behind the Galleon. The one in the lead was stout and muscular, his bald head tattooed with esoteric symbols. He was unarmed save for a large smith's hammer that hung from his belt. This was Montador's primary contact, Waldron Faller, who was also the senior mechanik of Black Anchor and had partial ownership of the company. Those with him were obviously guards, each armored in a knee-length mail hauberk and carrying a short-hafted battleaxe and a heavy blunderbuss.

"Captain!" Waldron Faller exclaimed as he spread his brawny arms. "Tell me what you think of her. A real beaut, don't you agree?"

"I can safely say I have never been so eager to part with my own money," Montador said, striding forward to clasp Waldron's hand in his own.

"Good gods, I can't wait to get a closer look at that beast!" Dirty Meg exclaimed, a grin wrinkling her wide face. "But is that trident launching mechanism the same as the harpoon cannon you installed on the *Dark Passage*? I heard the release clamps were prone to breakage."

Faller's smile became strained. "Every system on this machine has been tested and refined. You'll have no problems with her." Meg opened her mouth to ask another question, but he cut her off. "As much as I'd like to talk shop with a fellow wrencher, a demonstration is in order."

"I'd sure like to see it in action," Montador said. When Dirty Meg gave him a dark glare, he muttered, "Don't worry; I'll let you crawl all over the bloody thing before we take her aboard the *Calamitas*. Right now, I want to see what she's got."

Faller raised his right hand into the air. The noise of the bustling harbor and the foundry were suddenly drowned out by a hissing blast of steam and the roar of the Galleon's three smokestacks as the warjack came to life. Its right arm straightened out and rose to chest level, pointing its trident out at the harbor. Its single eye glowed red.

"Who's controlling it?" Fiona whispered to Bartolo, leaning close. "There's a warcaster here, somewhere."

Montador frowned. He was considerably less sensitive to such things than Fiona. He scanned those nearest but saw no immediate signs. "No idea."

"My friends," Faller shouted, "if you'll cast your gaze to the barge at the end of the dock . . ."

Montador had seen the scow sitting low in the water when they'd arrived. He looked at it more closely and saw that thick, rust-pitted slats of beaten iron draped its ugly bulk, weighing it down.

Faller held up his right arm again and clenched his fist. There was a muffled boom, and the Galleon's trident flew from the end of its arm trailing a length of chain. The triple points of the mammoth harpoon slammed into the armored scow at a downward angle, perforating both the thick iron and the wooden hull beneath.

The high-pitched whir of a mechanikal winch sounded from deep inside the Galleon, and the chain drew taut. The scow was reeled quickly through the water as the colossal leaned back and braced its feet to steady itself, prompting the metal deck plating beneath it to groan and pop. Before the scow reached the pier, Faller dropped his arm, and the six cannons across the Galleon's chest roared to life with flashes of flame and clouds of smoke. Two plumes of water indicated where cannonballs had missed their target, but

the others impacted the scow's hull, exploding wood apart and splitting the ship in half. The wreck sank beneath the water as the Galleon's trident retracted loudly.

Faller made a swiping motion across his neck. The Galleon's boiler quieted, and its eye's red light faded.

"That trident looks to have impressive range for the weight," MacNaile said under his breath to Montador. "And those cannons make for a nice little broadside."

Meg asked, "Is the trident ready to be fired again?"

The senior mechanik nodded proudly. "It has three launching charges. The cannons are self-reloading, eight shots apiece. If you run out of ammo, send it in. Between the cargo claw and the trident nothing will last long."

Meg gave the captain an impressed look. He nodded and said, "Ideally I'd like a pair of these. Any discount for two?"

Faller's grin disappeared, and his guards moved a bit closer. "This is the only one ready, but two more are in various stages of assembly. However . . ." Montador scowled and waited. He could sense his companions tense. Faller sighed and gave a tight smile as he said, "Naturally an opportunity like this attracts competition. Two days ago another buyer arrived to put in a bid—on the entire production run. I'm willing to open up bidding between you two, and he'll abide by the result."

"*Bidding?*" Montador shouted, his face reddening. "*I'm* the bloody buyer! I should level this whole bloody harbor and take what's mine." He jerked his head to where the *Calamitas* loomed beyond the pier, dwarfing every other ship on the water, with Fiona's own heavily armed vessel anchored beside it.

"You could do that, Captain," a deep, commanding voice said from behind the Galleon. "But you'd miss an opportunity. And make enemies even Broadsides Bart can't afford."

The man moved into the light, walking with a pronounced limp. His leg was supported by a heavy a brace, but coal smoke trailed from exhausts in his warcaster armor, and Montador noticed a peculiar modified mechanikal blade at his hip and the butt of a scattergun projecting over his right shoulder. His right arm had been replaced entirely with a mechanikal prosthetic, and his weathered face bore heavy scarring. Just behind him a tall, thin figure moved with a duelist's casual grace, his own face partially obscured beneath the cowl of a heavy gray cloak.

"I'd say we found our warcaster," Fiona said under her breath.

"Asheth Magnus," Montador said, his voice carrying both amazement and disgust. He had hoped Faller was bluffing to inflate the price. But if there was one man who had the resources to bid against him on multiple Galleons, it would be the notorious ex-Cygnaran mercenary. "Aren't you one of the most wanted in Cygnar? Some risk, coming here. What brought you out of your hole?" He eyed the youth behind Magnus with curiosity, noting his arrogant, hawkish look.

"He wants our bloody colossal, Captain," Dirty Meg said and spat. Her hand tightened on her heavy wrench.

Dougal MacNaile growled, "Let's see him try and take it."

"Yes," Fiona said, an excited lilt to her voice. "I'd like to see that as well."

"Come, now." Magnus' voice was quiet and dry. "Why so eager to pick a fight? We have a matter to discuss."

Tension was thick in the air. Montador made an adjustment with his left arm to prepare the holdout hidden in his own prosthetic for firing. "I suppose we can spare a moment to listen to the great Asheth Magnus," he said, his voice only slightly sarcastic. "But know that standing between me and what's mine can be dangerous." He looked to Faller, who was watching the exchange. "That goes for you also, my friend."

The senior mechanik inclined his head slightly. "Gentlemen, I leave you to your discussion. Magnus, you know where to find me once you reach an agreement." He and his guards disappeared into the foundry.

Magnus let him go, then said to Montador, "I am not interested in a bidding war. In fact, I have a way you could leave here richer rather than poorer: under my contract."

MacNaile grunted, and Montador raised a bushy eyebrow. "You wish to *hire* me?" He chuckled. "I don't come cheap, sir. And I'm feeling especially pricey today." Next to him, Fiona laughed appreciatively.

"I'm interested in an open-ended contract together with Fiona and your entire fleet, at twice your regular rate." Montador felt his eyebrows rise at the offer even as he heard Dirty Meg's sharp intake of breath. Magnus continued, "Once we have the Galleons, the *Calamitas* can take us to Five Fingers. If things go as planned, you'll still be the first to employ them in battle. Even better, their upkeep will be at my expense."

"That's an awful generous offer," Montador admitted, feeling rising excitement. He had been prepared to drop a small fortune to get his hands on a colossal or two, but he far preferred making money to spending it. It was also clear Magnus was up to something big. "But I have to say, I'd rather not see Five Fingers in flames. I have quite a few friends there."

Magnus laughed. He said, "Never fear, my war is not with that city. It will serve as a place to lie low, gather supplies, and recruit some additional men."

Montador's mind raced. The Four Star Syndicate had to be part of this, he considered. It sounded as though Magnus was putting together an army beyond the scope of any mercenary contract he had heard of. He glanced at Fiona, but as usual her ivory features were unreadable. "I dislike offers that sound too good to be true. I'd like to see the color of your gold."

Magnus reached beneath his cloak and pulled out a cloth-wrapped bundle. He tossed it to the sea captain, who caught it deftly. It was quite heavy for its size, and Montador was not surprised when he unwrapped it to reveal a bar of gold, stamped with the mark of the Leryn-Corvis Bullion Exchange. "I've recently come into quite a lot of money," Magnus said casually.

> **THE SIX CANNONS ACROSS THE GALLEON'S CHEST ROARED TO LIFE WITH FLASHES OF FLAME AND CLOUDS OF SMOKE.**

The Ordic warcaster handed the gold bar to Fiona, whose expression brightened as she examined it. He scowled and pretended to consider, but his decision had been made the moment Magnus had mentioned the open-ended contract. The rogue warcaster was up to something, something big. Montador would take his gold, see what he had in mind, and then sell the information to the King of Ord, whose letter of marque he bore. If things went south . . . well, the Meredius was a big place, and warcaster armor was heavy—heavy enough to send a crippled man to the bottom, should he fall overboard.

Montador smiled hugely and extended his right hand to Magnus. "We'll take you and your *merchandise* aboard as soon as you're ready to leave."

GENERAL OSSRUM
MERCENARY RHULIC WARCASTER

Battle is the greatest expression of the Rhulic soul. No other endeavor measures our strength, our spirit, and our resolve so thoroughly.

—General Ossrum

GENERAL OSSRUM						
SPD	STR	MAT	RAT	DEF	ARM	CMD
4	6	7	6	14	17	9

HAND CANNON			
RNG	ROF	AOE	POW
12	1	–	12

OATHKEEPER	
POW	P+S
7	13

FOCUS	6
DAMAGE	18
FIELD ALLOWANCE	C
WARJACK POINTS	+5
SMALL BASE	

FEAT: PERFECT PLAN

Alone among Rhulic generals, Ossrum knows the value of seizing the initiative. By his power he can instill his troops with a sudden burst of irrepressible speed and mobility, all while shielding them from retaliation. Moving swiftly across the battlefield they shrug off incoming fire as they secure key objectives and put the enemy on the defensive.

While in Ossrum's control range, friendly Rhulic models gain +2 ARM. Friendly Rhulic models/units activating in this model's control area gain +2 SPD and Pathfinder. Perfect Plan lasts for one round.

Mercenary – This model will work for Cygnar, Khador, and the Protectorate.

GENERAL OSSRUM

Martial Discipline – Friendly living Faction warrior models with small or medium bases can ignore friendly Faction warrior models in this model's command range when determining LOS and can advance through friendly Faction warrior models in this model's command range if they have enough movement to move completely past them.

Rhulic Warcaster – This model can have only Mercenary Rhulic warjacks in its battlegroup and can reactivate only friendly Mercenary Rhulic warjacks.

OATHKEEPER

⊘ Magical Weapon

Critical Decapitation – On a critical hit, double the damage exceeding the ARM of the model hit. A model disabled by this attack cannot make a Tough roll.

SPELLS	COST	RNG	AOE	POW	UP	OFF
BULLET DODGER	2	6	–	–	YES	NO

Target friendly model gains +2 DEF against ranged attack rolls and Dodge. (A model with Dodge can advance up to 2″ immediately after an enemy attack that missed it is resolved unless it was missed while advancing. It cannot be targeted by free strikes during this movement.)

ENERGIZER	*	SELF	CTRL	–	NO	NO

This model spends up to 3 focus points to cast Energizer. Models in its battlegroup that are currently in its control area can immediately advance up to 1″ for each focus point spent. Energizer can be cast only once per turn.

FIRE FOR EFFECT	3	6	–	–	YES	NO

Boost the attack and damage rolls of target friendly Faction model's first ranged attack each activation.

SNIPE	2	6	–	–	YES	NO

Target friendly model's/unit's ranged weapons gain +4 RNG.

STRANGLEHOLD	2	10	–	11	NO	YES

A model damaged by Stranglehold forfeits either its movement or its action during its next activation, as its controller chooses.

UNSTOPPABLE FORCE	2	SELF	CTRL	–	NO	NO

While in this model's control area, models in its battlegroup gain Bulldoze. Unstoppable Force lasts for one turn. (When a model with Bulldoze advances into B2B contact with an enemy model during its activation, it can push that model up to 2″ directly away from it. A model can be pushed by Bulldoze only once per activation. Bulldoze has no effect when a model makes a trample power attack.)

Warriors who possess the fighting spirit and irrepressible brilliance of General Ossrum Dhurg fear not the perils of war but rather the possibility of an ignoble death off the field of battle. In his prime Ossrum earned fame for favoring his startling improvisation and adaptability over time-honored Rhulic tactics. He believes in taking the fight to the enemy and picking his own ground. His men regard him with a mix of respect and affection, not merely for the victories he brings their clans but also because he asks nothing of them he will not do himself.

Born to Great Clan Dhurg, one of the thirteen founding clans of Rhul, Ossrum has always served as a professional soldier, fighting alongside and eventually commanding the forces of Hammerfall Fortress. He heard the call of war from the youngest age, seeing action early in the feuds between the disenfranchised warriors of Rhul's poorer western clans. Ossrum first distinguished himself by beating back incursions by Khadorans seeking to "clarify" their shared borders. Rather than simply defending Rhulic territory, he drove into the enemy, repelling them time and again.

Ossrum's disdain for traditional tactics and preference for bold maneuvers quickly earned him a mixed reputation. While his juniors admired his inventiveness, he often drew the ire of those to whom he reported. Despite the testimony of his detractors, the Dhurg stone lord took notice of Ossrum's victories and eventually awarded him the vaunted title of general, authorizing him to command the combined soldiers of lesser clans. This honor only increased the animosity from elder clan lords, who could not stomach his methods.

As age begins to catch up with him, Ossrum sees his best and last chance for glory in the conflagrations sweeping across western Immoren. The wealth he earns matters little; anything beyond that required to restock supplies and pay his men finds its way back to Clan Dhurg. Ossrum continually scrutinizes his assets, ensuring his men remain in fighting shape and confirming his warjacks stand fueled and ready. Those who employ Ossrum secure a fighting force equal to any that can be mustered by the standing armies of the Iron Kingdoms. Always on the advance, General Ossrum greets each morning with fresh enthusiasm, intending that should the day be his last, it will end in glory.

GALLEON

Dear Honored Sirs,

Black Anchor counts you among its noblest friends and patrons.

Without your dedication to our services and goods, our modest company could never have reached the pinnacle of success we now enjoy. You have shown the discernment of a connoisseur and unflinching dedication to the highest standards—standards we strive not only to meet, but to exceed. We will proudly stand by our product even when set against the best machines any kingdom arsenal can produce! You may have encountered such hyperbole from our competitors in the past, but you know we do not make such claims lightly.

It is for this reason we send you this missive. You stand among the select few in all of western Immoren who possess the hard-earned wealth and the foresight to take advantage of groundbreaking opportunities such as the one we now offer. With these considerations in mind, we give you the chance to be the among the first to own the most powerful implement of war ever created. We encourage you to act quickly. Such a chance may not come again, and we anticipate a high degree of interest.

We call it the Galleon, a construct as massive and unyielding as the ships from which it draws its name. It has been perfectly designed to advance the interests of those who earn their living as swords for hire and takes into account the wide-ranging needs of that noble profession.

The Galleon towers over even the largest of the warjacks that came before it, and yet it retains all the flexibility of those smaller cousins. Furthermore, its arsenal includes sufficient instruments of defense and offense to make those of a fortress pale in comparison. Never has so much firepower been concentrated in a single walking arsenal. Engineered to provide you the battlefield control you demand, the Galleon will grant you the freedom to go where you want, when you want, and vanquish anyone who stands in your way. It does so with advanced mechanikal innovation, exhilarating steam-powered performance, and remarkable precision.

The Galleon is easily maintained to take the fight to your enemies for decades to come! Our expert mechaniks are prepared to train any qualified steam worker in the upkeep of this modern marvel.

We look forward to further correspondence with you as together we open an exciting new chapter in both our partnership and the pursuit of peace in western Immoren.

Sincerely,

Waldron Faller
Chief Mechanik
Black Anchor Heavy Industries

GALLEON
MERCENARY COLOSSAL

The bigger the engine, the bigger the guns, boy. That's as true on land as it is at sea.

—Broadsides Bart

GALLEON						
SPD	STR	MAT	RAT	DEF	ARM	CMD
5	16	6	5	9	19	—

GUN PORT				
	RNG	ROF	AOE	POW
L	14	1	3	13

GUN PORT				
	RNG	ROF	AOE	POW
R	14	1	3	13

HARPOON CANNON				
	RNG	ROF	AOE	POW
R	10	1	—	15

CARGO CLAW		
	POW	P+S
L	3	19

TRIDENT STRIKE		
	POW	P+S
R	5	21

FIELD ALLOWANCE	2
POINT COST	18
HUGE BASE	

GUN PORT

Rapid Fire [d3] – When you decide to make initial attacks with this weapon at the beginning of this model's combat action, roll a d3. The total rolled is the number of initial attacks this model can make with this weapon during the combat action, ignoring ROF.

HARPOON CANNON

Drag – If this weapon damages an enemy model with an equal or smaller base, immediately after the attack is resolved the damaged model can be pushed any distance directly toward this model. After the damaged model is moved, this model can make one normal melee attack against the model pushed. After resolving this melee attack, this model can make additional melee attacks during its combat action.

CARGO CLAW

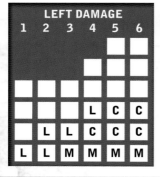 **Open Fist**

LEFT DAMAGE					
1	2	3	4	5	6
				□	
			□	□	□
□	□	□	□	□	□
			L	C	C
	L	L	C	C	C
L	L	M	M	M	M

RIGHT DAMAGE					
1	2	3	4	5	6
□	□				
□	□	□			
□	□	□	□	□	□
C	C	R			
C	C	C	R	R	
M	M	M	M	R	R

HEIGHT / WEIGHT: 33´, 71 TONS

ARMAMENT: DUAL SETS OF TRIPLE GUN BATTERIES (LEFT AND RIGHT CHASSIS), TRIDENT HARPOON CANNON (LEFT ARM), CARGO CLAW (RIGHT ARM)

FUEL LOAD / BURN USAGE: 2,500 LBS / 5 HRS GENERAL, 40 MINS COMBAT

INITIAL SERVICE DATE: 608 AR

CORTEX MANUFACTURER: FRATERNAL ORDER OF WIZARDRY

ORIG. CHASSIS DESIGN: BLACK ANCHOR HEAVY INDUSTRIES

The raw might of a naval ironhull now walks the lands of western Immoren as the Galleon. When unleashed upon a battlefield, the Galleon fires a rolling broadside comparable to that of a small ship of war. The colossal interrupts its deafening percussion only to reach out with its enormous cargo claw to toss a warjack like a rag doll or to use its massive trident to reel in resilient foes and finish them off at close range with a series of punishing blows. The Galleon commands a high price, but for those mercenaries who have the fortune to spend, it fights as a symbol of unquestionable affluence and might.

Only the Black Anchor Heavy Industries consortium could have dreamed of bringing together the engineering specialties and manufacturing capability needed to create a weapon like the Galleon. The feat required tremendous resources, hundreds of laborers, and dozens of highly skilled craftsmen and mechaniks, including those who might otherwise be employed by military armories.

Originally known as Black Anchor Shipwrights, the company originated in the southern Cygnaran port city of Clockers Cove several decades ago. Established to fabricate high-quality hybrid sail/steamships, it soon attracted a number of ambitious and talented engineers and mechaniks, including Steam and Iron Worker Union members who had enjoyed employment with prestigious factories such as the Cygnaran Armory, Engines West, and Rohannor Steamworks. Black Anchor quickly gained a reputation among private merchant guilds and privateers for being able to solve difficult engineering challenges and for producing ships capable of running naval blockades—those built for speed but also armed to the teeth. As a relatively lawless port, Clockers Cove served as the perfect staging ground for the outfit's industry, and Black Anchor thrived by aiding clients who valued discretion. For example, the company designed and manufactured the truly massive steam engines, pontoons, and specialized armament Captain Bartolo Montador used to refit the *Calamitas*. That large-scale engineering project paved the way for what was to come.

As Black Anchor's reputation and wealth grew, so did its facilities. Eventually, the organization expanded into the business of repairing and assembling steamjacks; within short order, it was outfitting labor 'jacks with weaponry. Facilities once built to service ships increasingly began to create parts for both labor 'jacks and decommissioned warjacks. As Black Anchor became more adept at reproducing 'jack chassis invented by others, it added several notable and wealthy mercenary outfits and independent warcasters to its growing clientele. Soon the warjack side of the business became dominant. Though the company still produces the occasional private vessel, its governing board renamed the entity Black Anchor Heavy Industries to reflect its change in focus.

Black Anchor's competence ultimately attracted the attention of powerful financial backers, including benefactors from the wealthiest merchant houses of Ord. With such resources, the company began to conceive and launch truly ambitious projects. It also established a reliable grapevine through its union steamos, who frequently communicated with counterparts in various military armories. It was not long before Black Anchor's owners learned of colossal factories operated by the Cygnaran

Armory in nearby Caspia as well as the Rigevnya Complex in Korsk. Loath to back down from a potentially lucrative challenge, Black Anchor decided to gamble and see if its own production capabilities were up to muster.

Thus began the most ambitious mechanikal project ever undertaken by a private interest. Even as its lead mechaniks began to draft the schematics, Black Anchor retrofitted one of its largest dry docks in order to produce its first colossal. Company negotiators secured arrangements with the Fraternal Order of Wizardry to acquire a limited run of custom-built, oversized arcanum cortexes—an expensive grade normally intended for heavy 'jacks.

Possessing such a rich nautical history, Black Anchor naturally drew upon its expertise in maritime engineering to construct and arm the Galleon. Indeed, the weight of the colossal's guns is identical to that favored by Black Anchor frigates, and its huge trident shares design elements with the massive harpoon cannons used by commercial whalers. Since its first test runs along the docks of Clockers Cove, the Galleon has raised some eyebrows, particularly among agents of the Cygnaran Reconnaissance Service, who noted that the first of these machines was loaded onto an Ordic privateer vessel connected with the Four Star Syndicate. The existence of such a dangerous weapon ensures an interesting—and undoubtedly profitable—future for those mercenary companies with the resources to procure a colossal of their own.

GALLEON CONCEPTUAL DESIGNS

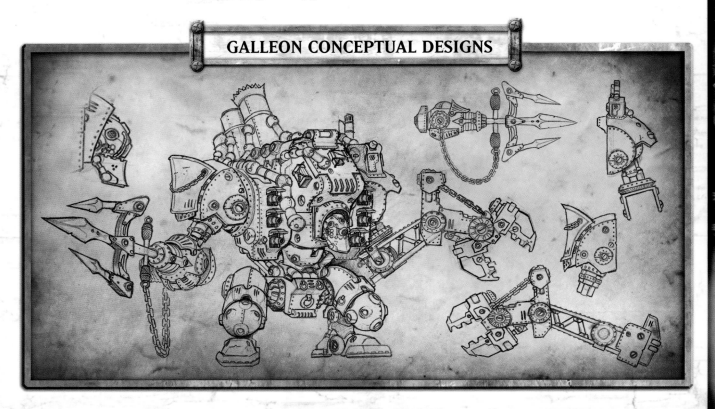

ALEXIA, MISTRESS OF THE WITCHFIRE
MERCENARY EPIC CHARACTER CAVALRY SOLO

Alexia's very presence cleaves through destiny unraveling the weft of fate.

—Sybeth Roane

ALEXIA						
SPD	STR	MAT	RAT	DEF	ARM	CMD
8	4	6	5	15	16	9

WITCHFIRE	
POW	P+S
8	12

MOUNT
POW
10

DAMAGE	10
FIELD ALLOWANCE	C
POINT COST	4
LARGE BASE	

Mercenary – This model will work for Cygnar and Khador.

Animosity [Morrowan] – This model cannot be included in an army that includes one or more models of the listed type.

ALEXIA

✠ Fearless

☻ Terror

Arcane Vortex – This model can immediately negate any spell that targets it or a model within 3" of it by spending 1 soul token before the RNG of the spell is measured. The negated spell does not take effect, but its COST remains spent.

Ghost Shield – This model gains +1 ARM for each soul token currently on it.

MAGIC ABILITY [8]

• **Grave Summons (★Action)** – When this model uses Grave Summons it can spend any number of soul tokens. For each soul token spent put one friendly Thrall Warrior solo into play anywhere completely within 3" of this model.

• **Hellfire (★Attack)** – Hellfire is a RNG 10, POW 14 magic attack. A model/unit hit by Hellfire must pass a command check or flee.

Soul Collector – This model gains one soul token when a living enemy model is destroyed in its command range. This model can have up to three soul tokens at a time. During its activation, this model can spend soul tokens to gain additional attacks or to boost attack or damage rolls at one token per attack or boost.

WITCHFIRE

⊘ Magical Weapon

Mage Killer – Gain an additional damage die on this weapon's damage rolls against models with Spellcaster or Magic Ability.

TACTICAL TIPS

MAGIC ABILITY — Performing a Magic Ability special action or special attack counts as casting a spell.

GRAVE SUMMONS — The Thrall Warrior models can activate the turn they are put into play.

Shadows obscure her every movement, but the name Alexia Ciannor is known across the war-torn Iron Kingdoms. She has garnered a reputation for pitilessness, blasphemy, and sorcerous power that seems out of proportion for one so young. Where she goes, chaos and destruction follow, and those she chooses to fight beside—for whatever inscrutable reasons—fear her as much her enemies do. Her mastery of the dread blade called the Witchfire has increased in just a few short years, and now the dead do her bidding gladly, rising at her command like soldiers eager to fight for their queen.

Since the nightmarish events of the Longest Night in 603 AR, Alexia's infamy has only grown. Those few who knew her in those days say she has grown madder still, haunted by the ghost of her mother and those who burned alongside her in that ghastly trial. Some suggest that since then, the chorus of specters in her head has been joined by the dozens, perhaps hundreds, of souls that have perished at the end of the Witchfire.

Her motives have grown even less discernible as she has made her way across the battlefields of the Iron Kingdoms. Mounted upon an undead steed whose eyes blaze with the necromantic power that animates it, Alexia simply appears on the eve of bloody conflicts to join the fight. She seems as happy to fight for one side as the other, taking her pay in coin and the corpses of the enemy. To what ultimate end Alexia uses the thralls she raises is a question shrouded in darkness. What is certain is that as the wars across western Immoren grow in scope and intensity, so has her mastery over the Witchfire—or perhaps, its mastery over her.

Those Morrowan priests and witch hunters who follow Alexia's trail have begun to wonder if her wanderings are not part of some occult design they cannot yet fully comprehend. Perhaps her desire to resurrect the spirit of her mother is only a diversion, a feint by powers to whom Alexia is herself only a pawn.

MODEL GALLERY

ARTIFICER GENERAL NEMO
Epic Warcaster

STORM CHASER ADEPT CAITLIN FINCH
Character Solo

ALEXIA, MISTRESS OF THE WITCHFIRE
Epic Character Cavalry Solo

VLADIMIR TZEPESCI, GREAT PRINCE OF UMBREY
Epic Warcaster

STORMWALL & LIGHTNING PODS
Colossal & Solos

CONQUEST
Colossal

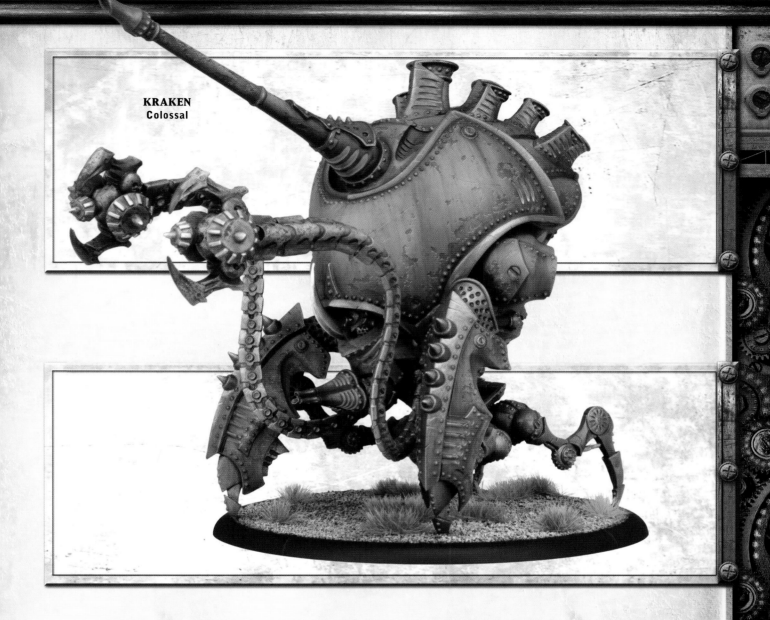

KRAKEN
Colossal

PAINTING COLOSSALS

Large models like colossals pose very different challenges for a painter than smaller figures. For example, their large and well-defined shapes nullify the difficulty inherent in painting fine details. Painters will, however, find the sheer volume of surface area a significant test. In particular, realizing solid, even basecoats over these large surfaces is tough even when using larger brushes.

By far the most useful tool to tackle these large areas is an airbrush, and many of the techniques in this section are designed with that in mind. Formula P3 paint works wonderfully with an airbrush. To attain the best possible results use a 50/50 mixture of water and blue window cleaner as an airbrush medium to dilute your paint to the desired consistency and then strain the mixture through a piece of fine wire mesh or nylon stocking. If you do not own an airbrush you can use spray paints instead; just be sure to choose spray paints with a matte finish.

With a little bit of daring, these techniques are accessible to all airbrush skill levels, allowing painters to realize eye-popping detail in a relatively short period of time.

TWO-TONE PRIMER

Using a two-tone primer coat is a sure and simple way to kick-start your colossal painting. First, apply an opaque layer of Formula P3 Black Primer over the entire model in two light coats, ensuring that the deep recesses receive a solid coating while retaining detail. Then apply a second tone of primer from above to provide a general idea of where the highlights and shadows will fall on the finished model. Use a blow dryer to harden the primer between layers. The main advantage of two-tone priming is that it dramatically speeds up the basecoat stage. It can also be used in a variety of clever ways, as you'll see in the following articles.

SPONGE PAINTING

"Sponge painting" is a term for applying paint using a dabbing or stabbing motion. You don't need to use an actual sponge for this technique; a small scrap of blister foam or a large round paintbrush works just as well. The important part of the technique is the motion you use to apply the paint. Remember to rotate the sponge or brush on the upswing of each stroke to prevent repeating the same stamp pattern.

SALT WEATHERING

The salt weathering technique simulates chipped paint quite effectively. First paint an underlayer— usually in rusty brown tones—that will show through wherever the paint is later chipped. Then apply clean water to the areas of the model you'd like weathered and sprinkle kosher sea salt over them. Next, apply a layer of paint using either spray primer or an airbrush. Finally, use a nylon brush with stiff bristles to scrub the area vigorously, which removes the salt to reveal flecks of the underlayer. The resulting surface can be worked further to create convincing rust effects or left as is for a quick route to a beautiful gaming model.

HAIRSPRAY WEATHERING TECHNIQUE

The hairspray technique recreates the rusting process on a micro scale. First paint an underlayer over the model that will be revealed as the paint chips away. Next apply a heavy layer of hairspray to the model. Then, using an airbrush, apply basecoat and highlight in light layers. Brush clean water onto the model where weathering is desired. Next use a nylon brush with stiff bristles to scrub the area vigorously. The water penetrates the top paint layer and dissolves the hairspray, so the scrubbing will separate the top layer from the underlayer in a realistic manner. Finally, apply a matte sealant to allow the surface to be worked further and to prevent further chipping.

■ Khador Red Base		■ Cold Steel		■ Brown Ink	
■ Khador Red Highlight		■ Battlefield Brown		■ Blue Ink	
■ Pig Iron		■ Exile Blue		□ Mixing Medium	

CONQUEST

Step 1) Begin by using the two-tone primer technique, starting with two light layers of Formula P3 Black Primer. For the second tone, apply a layer of rust-colored automotive primer from overhead. (You can buy rust-colored primer at most auto-supply stores. Alternatively, you can apply a similar color using drybrushing or an airbrush.)

Step 2) Airbrush a layer of Khador Red Base onto the flat surfaces of the model. Don't worry if overspray hits other areas of the model.

Step 3) Add Khador Red Highlight and some airbrush medium (a 50/50 mix of water and blue window cleaner) to the airbrush paint reservoir and apply highlights. Add more Khador Red Highlight to the reservoir for successive layers of highlights until you achieve the desired effect.

Normally you would now black out the areas that you will paint metal, but instead just drybrush those areas with Pig Iron followed by a lighter drybrush with Cold Steel. The airbrush overspray that you leave under the Pig Iron will add some character to the metal.

Step 4) Apply a paint wash of Battlefield Brown mixed with Exile Blue and a dot of mixing medium to the steel areas.

Step 5) Mix Brown Ink with Blue Ink and apply it as a glaze to shade the metal further.

Step 6) Paint the remaining parts of the model using the standard methods detailed in *Forces of WARMACHINE: Khador* and the weathering technique from the Gun Carriage detailed in *WARMACHINE: Wrath.*

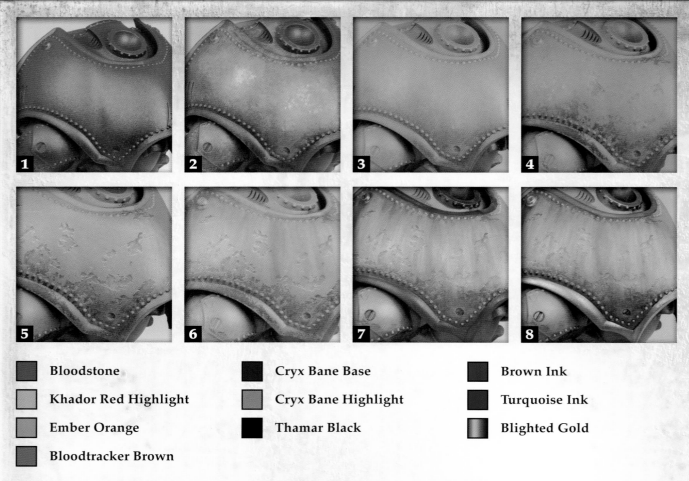

■ Bloodstone	■ Cryx Bane Base	■ Brown Ink
■ Khador Red Highlight	■ Cryx Bane Highlight	■ Turquoise Ink
■ Ember Orange	■ Thamar Black	■ Blighted Gold
■ Bloodtracker Brown		

KRAKEN

Step 1) Begin by using the two-tone primer technique, starting with two light layers of Formula P3 Black Primer. For the second tone, apply a layer of rust-colored automotive primer from overhead. (You can buy rust-colored primer at most auto-supply stores. Alternatively, you can apply a similar color using drybrushing or an airbrush.)

Step 2) Using the sponge painting method, apply a chaotic rust texture to the model. Bloodstone, Khador Red Highlight, Ember Orange, and Bloodtracker Brown are all good colors to use in this step.

Step 3) Apply two thorough coats of hairspray to the model, allowing the coats to dry between applications. A blow dryer will speed the drying process significantly. Apply a light coat of Cryx Bane Base mixed with Cryx Bane Highlight to the model. It is important to make this coat of paint fairly light and to avoid total coverage so that the water used in the next step can penetrate the top layer of paint to dissolve the hairspray. A good rule is to make sure that you can just barely see the rust showing through the layer of paint.

Step 4) Brush clean water onto the surface of the model and then use a stiff-bristled brush to gently abrade the surface, removing the top layer of paint. On areas where it is difficult to get the paint to chip away, use a sharp pin to scratch through the top layer. After achieving the desired effect, seal the model with a spray-on matte sealant and allow it to dry.

Step 5) Using a fine detail brush, trace a thin line along the top edge of each chip using Thamar Black. Then trace the bottom edge with Cryx Bane Highlight.

Step 6) Add translucent drips to the model using a mixture of Cryx Bane Base and mixing medium. To apply the drips, paint a line at the level of the rivets. Before the paint begins drying, use a second, damp brush to pull the paint downward and create the drip effect.

Step 7) Apply several layers of glaze mixed from Brown Ink and Turquoise Ink to finish the effect, then black out the metallic areas to prepare it for painting.

Step 8) Paint the blighted gold using the standard method described in *Forces of WARMACHINE: Cryx* for a dramatic final effect.

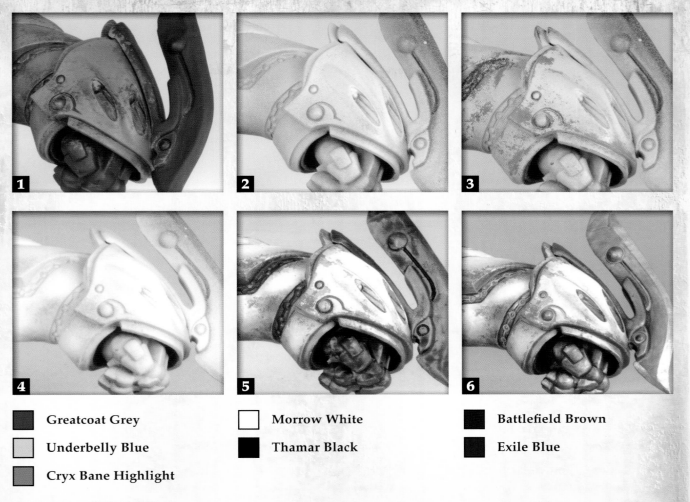

■ **Greatcoat Grey**	□ **Morrow White**	■ **Battlefield Brown**
□ **Underbelly Blue**	■ **Thamar Black**	■ **Exile Blue**
■ **Cryx Bane Highlight**		

HYPERION

Step 1) Begin by applying a solid coat of Formula P3 Black Primer, then use the sponge painting technique to add a layer of Greatcoat Grey.

Step 2) Apply two thorough coats of hairspray to the model, allowing the coats to dry between applications. A blow dryer will speed the drying process significantly. Apply a light coat of Underbelly Blue mixed with Cryx Bane Highlight to the model. It is important to make this coat of paint fairly light around the edges while fading to a solid opacity at the center of each plate. This is so the water will penetrate the paint more easily to dissolve the hairspray around the edges where you want the weathered look.

Step 3) Brush clean water onto the surface of the model and then use a stiff-bristled brush to gently abrade the surface, removing areas of the top layer of paint. After you achieve the desired effect, seal the model with a spray-on matte sealant and allow it to dry.

Step 4) Once again apply two more thorough coats of hairspray to the model allowing the coats to dry between applications. Then, once the hairspray is dry, apply a top coat of Morrow White using the airbrush.

Step 5) Brush clean water onto the surface of the model and then use a stiff-bristled brush to gently abrade the surface, removing areas of the top layer of paint. Make sure the areas of chipping from step 3 are revealed during this process. After you achieve the desired effect, seal the model with a spray-on matte sealant and allow it to dry. Black out the metallic areas on the model with Thamar Black.

Step 6) Apply translucent shading with a mixture of Battlefield Brown and Exile Blue. Then using thin glazes of Morrow White, apply highlights sparingly.

Finally, paint the metals and glow effects using the methods described in *Forces of WARMACHINE: Retribution of Scyrah* for a final effect that is quite striking.

THE SOUTHERN THORNWOOD

Major Victoria Haley focused her will through the Cyclone to direct a hail of bullets into the mechanithralls pouring from the breach in the crumbling wall. With another part of her mind she maneuvered her Firefly into a better position near the periphery. It fired its storm blaster amid several bile thralls rushing her trenchers from that direction, and lightning arced through them. One of her stormsmiths raised his staff and adjusted his gear to triangulate between the Firefly and another of his peers on the far side of the field. He threw a switch, and the air crackled as surges of energy electrocuted several of the undead that had gotten past the forward line.

Haley looked through the eyes of her Hunter ranging farther afield, where it raced nimbly through the underbrush and around the trees, searching for whatever entity was directing the thralls. She fired its cannon to neutralize a bloat thrall that had been sending gouts of caustic death over the trees. A squad of rangers accompanied the light 'jack, occasionally shooting targets of opportunity as they sought to gain a better sense of the disposition of the enemy. Nearer Haley several squads of trenchers and long gunners added volleys of withering fire.

She reached out mentally for Thorn but failed. Disorientation washed over her until she remembered again that her Lancer was not with her. It had been her idea to lend the 'jack to General Nemo, but actually handing it over and extracting her mind from its cortex had filled her with an intense sense of loss. It was not the first time she had given the machine to another temporarily, but it was the first time since the poison had stripped her of her magic. She had approached the decision with admirable logic: not only would others get better use out of its arcane machinery, but not having it at her disposal would remove the temptation to unleash her powers at a distance. Actually letting it go, however, had been an admission that she was truly crippled.

Even without Thorn, she had already forgotten her limits more than once, such as when she had begun to extend her hand to summon an explosion of temporal distortion. Pain had flared in her chest and head while her pulse pounded frantically, and she could feel tendrils of the poison spreading. To avoid this she endeavored to keep her mind focused entirely on her machines, immersing herself in the flow of information between their cortexes.

Even without calling on her magic she felt spasms of occasional pain, which she attempted to conceal from her fellow officers, particularly General Nemo. Her stamina was diminished also, and her legs felt weak even after such a short battle. Only her mechanikal arm was reliable; she had taken to using it to hold Echo and using the weapon as a support. It was imperative she prove her usefulness. She would endure and become stronger. She pushed herself each day a little more, testing her limits, taking care not to betray the exhaustion she felt until she finally collapsed on her cot in private.

This particular battle against Cryx felt satisfying, as it demonstrated her skill with warjacks had not diminished. Several brigades from the 2nd and 5th Divisions had been advancing for weeks into the Thornwood under General Nemo's command. They had spread out in a relatively wide sweep to neutralize any Cryxian strongholds or lairs. Eventually they were to combine their forces with other segments of the First Army that had joined the mission into the forest alongside the Khadorans. Now that CRS rangers and Widowmakers were cooperating rather than trying to eliminate one another, they had been able to discover several previously unknown Cryxian facilities, each overrun with undead. The ruins where they now fought were part of a long-abandoned fortress in the Bloodsmeath. More recently, Cryx had erected several necrotite mining facilities here to distill the concentrated fuel that powered helljacks and bonejacks.

Haley felt a surge of jealousy to see Captain Darius and the Stormwalls fighting on her left flank. She could not resist sending her Firefly closer to watch through its eyes as the colossals got their first taste of battle. General Nemo had deferred the honor of their initiatory fight to Darius. Cygnar's foremost mechanik was tasked to put the machines through their paces and ensure their weaponry and loading systems were working smoothly. He had apparently nicknamed the first two Stormwalls Deluge and Blitz.

Several field mechanik crews kept ready nearby, prepared to spring into action against any mishap with the expensive machines. Leading the army's small battalion of field mechaniks was none other than Captain Arlan Strangewayes, another of Cygnar's legendary mechaniks. Listening to Nemo, Strangewayes, and Darius talk shop about their new machines had been diverting during the march from Corvis, soured only by the watchful Khadoran eyes also upon them. Not many Khadoran soldiers accompanied this regiment, but a few Winter Guard squads lingered nearby, no doubt sent to observe the Stormwalls and report back to their superiors.

Nemo complained that the Thornwood would make a poor test ground for the machines and kept talking about the old Colossal Wars and the Trollkin Wars. Darius insisted the Stormwalls had none of the flaws of the original colossals from those times. These had been designed specifically for speed and agility despite their mass. Strangewayes groused about the number of moving parts—or, as he put it, the "fiendish complexity"—of a hybrid steam and voltaic system but seemed fond of the machines nonetheless, constantly tending to them and making adjustments.

Through the eyes of her Hunter, Haley spotted activity deeper in the forest just as the nearest rangers caught the movement. She was already shouting, "Reinforcements from the north! Take cover!" as the rangers dove behind the nearest trees. The trencher infantry and commandos went prone, while long gunners rushed back and allowed the warjacks to take the fore. Haley caught Darius' eye and pointed. He nodded and moved into action, runes springing forth around him and the pair of Stormwalls. Haley called to her captains, "Hold fire until my signal!"

A fresh tide of steam-fisted mechanithralls crashed through the underbrush. Darius had sunk a pair of mines along that perimeter and detonated them now, obliterating the first thralls. Then the Stormwalls opened fire, and Haley could not help sucking in an appreciative breath. The sound of chain guns spinning up to unleash a torrent of bullets was awe-inspiring, and she sent her Cyclone to add to the onslaught. Bullets pierced through pallid flesh, dropping thralls by the dozens, while the Stormwalls' main guns delivered punishing shells. Rifle fire from Darius' men joined the barrage, and the first wave of mechanithralls dropped, but more followed as soldiers hastily reloaded. All the while, helljacks and bonejacks loped toward the colossals. Sword knights stood nearer to the machines on the flanks with Caspian battle blades drawn, ready to strike down any thralls that closed.

The top hatches on the Stormwalls opened to launch storm pods in high arcs to land behind the nearest enemies. The massive coils atop each colossal's shoulders flickered blue and then surged with lightning that crashed forth to send a blinding line of searing power, turning everything to ash between each pod and its colossal. Using these galvanic beacons as additional points for triangulation, lightning crashed repeatedly down amid the smoking field, striking thralls and damaging bonejacks in front of the warjacks as the stormcallers did their work.

"Bile thralls at the flanks!" one of the rangers shouted, and she saw that biles were approaching from around the crumbled fortress walls amid the distraction of the central battle. A squad of Winter Guard positioned there desperately opened fire with blunderbusses, taking out several. Despite these efforts, one got close enough to purge, spraying caustic fluids across four of the unfortunate Khadorans. She split her soldiers and sent the Firefly charging into the midst of the remaining bile thralls, spitting them with its electro glaive before they could also purge. The rescued Winter Guard backed away while firing on the remaining enemies.

After Darius imbued the two colossals with runic power, they charged forward to confront the dwarfed helljacks. Deluge swept its enormous left fist through a half-dozen thralls that had swarmed close, sending them scattering. Then with its right fist it impacted the nearest Slayer with a deafening sound of metal on metal and sent the helljack flying backward to crash into the Reaper behind it. Blitz shrugged off a Reaper harpoon as a Slayer raked deeply into the steel of its legs and then the colossal battered both helljacks to oblivion in several punishing blows. Where its fists impacted, voltaic coils surged to send lightning streaking into the nearest thralls. Sword knights charged into the fray alongside the Stormwalls to cleave into helljacks with their battle blades.

BULLETS PIERCED THROUGH PALLID FLESH, DROPPING THRALLS BY THE DOZENS, WHILE THE STORMWALLS' MAIN GUNS DELIVERED PUNISHING SHELLS.

Haley directed her Hunter to fire armor-piercing shells to finish the last bonejacks, and in a few short moments the area was cleared of Cryx. Smoke rose from the wreckage of a dozen shattered 'jacks and from hundreds of rifle barrels, and the Cygnarans looked with stunned amazement at the burning wreckage of trees and thorny shrubs that had been cleared in the vicinity. Then a great cheer went up from the soldiers, directed at the Stormwalls. Haley approached Darius and nodded her admiration, still feeling lingering jealousy.

Darius seemed a little stunned at the performance of his machines and exclaimed, "Now *that's* a successful field test!"

Haley's laugh was cut short by a spike of physical pain in her chest. "I'd have to agree," she said, trying not to let it show as she watched the mechaniks, directed by Strangewayes, swarm over the Stormwalls. They worked to reload ammunition and repair damage, paying particular attention to Blitz's leg where the helljacks had hit hardest.

One of the rangers returned, his face anxious. He said, "That last batch came up from a cave opening just north of here, Major. Looks empty, but we only peeked in a little ways."

Haley nodded. "Add it to the map, and take word to Captain Bridgeway that I need him to use his Avenger's

seismic cannon to bring it down. Be thorough, and look for additional openings." Bridgeway was one of the division's senior gun mages and an expert 'jack marshal.

Haley almost felt normal amid the battle's aftermath, until she took another step and was nearly overcome by dizziness. She staggered and caught herself by leaning on Echo. Darius spotted her difficulty and turned his rig toward her, his face showing concern. "Are you all right, Major?"

"I'm fine. It's nothing," she said quickly. She gritted her teeth and stood straighter as she ordered her subordinates to resume the march.

THE NECROFACTORIUM

Deneghra strode like a dark tempest from the chamber where Karchev was being kept. Attempting to shape the mind of the unbending Khadoran warcaster was like trying to break an anvil with her bare hands. Asphyxious had shown no willingness to participate in the endeavor, and she now felt his intervention would be necessary.

Today she had been tempted to murder her captive and be done with it, but she knew Asphyxious would disapprove.

As she passed through the lower chambers of the complex, she mulled over the recent reports on the advance of the allied Cygnarans and Khadorans. She saw Mortenebra approaching on her many spider-like legs and moved to the side. "Master Necrotech," Deneghra said politely.

"Wraith Witch," Mortenebra replied in a sharp tone, coming to a stop and looking at her fixedly. "Good. You can save me some time by relaying a report to Lord Asphyxious."

Deneghra's eyes narrowed and she said, "I asked you to bring any matters to my attention first. You should not trouble him with details."

The movement of the ancillary legs and scavenger claws behind Mortenebra's back now suggested agitation. "Asphyxious made specific demands to be regularly informed about the Kraken progress. I would rather be at liberty to send Deryliss to inform him how little has changed, but the last time I did so I nearly lost an irreplaceable skarlock."

This brought Deneghra up short. Why would Asphyxious leave her in the dark? Most of the older Krakens were confined to the extensive arsenal of Lich Lord Scopulous, who was frugal about contributing toward efforts on the mainland, and therefore they were rarely seen. After Mortenebra's arrival, Asphyxious had set her to work forging new colossals for his use at the necrofactorium. "I thought we had completed several Krakens already. Has there been a problem?"

"Six," Mortenebra corrected. "I have built *six* Krakens, each perfect, and created to Lich Lord Asphyxious' specifications. Yet they are useless."

"Useless?" Deneghra asked, alarmed. "What do you mean?"

"They are inert and unresponsive. That was my message. If you would convey this, I can return to solving the problem. The only explanation is that the plans I was given, which included cortex modifications of Lord Asphyxious', are flawed. Reverting them will take time."

Deneghra's eyes widened. "Do *not* revert the cortexes, not without orders. I will speak to Asphyxious. See if you can determine the nature of the problem without deviating from his instructions." She knew too well how exacting the lich lord was in these matters. He was not prone to flawed design, although given his recent erratic behavior and decisions, Deneghra was not quite as confident about this as she might have been.

"Very well," Mortenebra said, "Although I have already done so exhaustively." Mortenebra spun around and scuttled back into the bowels of the complex.

Entering unannounced into Asphyxious' inner audience hall, Deneghra saw him speaking to a ghostly entity near the rear of the chamber, even as she shifted to a wraithlike state. Doing so she was better able to distinguish the being as one of the peculiar mechanikal creatures favored by Lich Lord Malathrax. Even as she identified it, the creature slipped away into the walls and was gone. Given the state of affairs between the two liches, she could not fathom what could possibly require such a courier. It made her distinctly uneasy.

Asphyxious turned to face her with no acknowledgement of having been interrupted. "Deneghra, what news?" She bowed and offered an unvarnished account of the Kraken situation, anticipating his seething wrath. Instead, he said, "Ah. This is of no concern. Thine instructions to Mortenebra were correct. There is no flaw in the plans."

"The fact that the Krakens are unresponsive is no concern?" Deneghra asked, confounded.

"None at all," he replied brusquely. He seemed distracted, lost in thought.

She said, "My assessment of the strength of the necrofactorium's defenses relies on the Krakens held in reserve. If they are not battle ready, the threat represented by the approaching Khadoran and Cygnaran armies is much more severe. I have received confirmation that several of the new Khadoran Conquests have broken through our blockade intact, and two Cygnaran Stormwalls were seen leaving Corvis. Without the Krakens to counter—"

"Enough!" Asphyxious' voice rang with command, a tone he had not taken with her in years. She felt as if she had been slapped. "I am glad our enemies bring their machines. It will make them overconfident, and once we defeat them, they will make for good salvage."

"Of course, my lord," Deneghra replied. "I do think it would be wise to send additional forces into the field to prepare ambushes before they consolidate, though. I can personally oversee these efforts. We can do considerable damage and deplete their numbers before—"

"No." He interrupted her again, in that same tone. "Thou will ready thine army on the perimeter of the necrofactorium. *As we initially discussed.* If they believe themselves prepared for the fight, all the better. Let them come. Now, leave me, tiresome creature! Trouble me no more with thy foolish and meddlesome suggestions!"

From the force of the bonds that tied her to him, she was already turning to leave before she had absorbed the impact of the words. Her mind was in turmoil, brought back to distant memories from her youth, when she was still being shaped to the life of a warwitch. Not since those days had Asphyxious shown such open disdain, and even then only when she had displeased him with her inability to retain the lessons. What had happened? Had the bond between them become so tenuous?

Even as she grasped at these explanations, a more chilling thought presented itself: his conversation with Malathrax's agent. Since her meeting with the Coven she had felt a lingering sensation of being watched. Had Asphyxious learned of the arrangements she had made behind his back? It would explain his reluctance to listen to her advice. She had lost his trust. She tried to put the thought aside but felt it eating at her, like a disease. Eager for the distraction of battle, she focused on the task at hand. She would gather their army and stand against the enemy.

Artificer General Nemo stared out along the ranks of the assembled allied forces. It was an awe-inspiring sight. The First Army of Cygnar stood in ranked formation for inspection directly alongside the 2nd Army of Khador. It was strange to consider these were the same once-embittered soldiers who had stood on opposite sides of the trench lines protecting Ravensgard and Northguard.

All in all, the casualties thus far had been relatively light. Nemo mistrusted the general lack of reconnaissance on the enemy. It made the expedition feel reckless, unlike the careful orchestration that had brought Irusk such fame. That said, they had crossed unmolested through several choke points perfect for ambush. Cryx had opposed them only where they had found cave warrens of the undead, fighting bitterly but futilely to prevent Cygnar from collapsing them. It seemed possible their numbers were not as great as originally feared, with the strike against Point Bourne having cost them. If that was true, finishing them now—before they could regroup and acquire reinforcements—was the right move. Lord Commander Stryker was certainly so inclined and was clearly pleased with their rapid pace. There was talk of sending forces down into the caves with explosives, but that had ultimately been rejected. The risk in those unknown warrens was too great; better to simply collapse access and march on.

Nemo's eyes were drawn again to the Stormwalls, now baptized in battle by Captain Darius. He had taken control of one for the upcoming clash and transferred the other to Captain Kraye, who seemed well suited to take advantage of its considerable firepower. Darius handled a host of heavy warjacks brought from the armories of Point Bourne, Stonebridge, and Corvis. Every warcaster present was controlling more 'jacks than was typical, with additional machines distributed to their most capable marshals.

There had been no sign of Captain Allister Caine or Major Markus Brisbane. Caine's absence was not a surprise to Nemo, who knew the Second Army had borrowed the gun mage and his escort for some secret operation in the south. Siege's absence was more worrisome. The officers from Stonebridge had expected him. Irusk had reluctantly admitted one of his kommanders and a standing legion were missing and that the senior officer had been coordinating with Brisbane. Nemo considered it inconceivable that a soldier of Major Brisbane's caliber might have had a mishap, but in war nothing was certain.

Lord Commander Stryker approached, offering a tired smile. The look they shared hinted at the depth of the long and sometimes difficult history between them. "General, why are we waiting?" he asked.

"I don't know," Nemo grumbled. "Let's find out."

With Stryker and Storm Chaser Finch following, Nemo approached Irusk where he was reviewing his troops and said, "Our forces are ready, and we do not have ample supplies. You claim to know the location of our enemy. Let us act on that knowledge."

Stryker interjected, "Speaking of which, how is it you have such accurate reconnaissance, Kommandant?"

Irusk stared at them with his typical stone-faced stoicism, only raising a single eyebrow. "You have no need of such information. As to why we have waited, you shall see shortly." He offered a cold smile.

It was only another hour before those gathered heard the approaching rumble of powerful steam engines, and there was a stir amid the Khadorans of the arrayed armies. Their temporary encampments occupied an open area they had cleared by chopping back the trees and underbrush. Visibility was still severely limited by the forest.

Major Haley joined them as they walked west deeper into the Khadoran area, hearing the sounds of cheering ahead. The reason was quickly apparent. The arrivals looked to be a sizable Rhulic mercenary force and a smaller company of Khadoran soldiers, all battle-weary. Their stunned expressions and the scowls the Khadorans directed at the nearby Cygnarans showed they had just recently learned of the alliance. The sight of them was eclipsed by several Khadoran colossals ponderously moving through the opening made for them as soldiers cleared the way. Nemo felt a twinge of bitterness at the sight of the tremendous machines, even larger than the Stormwalls, but built with typical Khadoran lack of finesse. They moved with none of the grace and fluidity of the Cygnaran colossals and poured clouds of heavy smoke into the air from rows of stacks across the heavy boilers on their backs.

Nemo realized his Stormwall had taken a step in that direction, causing some alarm among the Cygnaran soldiers. He settled the great machine, reminding its cortex that these were allies even as he reminded himself. The Stormwall had been responding to his own animosity at the certainty that the Khadoran machines likely incorporated elements of his own designs, stolen by spies. He tried to put the thought aside.

Irusk turned to Nemo and said, "General Nemo, behold the Conquest. This was why we waited." He was positively smug. He then moved to greet the officers among the new arrivals.

While Irusk was congratulating the young and unfamiliar warcaster who had apparently been responsible for delivering the machines, a powerfully built Rhulic warcaster approached, an unlit pipe in one hand. Nemo recognized General Ossrum of Clan Dhurg, a veteran campaigner and perhaps the only one among the gathering who might be older than himself. "General Ossrum," Nemo said and offered his hand. "I was not aware you were joining us."

"General Nemo." Ossrum shook his hand as he squinted and took in the scope of the assembled armies. "My contract is completed." As he filled and lit his pipe he continued, "Looks as though something serious is afoot."

Nemo could not help but chuckle. "That's one way of putting it. We intend to drive Cryx from the forest for good." The Rhulic warcaster raised his eyebrows, and Nemo could see his interest was piqued. Irusk stepped back toward them staring at Ossrum thoughtfully, perhaps considering what the junior warcaster had told him.

"Well, Kommandant," Ossrum said to Irusk in passable Khadoran, "thanks for your business. Can't say it's been a pleasure." Nemo had been expecting the general to make a sales pitch, knowing the mercenaries of Clan Dhurg were always interested in earning more coin. He felt perhaps there was a touch of theatrics as the dwarf turned away, giving a sharp whistle and making a circling motion with one hand to signal the Rhulic soldiers it was time to leave.

"General Ossrum," Irusk said. Ossrum turned as if surprised, and Nemo suppressed a knowing smirk. "Can I persuade you to join us in the fight ahead? A heavy purse would make the long hike north less painful, yes?"

Ossrum frowned and sucked on the stem of his pipe as if this were a novel thought. "Lost a lot of 'jacks getting here. I was planning to resupply and pick up replacement soldiers at Hammerfall before taking on more work. We're also low on ammo and fuel."

Having gone through a similar routine with Gorten Grundback after the Llaelese War, Nemo knew this could go on for hours if left to its natural course. "Ossrum," he said firmly. "We are on a tight schedule. The Khadorans will pay eighty percent of your usual fee," he held up a hand as Ossrum's face reddened and he opened his mouth to retort, "and the Cygnaran treasury will pay an additional seventy percent. That will bring your payment to one and a half times your usual. Is that acceptable? That includes access to ammunition and coal." Nemo caught Irusk's eye and saw the kommandant's initial annoyance at the interjection replaced with resignation. He nodded once.

Ossrum's eyes glittered and he smiled as he withdrew his pipe to say, "Let's put it in writing."

Although nowhere near as impressive as what was below, the surface above the Thornwood Central Necrofactorium included several low structures with fortified access points and numerous slender smokestacks rising up to vent noxious fumes. These facilities were simply the upper portion of a buried structure of far greater complexity, one that Asphyxious was already preparing to reveal when the need arose. Machinery was in place to push aside the thin layer of surface earth and elevate the central structure. Initially it had been planned this would not be necessary for years, if not decades. With the approach of the allied armies, though, Deneghra knew they would likely trigger the mechanisms soon.

There were defensive advantages to both states. As it was, the necrofactorium was extremely difficult to find amid the forest despite the smokestacks. The central facility was surrounded by a chain of steep hills that created a small forested valley with only two choke points allowing access. Any incidental traffic through the region would be inclined to veer away, along the edges of the outer hills. Thralls under Deneghra's supervision had augmented these natural barriers in many ways and had created emplacements for numerous bloat thralls as well as concealed firing positions for pistol wraiths. On the other hand, the hidden structure contained a number of soul-empowered necromantic weapons that could be employed only once the building was fully elevated from the depths. Deneghra was certain they would need those defenses to repel an army the size of the one that approached.

> **"WE INTEND TO DRIVE CRYX FROM THE FOREST FOR GOOD." THE RHULIC WARCASTER RAISED HIS EYEBROWS, AND NEMO COULD SEE HIS INTEREST WAS PIQUED.**

Deneghra gathered her force near one of the entrance points into the valley, and the Witch Coven of Garlghast occupied the other. Nightmare stood beside her, claws clenching in anticipation of imminent battle, while an array of helljacks and bonejacks stood scattered among the undead filling the field ahead, all ready to answer her call. She stood on a slightly elevated position back from the valley entrance. That particular ingress was choked with thorn-covered bushes and withered trees intended to hinder both movement and visibility for any intruding forces. Even without being able to see them directly, Deneghra could hear the rumble of the allied armies as they made their advance.

That the enemy had pinpointed their location so quickly disturbed her. She had not anticipated their arrival for weeks and had expected she would need to guide them to their destruction. Most likely, they had some means to detect the powerful necromantic energies concentrated here. Ultimately it did not matter how they had found the valley; there was no way to avoid a confrontation now. Deneghra just wished she was as confident of their defenses as Asphyxious seemed.

Man-O-War bombardiers were the first to march to their deaths through the narrow valley, wielding their buzzing chain blades to carve through the dense underbrush and clear the way for the rows of assault kommandos behind them. Mechanithralls and brute thralls descended upon them, heedless of losses, and overwhelmed the first lines. There followed the sound of bloat thralls firing their caustic fluids outward against other advancing forces still pushing through. The enemy ranks were thrown into slight disarray by the sudden onset of battle, but they soon recovered, and heavy Khadoran warjacks strode forward to clear the nearest thralls.

The sound of rifle fire began and quickly intensified as soldiers she could not yet see fired on the nearest exposed Cryxians. Pushing through the forward Khadorans came soldiers in the blue armor of Cygnar and with them the sounds of lightning and thunder. Projectiles from distant artillery began to soar over the surrounding hills and explode among the withered trees, splintering or toppling them entirely. They were firing blind, and Deneghra knew her bloat thralls likely had a better vantage from their positions along the ridged hillside, where they launched caustic death into the forces beyond. She could identify the distinct sounds of detonations as several as the bloat thralls were found and eliminated. Beyond this, sounds of similar escalating battle reached her from the opposite end of the valley, where the Witch Coven was positioned. Deneghra could hear the familiar howls of the Deathjack as it joined the carnage with bestial enthusiasm.

Having thought the enemy would try some simple probing strikes before committing in full, Deneghra summoned a pistol wraith to relay a message to Asphyxious. "They are massed in greater strength than anticipated," she conveyed. "Tell him to send reinforcements immediately, and to raise the central tower!"

Assault kommandos in alchemically treated armor pressed forward into the valley firing their carbines, heedless of the bile that ate through other soldiers. Some wielded flamethrowers and wore heavy masks and tanks to spray long plumes of blazing liquid out among the incoming thralls and bonejacks. The forward companies of kommandos penetrated the valley, but Deneghra waited for the narrow gap to fill with storm knights before she gave the mental signal to her machine wraiths atop the sides of the defile. There were low thumps as large reservoir tanks of bile fluid were burst by the wraiths on either side, sending a tide of caustic fluid flooding the channel. The screams of the dying sang in her ears as the knights realized the uselessness of their armor amid a torrent of acidic fluid. As the enemy reacted, the wraiths descended to seize control of the nearest warjacks and turn them against their own forces.

Additional warjacks pushed forward to clear both sides of the ravine, followed by squads of infantry. The battle became chaotic as Deneghra used her will to direct groups of undead into the fray, relying heavily on the large numbers of mechanithralls and bile thralls at her disposal. Numerous necrosurgeons were scattered among them—as storm knights and trenchers who charged into the melee were smashed down by steam-powered fists, their bodies were pulled aside to be transformed into ready reinforcements. Similarly, necrotechs waited nearby to seize parts from downed warjacks along with various body parts to create explosive scrap thralls and send them forth.

Khadoran Juggernauts, Marauders, Devastators, and Kodiaks crashed into her undead troops to tear great ragged holes in them and make room for the advancing allies. Devastators opened their shells to unleash tremendous explosions, momentarily clearing the immediate area, only to have more thralls then surge against them. Cygnaran Ironclads, Centurions, Hammersmiths, and Stormclads crashed into the forested clearing before the necrofactorium, seizing ground from the walking dead. Deneghra dispatched her helljacks judiciously, but the sheer scope of the incoming army began to grind down her sense of superiority. She was not accustomed to feeling outnumbered. Not here.

The incoming artillery bombardment arcing down from beyond the ring of outer hills became fiercer as mortars and cannons were pushed closer by their crews. Any reinforcements Deneghra sent forward were quickly chewed apart amid this conflagration or met by the fire of Defenders, Grenadiers, Destroyers, and Demolishers. She saw trenchers rushing forward with foolish courage to die by the dozens, the hundreds. Nonetheless, by their efforts they seized the upper hills on the far side of the valley and began to situate chain guns and cannons. They were soon joined by Winter Guard positioning their mortars and field guns.

Deneghra had to fall back and directed the Withershadow Combine to move as well when teams of trencher and Widowmaker snipers took the high ground and began to fire on key targets of opportunity. With gun mages adding their fire, they managed to seize the outer perimeter from the pistol wraiths, bile thralls, and bloat thralls. This paved the way for ranks upon ranks of long gunners and Winter Guard riflemen to take up position and fire down into the valley with devastating consequences. Man-O-War soldiers charged through the choke point, their heavy boots sizzling in pools of acidic bile. Shocktroopers at the fore advanced in shield wall formation to cover the advance of additional heavy infantry, including storm knights and Iron Fangs. Deneghra's helljacks fired on them continuously, taking a toll but not appreciably slowing them.

One by one she sent forward Deathrippers and Defilers, igniting her power through their arc nodes to summon destruction amid the enemy. She inflicted the curse of shadows on the front line of Man-O-War as the first wave of her bane thralls charged through, allowing them to penetrate deeper into the heavy infantry ranks and sow death with their massive axes. Bane knights and soul hunters swept up the hillside to slaughter long gunners left exposed and were set upon in turn by Stormguard from the rear ranks.

The battle hovered indecisively as long minutes passed amid the chaotic maelstrom. The sky flickered with lightning from dark clouds, and heavy rain began to fall. Cygnaran manipulation of the weather soon produced a heavy downpour amid frequent lightning strikes, joining the crackling of electricity along the ground from storm chamber blasts and arcs. The slick ground made footing treacherous and became worse as mud mixed with blood, corpses, and tides of bile. In this environment her Leviathans and Harrowers served her well, sweeping in where they could to reap the living with claw and perisher.

Through the haze Deneghra sought to locate enemy warcasters, intending to isolate them one by one for quick and decisive strikes. It was the only way she could see to stop the enemy momentum.

Lich Lord Terminus pressed on through the forest with his new army behind him. The expedition into eastern Llael had not proceeded as planned, but his goals there had been achieved. The armed might of the mortals in that despoiled and half-ruined land were scattered and made ineffectual from their fear of Cryx. They could focus only on what was immediately before them, a predictable outcome when their homes were threatened.

Yet his anger was aroused at how other elements of their plan had begun to unravel. The vulnerability of Lord Venethrax's position was unacceptable—and a matter he intended to rectify personally. He was focused on reaching that much-diminished column when Lord

Malathrax emerged from the shadows in front of him. The movement of wraiths among the shadowy trees behind him suggested some nominal escort.

"Lord Terminus," Malathrax said respectfully, his masked face transforming to a leering beast. "I am pleased to find you."

Towering over the other lich lord, Terminus stared down with barely restrained malevolence. "Malathrax. You should be with Lord Venethrax."

"I have just come from him, but as you know my skills are better suited to disseminating information than seeking battle. Venethrax sent me to you after I received certain critical facts. Time is of the essence."

Terminus was generally willing to indulge the spymaster, who had often been useful to him, having provided key intelligence during the intricate feints and landing operations the mainlanders referred to as the Scharde Invasions. "Then speak."

"I know you are eager to reach Lord Venethrax's side, and reinforcements are much needed there. That said, our priorities must be carefully weighed. Venethrax's column is at risk, but he is well equipped to deal with lesser threats. Whereas I have word of a singular opportunity to simultaneously strengthen our position while diminishing a rival of yours who has stood as a persistent obstacle in our endeavors." Malathrax's silver-plated face took on a cherubic guise.

Terminus' glowing eyes simmered. "Cut to the quick of this."

"Asphyxious has proven reluctant to support Venethrax, and I wonder if he had a hand in the disaster that nearly buried our column. Even your fresh army comes not from him but from one of his minions who begins to realize the scope of her master's selfish megalomania."

Terminus' head tilted slightly. "What do you know of this?"

Malathrax spread his hands and said, "Never underestimate the scope of what I know, Lord Terminus. It is time Asphyxious paid for his hubris. Let us go to his necrofactorium and take that which he withholds. He will shortly be beset by Cygnar and Khador."

Terminus made a growling noise in his throat. "I left the Witch Coven with him to defend our production in the Thornwood. That war industry is vital."

"I do not suggest we allow the necrofactoriums to fall. But let us demonstrate our displeasure by removing the struts upon which his safety relies. I believe Deneghra is ready to turn from him, and I am certain Mortenebra can be convinced. You can pull back the Coven. We can sweep aside Asphyxious' ambitions and set in his place someone better suited. All this

we can accomplish, preserving the necrofactorium itself, and take all the troops we require. It is a chance we should not squander, worth taking a small diversion."

Peering down at the creature whose masked face shifted through several of its guises in quick sequence, Terminus pondered. "I will admit," he said at last, "the scenario has an undeniable appeal. But our first priority must be the athanc held by Venethrax. Until I personally assure it is safely in our grasp, a reckoning with Asphyxious must wait."

Despite the carnage, Khadorans and Cygnarans poured into the valley. Their swift occupation of the high ground on the outer hills had undermined Deneghra's plans. The gun mages and snipers prioritized necrosurgeons and necrotechs, and many of those near the front were gunned down. She had to hastily commit the second wave of bile thralls, sending as many as she could behind the forward advance of bane and bile thralls among the hills. A wraith engine howled in a battle frenzy and closed behind them, reaching out with scything claws to sweep through long gunners and feast on their souls. Two Storm Striders managed to climb the outer incline of the hills and unleashed powerful bolts of voltaic energy into the machine, prompting it to turn on them with a piercing shriek.

Standing in the rain and wind, Deneghra felt the battle could easily swing either way. The faces of the enemy showed their horror and weakening morale as the enthusiasm of the first charge faded and the body count rose. The nearest heavy 'jacks had torn many of the thralls to pieces but then had become mired amid the undead, vulnerable to the Slayers, Corruptors, and Seethers.

Then the colossals reached the valley, and everything changed.

One of the Cygnaran and two of the Khadoran colossals charged forward, augmented by the powers of their masters. With them came a veritable tide of fresh warjacks, Man-O-War soldiers, and knights. She recognized the marks of Cygnar's Storm Division together with Khador's 4th Assault Legion. The Stormwall arrived amid the booming of cannons and the whirring of chain guns. Directing it from atop his steed was Captain Jeremiah Kraye, who was taking shots while also controlling many of the other Cygnaran warjacks that ran forward, firing their own weapons with unnatural accuracy.

The two Conquests were controlled by Supreme Kommandant Irusk, and their cannons gave forth deep, bellowing reports as the machines waded into the fray. The enormous constructs dwarfed even otherwise massive heavy 'jacks. Several of her bonejacks got too near as she attempted to invoke a curse on the closest Conquest, and it swept its fists in a wide arc to scatter thralls and 'jacks. The Stormwall stepped up to a Slayer and backhanded it to send it flying into the nearest Reaper, toppling both, while its other lightning-wreathed fist crushed a Seether into scrap.

Desperate to stall their advance, Deneghra decided Kraye must die; then the Stormwall would stall and she could deal with Irusk. This thought reached Nightmare, and its bloodthirsty cortex assented with a certain frenzied mania. They both went incorporeal even as she sent the bulk of her heavy warjacks against the colossals. She transformed the nearest Man-O-War shocktroopers to shadow, and she and her favored Slayer swept through them like a cold wind. At her urging bane thralls converged from behind her to engage the troopers while she focused on Jeremiah Kraye. A badly damaged but still functional Deathripper crawled near enough for her to invoke acidic venom through its arc node to wash over the intervening stormblades, sending them screaming to their deaths.

Kraye reared back on his horse and fired his carbine twice in quick succession, finishing the Deathripper in an explosion of its skulled head. A Sentinel protecting Kraye turned toward her as she neared and fired a spray of bullets that passed through her spectral form. She became substantial as she thrust Eclipse to score a deep gash along the surface of its assault shield. This was superficial damage, but her weapon's power swallowed the warjack in darkness, then the 'jack reappeared from shadows behind Kraye facing away from Deneghra. Both Kraye and his Stormwall turned toward her, startled by her sudden appearance.

The mounted warcaster let his carbine fall by its strap to his side and drew his cavalry saber as he spurred his horse. She heard and sensed the Stormwall turn toward her as well, and she gathered her will and let loose a powerful wave of clinging darkness to stop both. The steam engines of the Stormwall strained as it sought to overcome the supernatural gloom holding it in place. Deneghra had cleared the way between Nightmare and Kraye. The 'jack suffered several close-range Charger cannon hits before it reached him, but then with a single great slash of its metallic claws it scraped him from the saddle and sent him flying, trailing blood, into the mud twenty feet from his horse. The steed's eyes rolled in fear, and it bolted. Kraye pushed himself up with one arm as blood dripped from multiple lacerations through the breastplate of his warcaster armor. If not for his power field, he would have already been dead.

Nightmare gave a bestial shriek and crouched before leaping to finish him. The ground shook as something massive approached. Deneghra felt and heard multiple booming cannons. Instinctively she jumped back and away as the ground around her erupted with explosive blasts. Shrapnel tore through her side. One of the Conquests, sent forward

with unnatural speed, intercepted Nightmare and towered above it. Each of its fists was as large as a heavy 'jack, and it brought one of them smashing down onto Nightmare, which crumpled with the sounds of metal snapping and shattering. When it struck again Deneghra felt a jarring disconnection and looked with disbelief through the rain at the heaped wreckage of her favored helljack.

Both the Stormwall and the second Conquest fired in her direction, even as an oversized shell smashed into the ground behind her and sprang open to reveal voltaic coils. She went insubstantial an instant too slowly to avoid the lightning that tore painful rents through her dead flesh, but then multiple shells passed through her as the world became noise and torn earth from multiple blasts. She scrambled to the side and back, summoning her undead.

Looking over her shoulder she saw Irusk striding through the mud toward her. He extended his hand and the air filled with the sound of incoming shrieks as arcane projectiles burst upon her position, tearing gashes in her body despite her ghostly state. She mentally sent her remaining Leviathans to intercept him but did not linger to watch. That the Stormwall kept fighting told her that her gambit had failed and Kraye had survived; otherwise its cortex would have been overloaded by backlash.

> **FOR A MOMENT DENEGHRA DID NOT RECOGNIZE HER TWIN, VICTORIA HALEY. SHE FELT A STRANGE VERTIGO LOOKING AT HER; SOMETHING WAS WRONG.**

Severely wounded but feeling none of the pain a living person would have, Deneghra managed to get behind a wave of thralls she had directed into the hail of bullets and shells sent her way. Through the eyes of a battered Defiler closer to the breach she saw more allied forces entering the valley, including Lord Commander Stryker as well as a female warcaster in Morrowan armor.

Another woman was with them, and for a moment Deneghra did not recognize her twin, Victoria Haley. She felt a strange vertigo looking at her; something was wrong. It wasn't her posture, although Victoria looked tired and fragile as she leaned on her spear. Rather, it was the missing sense of mental connection and spark she felt when her twin was near. It was as if Haley was hollow, an imitation. Though she had often sought her sister's death, this unnerved her far more than her failed attack on Kraye. Stryker's augmented Ironclad stepped on the Defiler whose eyes she had borrowed, and she lost track of her twin.

She continued to run toward the necrofactorium, her mind divided as she sent her remaining 'jacks and thralls into the battle as she tried to knit her damaged flesh together. Her defense of the valley had largely collapsed, and she was confused at the lack of reinforcements from the complex. Similarly, the machinery of the central tower had yet to be activated to expose its soul-driven weaponry and the larger doors for the reserve arsenal. Had Asphyxious ignored her? In an instant she felt a pang of grief and despair: he had left her to her death.

As she approached the nearest surface entrance, she was startled to see the distinct silhouette of Asphyxious walking toward her, his new weapon Daimonion in hand. Vociferon was behind him, carrying his staff of soul cages. Strangely, she felt relieved to know Asphyxious had come to finish her personally. She sank to her knees and awaited the killing blow. Instead he said, "Rise, Deneghra, thou hast done superbly. The enemy is positioned as I wished. Thank you for putting yourself in peril for my glory."

> **SCREAMING THE MADDENED HOWLS OF THE DAMNED, THE SOULS WERE FORCED TO CHANNEL THEIR POWER THROUGH THE TOWER'S MACHINERY.**

She looked at him stunned, then shakily got back to her feet. He placed a clawed hand on her shoulder, and necromantic power flowed into her to repair her remaining injuries. Profoundly confused, she said, "I sent for reinforcements . . ."

"Yes, and we shall unleash them momentarily. I wanted to ensure as many of the enemy as possible were in position before activating the final sequence. A risk, as they are closing from both sides, but necessary. I could not reveal myself too soon."

"Why not tell me?" she said indignantly.

"I am sorry, my dearest companion." To her ears, his voice conveyed genuine regret, although no other ear would have detected it. "I was forced to leave thee in darkness because I knew agents of Malathrax watched. It serves my purposes that both he and Terminus believe a divide exists now between us and that thou hast defied me. By this measure the others will seek to recruit thee into their confidences, to pit thee against me. For this to come to pass thy reactions had to be unfeigned. I expect in the days ahead he will come to thee, and make such overtures, and thou shall slowly see the worth in their offer. We shall speak of this again, but first there is a battle to be won."

"I understand," she said. Still reeling from this reversal of fortunes, Deneghra quickly collected her wits and looked behind her to where the last of their outer force was being torn to pieces by the allied armies. "We must raise the central tower!"

Asphyxious looked beyond her as if the onrushing army was only of trivial interest and said, "Yes, it is time." He raised his clawed hands, his sword in one, the other open, as green light poured from within his ribcage and spectral phantoms rose to spiral around him.

There was a deep rumbling from underfoot as the machinery of the necrofactorium activated, and a tremendous cloud of noxious vapors poured from dozens of slender smokestacks concentrated at the center of the dank and muddy valley. The central tower through which they had climbed from below and the earth surrounding it trembled as the structure rose through the soil, toppling the nearest trees. Numerous smaller black stone minarets clawed their way from below, like the talons of some tremendous beast that was awakening. Bronzed metal spires atop these gleamed with a greenish hue as the air filled with a deep, oscillating thrum that began to ascend in pitch.

The first wide, flat surfaces to break free from the earth were dual circular platforms, one to either side of the central tower. On the upper surface of each of these were three large metal apertures, which opened with a hissing of foul vapors even as the platform continued to rise. From within the noxious mist emerged the Krakens, which tremendous lifts had raised out of the innards of the building.

Asphyxious spoke again. "I did not know whom Mortenebra ultimately served and so could not trust her with these machines. These first Krakens have modified cortexes that will respond only to thy will and mine." He waved toward those nearest her. "Those three I grant thee." Without another word he strode in the direction of the other platform with its trio of colossals. Deneghra felt a surge of relief to know the machines actually worked and was profoundly touched at this proof of his trust. She knew she must prepare them at once.

The nearest Conquests had smashed through the last of the helljacks sent against them and were advancing, cannons firing. The explosions sprayed debris as Deneghra rushed to climb atop the slowly rising platform. The central area where a widening cylinder had become a tower was rising quickly, and from its horned peak came surges of green energy that lashed outward to strike the approaching enemies.

Deneghra's power field saved her from the wake of a Conquest's main guns as she slipped between the three mighty Krakens and extended her will to touch their cortexes.

Almost at once she felt their minds, powerful and different from those she had felt before but immediately responsive. The machines unfolded their harvesting claws as two leapt down from the platform, each firing a great hellblaster cannon that extended from its upper chassis like a great horn. Smaller flayer cannons spat death at the nearest foes, which included a stalwart group of storm knights that had rushed forward through the muck to confront Deneghra. As several fell, the others stumbled back and away, clearly terrified of the great machines. Harvester tentacles quickly seized them and hauled them, screaming, to where they were shoved into iris apertures on each Kraken's central torso. Those captured men would be imprisoned until their deaths could be exploited to empower the Krakens with the energies of their dying flesh and departing souls.

As she prepared to send forth the third Kraken, she heard several of the nearest smokestacks on the tower begin to topple, having been directly hit by fire from a Conquest. Two of the large pipes crashed into the gear works of an exposed mechanism that had just extended above the surface, part of the machinery necessary to lift the weapon spires of the inner tower to proper elevation. Knowing the tremendous force leveraged through them by the engines down below, Deneghra foresaw imminent disaster should those gears shatter or seize; the upper platform might even be sent plunging back into the depths. She urged the third Kraken to lash out with its tentacles, breaking loose the columns and clearing the gears of debris.

Turning back to the fray, she saw Irusk had directed one of the Conquests to fire on the necrofactorium tower. It took a step back to reposition as the Krakens leapt to meet it, but they were faster. Deneghra sent one of her last remaining Defilers closer to the machine and arced a curse through it upon the Khadoran colossal, weakening its armor just as the trio of Krakens drove forward to tear it apart with tentacles empowered by the bodies they had gathered. The Conquest staggered as one of its arms was torn loose. Its left leg crumpled beneath another blow and it fell with a deafening crash, crushing both men and machines. The other Conquest and Stormwall were closing, but both their hulls bore damage, while her machines were pristine and empowered with fresh kills.

The escalating thrumming sound reached a crescendo as the tower achieved its full height. Green hellfire lashed from the metal-tipped spires, igniting the living, while a flood of souls from the harvest at Point Bourne was disgorged from countless soul cages at the heart of the necrofactorium. Screaming the maddened howls of the damned, the souls were forced to channel their power through the tower's machinery. Some few tormented spirits broke free to rise wraithlike into the rainstorm already flooding the valley. Others were seized by the complex mechanism and sent along rows of the empowered spires to reach Asphyxious, Deneghra, the Witch Coven, and now Mortenebra. The master necrotech had just emerged from the newly revealed portal at the base of the central tower with a half-dozen iron lich overseers. A steady tide of fresh helljacks poured from that opening even as she strode forth to join the battle.

A dozen autonomous bonejacks raced toward Deneghra, and as they neared she seized control of their cortexes and then sent them scurrying to arc death upon her foes. The continuous surge of power from the influx of hundreds of souls combined with the exhilaration at directing three colossals. The sense of godlike power was only magnified when the landscape erupted around them and transformed into a vision of hell.

Darius had suffered badly in his clash with the Witch Coven of Garlghast and had at first been pushed back, but then the battle turned. Artificer General Nemo sent his Stormwall forward, directing it to fire its chain guns and main cannons into the minions of the Witch Coven, eventually forcing the retreat of the trio and their otherworldly floating sphere. At the fringes of his mental reach Thorn ran, using its tremendous maneuverability to position itself so Nemo could arc lightning where it was most needed.

Forward Kommander Kratikoff, Kommander Strakhov, and Captain Darius directed their own battlegroups to either side, spreading out to obliterate the thinning sea of thralls and helljacks. The multitude of warjacks and soldiers cleared the way toward the central entrance to the underground Cryxian lair. Supreme Kommandant Irusk had insisted his Greylords knew this to be the source of the incursion that had ravaged Point Bourne, and his entire army was eager for a reckoning. For once, the two armies were entirely united in purpose.

Stryker and Irusk had agreed to lead the attack on the main pass into this forested valley while Nemo and Sorscha, supported by the Rhulic mercenaries, led a smaller contingent into the other. They had taken the high ground along the perimeter and fired down onto the fray with their carbines and battle cannons. This combined with the seemingly imperishable Conquest and Stormwall had driven back the Cryxian horde.

Thunder and lightning created a constant din as Stormwall storm pods were launched and utilized by stormsmiths who found no lack of targets. Nemo's Storm Striders similarly had an ample field of fire, and he delighted in summoning his own lightning from the clouds to strike at bonejacks, necrotechs, and brute thralls. There had never been a battle better suited to his weaponry. The perimeter was established and numerous storm towers were rushed forward to guard their flanks, while trenchers labored to situate chain guns and cannons atop the upper hills.

Amid this display of Cygnaran firepower the earth began to shake, a fact at first lost amid the heavy tread of the colossals and the escalating storm. Through the haze and mist of the valley Nemo saw a looming tower flickering with green energy rising ahead of them. It seemed as though he was seeing the Temple Garrodh reborn, which chilled him to his marrow.

Necromantic energy surged from one metal spire to another, then lashed into the approaching allied army. Where these tendrils struck, men screamed and died. Even as their flesh fell from their bodies, they grinned lipless smiles as they turned their weapons on former comrades. Nemo's shouted orders were lost in the howling wind and rumbling, and then the ground dropped and broke open all around him.

Great gaping chasms appeared, and he realized deep tunnels riddling the ground around the central fortress were collapsing, strategically. The earth swallowed rank after rank of Iron Fang pikemen, Winter Guard, trenchers, and storm knights. One of his Avengers plunged below and then was set upon, its vision dimming as thralls hammered its chassis. Additional horrors clambered from these gaping trenches: mechanithralls, bile thralls, and bane thralls, but also the mindless drudges of the cephalyx. Enormous gouts of bile exploded amid the Cygnarans and Khadorans, transforming already uncertain ground into a sea of mud, gore, and bubbling acid.

Green hellfire blazed from the fortress towers and set afire the branches of the valley's remaining trees. Sickly radiance danced across their upper limbs, and their puckered bark showed tormented faces as shrieking spectral forms soared through them. Some of these manifested as machine wraiths that plunged into the nearest warjacks to seize control of them. Both the living and the inanimate turned on their own, and the landscape became a hellscape of carnage and confusion.

Haley had no time for thought as the shaking earth settled to reveal fresh thralls and drudges climbing up throughout the army. The barrels of her Cyclone's chain guns glowed orange from the heat of ceaseless firing and sent steam rising in the rain. Her Firefly was badly damaged, but she managed to send it to take out several thralls closing on a group of trenchers that were falling back and firing. Her right flank was held by Constance Blaize with her warjacks and Precursors, who were standing stalwart against the fresh assault but suffering casualties.

There was a tremendous crash as the rampaging Krakens toppled one of the Conquests, and Haley strode closer, adrenaline momentarily making her forget her weakened condition. As she urged her Hunter to fire on the nearest one, she saw Deneghra amid the Cryxian colossals, presumably directing them.

From between the Stormwall and the other Conquest charged the glowing form of Lord Commander Stryker, the coils on his back thrumming. He held Quicksilver raised above his head as he and his warjack Ol' Rowdy rushed the nearest Kraken. His sword was a shining streak as it cut through one of the clawed tentacles, its blade also shearing through the nearest armor-plated leg. Ol' Rowdy pounded the Kraken from the other side with its quake hammer. The colossal staggered, then leaned as Stryker leapt up to sweep his sword into its innards with a spray of sparks and twisted metal. The Kraken began to topple and Stryker had to dive out of the way. Ol' Rowdy interposed itself to deflect the crippled machine, whose bulk pressed the warjack into the mud, partially pinning it.

One of the Krakens tore through the crippled Stormwall and was beset by the last Conquest, but another closed on Stryker. Haley gasped as she saw its tentacle lash out, barely missing him. Ol' Rowdy was still struggling, trying to pry a bent leg from under the bulk of the downed Kraken. Without thinking Haley extended her hand and gathered her power, trying to reach into the foreign cortex of the Kraken to halt its attack as its other tentacle reared back like an angry serpent. Searing pain and white light erupted in her head as though a firebrand had struck her, and her heart beat erratically as pain shot through her chest and legs. She fell to her knees as she fought for breath, her vision swimming.

The incoming Kraken tentacle smashed into Stryker, shattering through his power field and knocking him backward into the mud, crumpling his warcaster armor. It groped for him again with its claws. Clutching her head in pain, Haley could do nothing.

Gallant intervened, blocking the Kraken's tentacle with its buckler, but was driven back as its shield and arm shattered beneath the colossal's strength. Blaize reached Stryker and pulled him to his feet and away even as her knights charged the Kraken to hammer it with their maces. In a single great sweep it crashed a tentacle through them to send broken bodies flying. Haley sent her Cyclone to charge forward and beat on it with its fists, but soon that 'jack also joined the wreckage scattered across the mud.

She got unsteadily to her feet as Blaize and Stryker limped toward her. There was blood on Stryker's face and he looked dazed. Behind him the Cryxian tower surged with unholy power, and Deneghra's body was limned with green fire. Haley had never felt so hopeless. When she locked eyes with her twin, she was startled to see pity in the wraith witch's expression.

Through the eyes of his Stormwall, Nemo saw the Cryxian colossals for the first time. Three moved from the roof of the nearest section of the fortress, the unmistakable silhouette of Asphyxious amid them. Nemo had fought in the Scharde Invasions, and he had stood atop the Temple Garrodh facing this same pernicious enemy, but he could not remember ever feeling greater dread. Asphyxious blazed with green energy, and his gleaming eye filled with hatred, glee, and malice as his power flowed into his rampaging machines. Nemo's Stormwall fired every gun at its disposal. Chain guns whirred and main guns fired, tearing several holes in the chassis of the nearest Kraken, but on it came.

Its appendages lashed out to scoop up sword knights and trenchers, its cannon firing necrotite-laden shells. Another Kraken crashed directly into the Stormwall and tore into it with metal-clawed tentacles dripping caustic liquid manifested by Asphyxious' necromancy. The Stormwall's left arm soon hung useless at its side, but blue runes surrounded Nemo as he imbued the machine with his own magic, letting it serve in place of damaged machinery. The colossal's blazing fists smashed into the bulbous surface of the Kraken. The Thunderhead joined in the attack, and together they battered the Cryxian machine until it moved no more. With its last lash, the Kraken crumpled one of the Stormwall's legs and knocked back the Thunderhead to shatter several of its voltaic coils.

The other two Krakens closed and put a quick end to the mighty Stormwall in a series of metal-buckling blows even as Sorscha's Conquest reached it. Despite the Khadoran colossal's might, Nemo knew it could not stand alone against two of the Cryxian machines. Asphyxious seemed a blazing green beacon of death as he charged into the midst of several Stormblades and carved through them with his sword. Bullets and cannon shells directed at him deflected off his power field. Nemo recognized that he was infused by souls, augmented by the skarlock that strode with him. He had seen the lich lord similarly augmented at Garrodh and knew the folly of their attack.

It seemed as if Nemo was surrounded by a city of the dead, a tableau of green fire and shrieking wraiths. This was the Thornwood, Cygnar's northern forest? It was as if he had been hurled into some living nightmare. With Caitlin Finch following close behind and sending lightning at anything that came close, Nemo reached Sorscha and yelled above the clamor, "We must retreat!"

Her attention had been focused on the clashing colossals, but then her cold eyes met his. Her jaw clenched in stubborn resolve, but after a pause she nodded. Already the Conquest staggered back, one arm shattered. Nemo shouted out to what subordinates he could reach, even as part of his mind still directed his warjacks in battle. He could see that Darius' position was overrun by helljacks racing from the fortress. Ossrum and the stalwart Rhulfolk held his flank, but not for long.

> ## IT SEEMED AS IF NEMO WAS SURROUNDED BY A CITY OF THE DEAD, A TABLEAU OF GREEN FIRE AND SHRIEKING WRAITHS.

If they were not to join the fallen in a mass grave, he knew they had to accept this bitter defeat. His eyes lingered one last time on Asphyxious, who strode amid the green flames and accepted each death around him as homage, a king of the dead and reaper of destruction, as pure an evil as Nemo had ever seen. That image seared into the core of his being as he yelled the orders to quit the field.

UNBOUND RULES APPENDIX

GENERAL
INCORPOREAL ADVANTAGE.

Replace the last line of Incorporeal with the following:

When this model makes a melee or ranged attack, before the attack roll is made it loses Incorporeal until its next activation.

CYGNAR
MAJOR VICTORIA HALEY. TEMPORAL SHIFT.

Replace the text of Temporal Shift with the following:

Enemy models/units activating while in Haley's control area forfeit either their movement or their action during their activations, as their controller chooses. At the start of your opponent's turns, he must declare which affected models/units he intends to activate that turn. Those models activate first that turn in the order you choose. Temporal Shift lasts for one round.

COMMANDER ADEPT NEMO. SUPERCHARGE.

Replace the text of Supercharge with the following:

When this model allocates focus during your turn, it can allocate up to 5 focus points to one warjack in its battlegroup that is in its control area.

OL' ROWDY. COUNTER CHARGE.

Replace the second line of Counter Charge with the following:

This model can use Counter Charge only once per round.

PRECURSOR KNIGHTS. SHIELD WALL (ORDER).

Replace the first line of Shield Wall with the following:

Until the start of their next activation, each affected model gains a +4 ARM bonus while B2B with another affected model in its unit.

PROTECTORATE OF MENOTH
GRAND SCRUTATOR SEVERIUS. DIVINE MIGHT.

Replace the text of Divine Might with the following:

Remove focus points from enemy models with the Focus Manipulation ability that are currently in Severius' control area. Enemy models cannot cast spells and lose the Arc Node advantage while in Severius' control area. Divine Might lasts for one round.

HIERARCH SEVERIUS. FIRES OF COMMUNION.

Add the following line to the end of Fires of Communion:

These models do not count toward the limit of four solos you can activate this turn.

THYRA, FLAME OF SORROW. ELITE CADRE [DAUGHTERS OF THE FLAME].

Change the last line of Elite Cadre [Daughters of the Flame] to the following:

(During your Maintenance Phase, if one or more models in a unit with Vengeance was destroyed or removed from play by enemy attacks during the last round, each model in that unit can advance 3˝ and make one normal melee attack.)

SANCTIFIER. CENOTAPH.

Replace the last line of Cenotaph with the following:

At the start of the turn this model's battlegroup activates, you can remove all soul tokens from this model to allocate it focus points, 1 for each token removed.

FIRE OF SALVATION. RIGHTEOUS VENGEANCE.

Replace the text of Righteous Vengeance with the following:

If one or more friendly Faction warrior models was destroyed or removed from play by enemy attacks while within 5˝ of this model during your opponent's last turn, at the beginning of your next turn this model can make a full advance followed by one normal melee attack.

TEMPLE FLAMEGUARD. SHIELD WALL (ORDER).

Replace the first line of Shield Wall with the following:

Until the start of its next activation, each affected model gains a +4 ARM bonus while B2B with another affected model in its unit.

WRACK. SUFFERING'S PRAYER.

Replace the second line of Suffering's Prayer with the following:

At the end of your Control Phase, this model receives 1 focus point if it does not have any.

KHADOR

SUPREME KOMMANDANT IRUSK.
TACTICAL SUPREMACY.

Replace the text of Tactical Supremacy with the following:

During a turn it activated, target friendly model/unit can advance up to 3" after all models have ended their activations that turn.

KOMMANDER ORSUS ZOKTAVIR.
ARCANE DEMENTIA.

Replace the third line of Arcane Dementia with the following:

If he destroyed three or more enemy models with melee attacks since the beginning of your last Maintenance Phase, do not roll to determine his base FOCUS; it is automatically 7.

ASSAULT KOMMANDOS.
SHIELD WALL (ORDER).

Replace the first line of Shield Wall with the following:

Until the start of its next activation, each affected model gains a +4 ARM bonus while B2B with another affected model in its unit.

IRON FANG PIKEMEN.
SHIELD WALL (ORDER).

Replace the first line of Shield Wall with the following:

Until the start of its next activation, each affected model gains a +4 ARM bonus while B2B with another affected model in its unit.

MAN-O-WAR SHOCKTROOPERS.
SHIELD WALL (ORDER).

Replace the first line of Shield Wall with the following:

Until the start of its next activation, each affected model gains a +4 ARM bonus while B2B with another affected model in its unit.

MAN-O-WAR DRAKHUN.
COUNTER CHARGE.

Replace the second line of Counter Charge with the following:

This model can use Counter Charge only once per round.

WAR DOG.
COUNTER CHARGE.

Replace the second line of Counter Charge with the following:

This model can use Counter Charge only once per round.

CRYX

LICH LORD ASPHYXIOUS.
SPECTRAL LEGION.

Add the following line to the end of Spectral Legion:

These models do not count toward the limit of four solos you can activate this turn.

PIRATE QUEEN SKARRE.
RITUAL SACRIFICE.

Change the text of Ritual Sacrifice to the following:

Remove target friendly warrior model from play. Skarre gains d6 additional focus points at the start of her next activation. Skarre can gain the benefit of Ritual Sacrifice only once per round.

DERYLISS.
ARCANE EXTENSION [MORTENEBRA].

Replace the text of Arcane Extension with the following:

At the start of a turn in which Mortenebra's battlegroup activates, if this model is in Mortenebra's control area, Mortenebra can allocate focus to warjacks in her battlegroup that are in this model's command range.

VOCIFERON.
ARCANE EXTENSION [ASPHYXIOUS, MASTER OF THE THORNWOOD].

Replace the text of Arcane Extension with the following:

At the start of a turn in which Asphyxious, Master of the Thornwood's battlegroup activates, if this model is in Asphyxious' control area, Asphyxious can allocate focus to warjacks in his battlegroup that are in this model's command range.

BANE KNIGHTS.
VENGEANCE.

Change the text of Vengeance to the following:

During your Maintenance Phase, if one or more models in this unit were destroyed or removed from play by enemy attacks during the last round, each model in the unit can advance 3" and make one normal melee attack.

MACHINE WRAITH.
MACHINE MELD.

Change the fifth line of Machine Meld to the following:

You cannot activate the warjack this round.

RETRIBUTION OF SCYRAH

HYDRA.
GRANTED: FOCUS BATTERY.

Change the last line of Focus Battery to the following:

Focus points remaining on this model count toward its focus allocation limit.

DAWN GUARD SENTINEL OFFICER & STANDARD.
GRANTED: VENGEANCE.

Change the last line of Granted: Vengeance to the following:

(During your Maintenance Phase, if one or more models in a unit with Vengeance were destroyed or removed from play by enemy attacks during the last round, each model in the unit can advance 3" and make one normal melee attack.)

HOUSEGUARD HALBERDIERS.
SHIELD WALL (ORDER).

Replace the first line of Shield Wall with the following:

Until the start of its next activation, each affected model gains a +4 ARM bonus while B2B with another affected model in its unit.

MERCENARIES

CAPTAIN DAMIANO.
DEATH MARCH.

Change the last line of Death March to the following:

(During your Maintenance Phase, if one or more models in a unit with Vengeance were destroyed or removed from play by enemy attacks during the last round, each model in the unit can advance 3" and make one normal melee attack.)

HAMMERFALL HIGH SHIELD GUN CORPS.
SHIELD WALL (ORDER).

Replace the first line of Shield Wall with the following:

Until the start of its next activation, each affected model gains a +4 ARM bonus while B2B with another affected model in its unit.

TROLLBLOODS

JARL SKULD, DEVIL OF THE THORNWOOD.
TACTICAL SUPREMACY.

Replace the text of Tactical Supremacy with the following:

During a turn it activated, target friendly model/unit can advance up to 3" after all models have ended their activations that turn.

SKALDI BONEHAMMER.
COUNTER CHARGE.

Replace the second line of Counter Charge with the following:

This model can use Counter Charge only once per round.

TROLLKIN FENNBLADES.
VENGEANCE.

Change the text of Vengeance to the following:

During your Maintenance Phase, if one or more models in this unit were destroyed or removed from play by enemy attacks during the last round, each model in the unit can advance 3" and make one normal melee attack.

TROLLKIN FENNBLADE OFFICER & DRUMMER.
VENGEANCE.

Change the text of Vengeance to the following:

During your Maintenance Phase, if one or more models in this unit were destroyed or removed from play by enemy attacks during the last round, each model in the unit can advance 3" and make one normal melee attack.

CIRCLE ORBOROS

MOHSAR THE DESERTWALKER.
DISJUNCTION.

Replace the text of Disjunction with the following:

While in Mohsar's control area this round, enemy models cannot be used to channel spells. During your opponent's next Control Phase, his models cannot leach fury and cannot have fury leached from them while in Mohsar's control area.

GNARLHORN SATYR.
COUNTER SLAM.

Replace the second line of Counter Slam with the following:

This model can use Counter Slam only once per round.

FERAL WARPWOLF.
BAYING OF CHAOS.

Replace the second line of Baying of Chaos with the following:

A warbeast can be affected by Baying of Chaos only once per round.

SKORNE

LORD TYRANT HEXERIS.
DEATH MARCH.

Change the last line of Death March to the following:

(*During your Maintenance Phase, if one or more models in a unit with Vengeance were destroyed or removed from play by enemy attacks during the last round, each model in the unit can advance 3" and make one normal melee attack.*)

SUPREME ARCHDOMINA MAKEDA.
ELITE CADRE [PRAETORIAN SWORDSMEN].

Change the last line of Elite Cadre [Praetorian Swordsmen] to the following:

(*During your Maintenance Phase, if one or more models in a unit with Vengeance were destroyed or removed from play by enemy attacks during the last round, each model in the unit can advance 3" and make one normal melee attack.*)

BRONZEBACK TITAN.
COUNTER CHARGE.

Replace the second line of Counter Charge with the following:

This model can use Counter Charge only once per round.

CATAPHRACT CETRATI.
SHIELD WALL (ORDER).

Replace the first line of Shield Wall with the following:

Until the start of its next activation, each affected model gains a +4 ARM bonus while B2B with another affected model in its unit.

IMMORTALS.
VENGEANCE.

Change the text of Vengeance to the following:

During your Maintenance Phase, if one or more models in this unit were destroyed or removed from play by enemy attacks during the last round, each model in the unit can advance 3" and make one normal melee attack.

PRAETORIAN KARAX.
SHIELD WALL (ORDER).

Replace the first line of Shield Wall with the following:

Until the start of its next activation, each affected model gains a +4 ARM bonus while B2B with another affected model in its unit.

HAKAAR THE DESTROYER.
RIGHTEOUS VENGEANCE.

Replace the text of Righteous Vengeance with the following:

If one or more friendly Faction warrior models was destroyed or removed from play by enemy attacks while within 5" of this model during your opponent's last turn, at the beginning of your next turn this model can make a full advance followed by one normal melee attack.

LEGION OF EVERBLIGHT

BLIGHTED NYSS LEGIONNAIRES.
VENGEANCE.

Change the text of Vengeance to the following:

During your Maintenance Phase, if one or more models in this unit were destroyed or removed from play by enemy attacks during the last round, each model in the unit can advance 3" and make one normal melee attack.

CAPTAIN FARILOR & STANDARD.
VENGEANCE.

Change the text of Vengeance to the following:

During your Maintenance Phase, if one or more models in this unit were destroyed or removed from play by enemy attacks during the last round, each model in the unit can advance 3" and make one normal melee attack.

MINIONS

BLOODY BARNABAS.
COUNTER CHARGE.

Replace the second line of Counter Charge with the following:

This model can use Counter Charge only once per round.